STATEMENT CONCERNING PUBLICATIONS OF RUSSELL SAGE FOUNDATION

Russell Sage Foundation was established in 1907 by Mrs. Russell Sage "for the improvement of social and living conditions in the United States of America." While the general responsibility for management of the Foundation is vested in the Board of Trustees, the responsibility for facts, conclusions, and interpretations in its publications rests with the authors and not upon the Foundation, its Trustees, or its staff. Publication under the imprint of the Foundation does not imply agreement by the organization with all opinions or interpretations expressed. It does imply that care has been taken that the work on which a manuscript is based has been thoroughly done.

CULTURAL DIFFERENCE AND MEDICAL CARE

The Case of the Spanish-Speaking People of the Southwest

By LYLE SAUNDERS

Associate Professor of Preventive Medicine
and Public Health (Sociology), University
of Colorado, School of Medicine

RUSSELL SAGE FOUNDATION
New York   ~   ~   *1954*

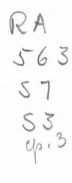

CONTENTS

3

*"He deemed it essential, it would seem, to know
the man before attempting to do him good."*

NATHANIEL HAWTHORNE

INTRODUCTION

THIS BOOK HAS BEEN CONCEIVED AND WRITTEN with two main purposes in mind. One is to present information about the Spanish-
speaking people of the American Southwest that may be useful
to medical and related professional people who work with members of that population group. The other is to use the situation of
the Spanish-speaking people and their relationships with the
English-speaking population among whom they live to illustrate
a few simple but highly important generalizations about medicine
and culture and the interrelations between them.

Professional and subprofessional workers in the fields of health
and medicine, welfare, and education, whose occupations involve
them in considerable interaction with Spanish-speaking people
in the Southwest, have an opportunity to observe that their
patients or clients or students at times behave in ways that are
thoroughly puzzling. A mother who obviously loves her child
waits until he is critically sick and almost beyond help before
seeking medical aid. A patient seriously ill with tuberculosis
leaves a hospital against medical advice to attend the wedding of
his brother. Children already much retarded are enrolled in
school months after the opening date and leave long before the
term ends. A family on public assistance, without enough money
for food, makes a down payment on an expensive television set.
A child dying of leukemia is taken from a hospital and placed
under the care of a *curandera*, a lay practitioner. These and similar
examples of behavior that might be listed readily are difficult
for professional people to understand because they derive in part
from somewhat different notions about the meanings and relative
values of health, education, welfare, family relationships, time,
work, and personal and professional responsibility from those

5

generally shared by persons who have received professional training. These differences, to the extent that they represent something more than idiosyncratic variations, are manifestations of a conditioning in and by a cultural group that includes among its beliefs, practices, and patterns of relationship many that are different from those of the dominant natively English-speaking population of the United States.

With the possible exception of Carey McWilliams' *North from Mexico* and John Burma's recently published *Spanish-Speaking Groups in the United States*, there has been no single book concerned with the whole Spanish-speaking population of the Southwest. The few good publications on the subject have dealt with one or another of the subgroups within the total population and, for the most part, have been concerned with describing and analyzing particular conditions and problems, without giving much consideration to the factor of cultural difference or its relation to those problems and conditions. The most penetrating studies of the culture of Spanish-speaking people in the Southwest have remained unpublished—mainly in the form of doctoral dissertations—or have been issued in such limited editions that copies are hard to obtain. Moreover, they have been written mainly from the point of view of the specialist in one of the social sciences and are not always so organized as to be of maximum value to a practicing professional person with a limited background in that field.

One of the purposes of this book, then, is to call attention to the fact that Spanish-speaking people in the Southwest share a distinctive culture which to some extent—varying from individual to individual and from situation to situation—exercises a determining influence on their behavior. A related purpose has been to provide enough information about that culture and its historical antecedents to enable professional people who work with members of the Spanish-speaking group to have some insights into factors that may underlie some of their behavior. The discussion is not intended to constitute a complete account of the culture of Spanish-speaking people. Rather, it is hoped that it may serve as an introduction to that culture which will sensitize people in the various professions to some of its implications and stimulate them to seek the more comprehensive sources that are available.

A second major purpose has been, as indicated above, to use the situation of the Spanish-speaking people and their relationship to various professional services and personnel to emphasize some aspects of the relationships between medicine, using that term in its broadest sense, and other parts of culture. The points to be made here are few in number and exceedingly simple to state. Like many generalizations in the social sciences, they seem so simple, so obvious as to be hardly worth mentioning. But their implications are neither simple nor obvious, and an adequate discussion of them could easily fill several volumes.

The first point is that the practice of medicine is a social activity. In whatever form it may take and wherever it may occur, the practice of medicine always involves interaction between two or more socially conditioned human beings. Furthermore, it takes place within a social system that defines the roles of the participants, specifies the kinds of behavior appropriate to each of those roles, and provides the sets of values in terms of which the participants are motivated. The way anyone behaves on either side of the therapeutic relationship is in part a function of his understanding of his social role in that situation and of the kind of behavior that is proper for it.

The second point to be emphasized is that medicine is a part of culture. In its totality, medicine consists of a vast complex of knowledge, beliefs, techniques, roles, norms, values, ideologies, attitudes, customs, rituals, and symbols, that interlock to form a mutually reinforcing and supporting system. Such a system is designated by the term "institution." Medicine as an institution is integrated with other major institutional complexes—government, religion, the family, art, education, the economy—into a functioning whole, which is culture. Each culture has its own unique system of elements constituting the institution of medicine. Some of the individual elements may be similar to or even identical with those of other cultures; some are certain to be different. Since in only the least complex societies, and possibly not even in those, can an individual encompass all of the culture of

the group into which he was born, subcultural groups exist; that
is to say, there are aggregations of people who have in common
some, but not all, of the elements of a given culture. In our culture, persons who are trained in a particular professional dis-
cipline, for example medicine, may be thought of as a subcultural
group.

When the practice of medicine involves the application of elements of the institution of medicine in one culture to the people
of another, or from one subculture to members of another subculture within the same cultural group, what is done or attempted by those in the healing roles may not be fully understood
or correctly evaluated by those in the patient roles. Conversely,
the responses of those on the patient side of the interaction may
not conform to the expectations of those on the healing side. To
the extent that this occurs, the relationship may be unsatisfactory
to everyone concerned.

When persons of widely dissimilar cultural or subcultural
orientations are brought together in a therapeutic relationship,
the probability of a mutually satisfactory outcome may be increased if those in the healing roles know something of their own
culture and that of the patient and are aware of the extent to
which behavior on both sides of the relationship is influenced by
cultural factors. An even higher probability of satisfaction may
result if the professional people are willing and able to modify
elements from their medicine so as to make them fit the expectations of the laymen with whom they are working.

The case of the Spanish-speaking people of the Southwest
admirably illustrates these points. The interaction of English-
speaking professional people and Spanish-speaking laymen in
medical situations is frequently hampered by their being members of different social systems and different cultures. Thus, they
define their roles somewhat differently, consider different kinds of
behavior appropriate in the situation, and evaluate its various
components differently. They share in any given instance of interaction a common interest in some aspect of illness or health, but
both tend to perceive the situation in terms of the complex of
elements that makes up the institution of medicine as they have

learned it from their cultural and subcultural participation and their ideas and feelings about proper role behavior. It is believed that the professional function of the English-speaking practitioner can be more effectively carried out if he views the situation in terms such as these and if he knows something about the specific cultural elements that influence the behavior of Spanish-speaking laymen and is willing to modify his own beliefs and procedures to the extent necessary to assure their cooperation.

My opportunity to work in a medical setting was largely the result of the deep interest of Dr. Ward Darley, now president of the University of Colorado, in having social science content and methodology introduced into the teaching and research activities of the University's School of Medicine, which at that time he directed. Through a series of discussions, initiated by Dr. Darley, with Dr. Esther Lucile Brown of Russell Sage Foundation, arrangements were made for my appointment to the teaching staff of the Department of Preventive Medicine and Public Health in the School of Medicine, a position that gave me many opportunities to observe interactions between Spanish-speaking laymen and a variety of professional people in both clinical and public health situations.

The idea for a book about Spanish-speaking people and their relationships with health facilities and personnel was suggested by Dr. Brown. In addition, she has carefully read several drafts of the manuscript, preparing each time detailed commentaries and criticisms. Her interest and enthusiasm, her keen critical judgment, her advice and assistance have placed me in her debt to an extent that no acknowledgment can appreciably diminish.

Helpful suggestions were also received from a number of friends and colleagues who read the first draft of the manuscript. Particularly valuable were the critical comments of Albert F. Wessen, Paul A. Walter, Jr., Benjamin D. Paul, George I. Sánchez, Julian Samora, and my colleagues in the Department of Preventive Medicine and Public Health, Drs. H. J. Dodge, Lloyd Florio, and Gertrud Weiss. Most helpful, too, was a series of conversations with Miss Geraldine Gourley, who furnished illustrative materials and insights into the behavior of Spanish-speaking patients.

Special thanks are due to Mrs. Dorothy Hannigan, who cheerfully typed the manuscript several times and offered numerous editorial suggestions.

Since the process of communication by written symbols is a somewhat imperfect one, no book ever says fully or precisely what its author had in mind. This one is no exception. But the effort to communicate will be sufficiently justified if, among those who read it, there are some to whom is transmitted even a small fraction of the very genuine and deep liking, admiration, and respect I feel for the Spanish-speaking people—*la gente de la raza.*

LYLE SAUNDERS

Denver, Colorado
September 10, 1954

Chapter I

FELICITY STREET

THE BUILDING AT 1407 FELICITY STREET in the city of Arcadia is an apartment house. It has not always been one. When constructed in 1898 it was one of the showplaces of Arcadia and was occupied by a single family, the Thompsons. They owned the canning plant, one of the largest department stores in Arcadia, and a bakery; and the entire family participated in local civic and social affairs. Their house was known to be one of the finest in town and frequently on a summer evening or a Sunday afternoon less prominent couples would stroll the few blocks from Main Street to see how the other half lived.

It has been many years since the Thompsons resided on Felicity Street. They moved to the newly developed Blossom Hills section the week after Woodrow Wilson was elected President for a second term, and the house was occupied for a few years thereafter by the family of a rancher who came to live in Arcadia so that his two daughters, just growing into their middle teens, could have the advantages of a city education. When they left, the house was sold to a lawyer who turned it over for a quick profit to an undertaker. This gentleman used it as a business establishment until the early 1930's, when it came into the possession of Mrs. Kathleen O'Keefe and was transformed into a boarding house for employed single girls. After Mrs. O'Keefe's death in 1945, the house, then somewhat run down, was taken over by Sellen Brothers, a real estate firm. Remodeled into apartments with only the minimum amount of work done in order to make the conversion, the building was again rented, this time to several families. Since then it has remained an apartment house and has been fully occupied.

Notes to chapters appear on pp. 247–283.

The present occupants of the 15 rooms and three baths of 1407 include 15 adults, 23 children, two dogs, three cats, a few rats, mice enough to keep two of the cats sleek and contented, and an assortment of lice, bedbugs, fleas, roaches, spiders, flies, and other pests. The human population are members of six families, or, more accurately, six households, since one includes a boarder unrelated to any member of the family with whom he lives; one consists of an unmarried mother and her infant daughter; and two include members of three generations, rather than the two considered normal for families in Arcadia. All are part of a population group[1] known in Arcadia as "Mexicans," although only three of the occupants of 1407 and an equally small proportion of their neighbors on Felicity and surrounding streets have ever been to Mexico.

This is to be a book in which the health practices and problems of the Spanish-speaking people of the American Southwest and the relationships of this population group to existing public and private health personnel and facilities will be used as an extended case to illustrate some of the areas and ways in which cultural factors[2] may and do influence the giving and accepting of medical care, using that term in its broadest possible meaning. Any one of a number of population groups might have been chosen to serve this illustrative purpose. The selection of the Spanish-speaking people was determined by several considerations. In the first place, they constitute the largest culturally distinct population group within the larger population of the United States,[3] so that any findings with respect to them or their health problems may reasonably be expected to have relevance for a large number of people. Second, there are numerous differences, both obvious and subtle, between their culture and that of the majority population, many of which have important implications for both attitudes and practices with respect to illness and health. Also, their distribution in the Southwest is such that in many localities their numerical concentration or high proportion in the total population brings them sharply to the attention of professional people in the various areas of medicine and health and contributes to public and individual health problems in which cultural factors may be readily seen to play an important part. And, finally, the Spanish-speaking people are a group in whom the writer has had a long and continuing interest.

Since we are to be so largely concerned here with the Spanish-speaking people of the Southwest—the group whom the inhabitants of Arcadia, as well as those of many other areas of the Southwest, refer to as "Mexicans"—it may be appropriate to begin with a closer look at the residents of 1407 Felicity Street.

Perhaps if we can learn something about this small group— where they came from, what they do for a living, how they live, what illnesses they have and what they do about them—we can better understand the health ways and problems of other inhabitants of the "Mexican" section of Arcadia and, to a lesser extent, those of Spanish-speaking people in all parts of the Southwest. This would not be so if Felicity Street and its occupants were unique to Arcadia. But they are not. Called by some other name, Felicity Street exists in Denver and Dallas, in El Paso, Phoenix, and Albuquerque, in Los Angeles and San Antonio. It exists wherever there are Spanish-speaking people living in urban areas in the Southwest.[4] It exists too, although in somewhat different form, in the smaller cities and towns and in agricultural villages. Felicity Street is less a location than a way of living, less a matter of geography than a matter of recurring conditions. Wherever it exists the individual people are different, but the conditions under which they live, the problems they face, the burdens they bear are much the same.

In viewing the inhabitants of 1407 we are not looking at all Spanish-speaking southwesterners, nor are we considering a sample that can be said to be typical or representative of the group as a whole. No sample so small could ever be fully representative of so heterogeneous a population. We are simply becoming acquainted with a few people, selected because they exemplify several kinds of health problems, who we have reason to believe are not greatly different in cultural background, ways of living, and point of view from a couple of million others. To the extent that our belief represents what actually exists, we can by learning about the people of 1407 Felicity Street also learn some-

thing about the inhabitants of similar streets elsewhere in the
Southwest.

THE OCCUPANTS OF 1407 FELICITY STREET

The ground floor of 1407 is occupied by three household
groups, the Treviños, the Gurules, and Simoneta Roybal and her
infant daughter.* Each of the apartments has a cold water tap;
no hot water is piped into any of them. These three households
and two from the upper floor share a common bath, a narrow
room lighted by a small frosted window at one end and a single
unshaded bulb that hangs from a long cord fastened in the center
of a high ceiling. The floor is covered with old, much worn
linoleum, buckled in places because of leakage from the tub.
There is an elaborate pedestal lavatory with heavy brass fixtures,
also an ancient much-ringed tub perched high on four legs, and a
toilet that flushes lethargically and noisily when the chain, leading to a water tank high up near the ceiling, is pulled.

The Treviños

The Treviños, who occupy the front apartment, have three
rooms, one of which, fitted as a kitchen, contains a sink, a four-
burner apartment-size gas stove, and an electric refrigerator.
There are five persons in the household, Linda, sixteen; Rosalie,
eighteen; Larry, twenty-three; Pedro, father of these three,
forty-eight; and Alessandro Flores, seventy-two, a boarder. Mrs.
Treviño died from pneumonia four years ago shortly after the
family came to Arcadia.

Pedro Treviño was born in a small village in north-central
New Mexico. He went through the third grade at the village
school but learned little there that has since been of value to him.

* It should surprise no one to learn that Arcadia, Felicity Street, the apartment
house at number 1407, and the inhabitants thereof are all imaginary. They easily
could exist, but they do not. Since an attempt was made to use names common
among the Spanish-speaking people of the Southwest, and since the conditions
described in this chapter are not uncommon among some portions of the Spanish-
speaking population—and among other population groups as well—the names of
actual persons or descriptions that fit actual conditions may inadvertently have been
used. If such usage has occurred, it is entirely coincidental. No reference to any real
person, living or dead, or to any actual family group is intended here and none
should be inferred.

The entire village was Spanish-speaking, so that during his childhood and youth his only contact with the English language was obtained during his brief period of schooling. As a boy and as a young man he worked as a sheepherder, first in and around his native village and then in other areas of New Mexico and, for a time, in Wyoming. When he was nineteen he married Adelina Trujillo, the daughter of a neighbor. Their first three children, each of whom was delivered at home and by untrained midwives, died before reaching the age of two.

In 1933, when Larry was two, Pedro and his family moved to Trinidad, Colorado, and a year later to Pueblo, where Pedro was able to find intermittent employment as a laborer. Since that time, with the exception of three seasons spent in cultivating beets, the family have been city dwellers. They came to Arcadia about four and a half years ago and have been living at 1407 Felicity Street for nearly two years. Mr. Flores joined them shortly after they moved in. The $45 a month he pays supplements the earnings of Pedro who is not and never has been regularly employed.

Pedro Treviño has never been very sick, nor has he ever been very well. There is no way to tell what diseases he may have had as a child, since no doctor was available in the village and thus no professional diagnoses were ever made. He remembers being ill on a few occasions and being treated with home remedies by his mother. But his recollections of just when he was ill or how he felt or what he may have had are not very clear. About eight months ago, while working on a construction job, he suffered a hernia which still gives him considerable discomfort. Surgery was recommended by the physician to whom he was taken by his employers, but he refused help of any kind. His reasons for not going back for treatment and not accepting surgery are confused. For one thing, he is afraid of hospitals and of surgery. Also, he feels generally uneasy when dealing with Anglos[5] in formal situations. He remembers unsatisfactory relationships with Anglos in official or professional positions. Another reason is that he more or less accepts whatever happens. And he is afraid that medical or surgical treatment will cost too much. Whatever the reasons may be, he has not sought help for his hernia. When the pain is severe, he takes a few spoonfuls of a preparation recommended to him by a neighborhood druggist, himself a "Mexican." Most of the time he is not particularly aware of the condition of his own health.

No physician attended Mrs. Treviño during her last illness. In the early stages she treated herself with a syrup made from frying down onions and then sweetening the juice with a little honey. When her condition became worse, she was given a remedy made of powdered oshá,[6] sugar, whisky, and hot water by a neighbor who was helping to take care of her. Her illness and death occurred during one of Pedro's periods of unemployment, and the local welfare department was asked to help pay her funeral expenses. It refused on the grounds that the Treviños did not meet the residence requirements for assistance. So Mrs. Treviño was buried in a coffin made by Pedro of lumber borrowed from a contractor for whom he had worked recently. Part of the cost of the funeral is still unpaid, although occasionally an extra dollar or two is diverted toward reducing the debt.

Linda Treviño has been under the care of a physician for a little more than a year. Picked up in a routine school health examination, sent to a diagnostic clinic, and found to have rheumatic heart disease, she has been a patient during that time in two hospitals and a convalescent home. She left all three against medical advice. The doctor who examined her last feels that she has a life expectancy at best of about five years, if she follows his advice, which includes constant bed rest. He is a little angry at the family because they do not insist that Linda stay in a hospital or convalescent home, feeling that they know the facts well enough but perversely refuse to cooperate. However, he has never talked directly to any of them except Linda and Rosalie.

Since leaving the hospital about six weeks ago, Linda has not been on bed rest nor has she followed any special therapeutic routine. She sometimes helps her sister with the housework and spends a good deal of time reading romance and movie magazines. She has used her illness as an excuse to stop attending school, but pays little attention to the implications of her condition. She is interested in boys and has caused a good deal of tension between herself and her father by going out at night unchaperoned and returning at what he considers improper hours. He is shocked by her freedom in associating with boys. She is resentful of what she considers his old-fashioned restrictions. Neither has any understanding of what lies behind the point of view of the other.

Linda is impulsive and headstrong and does not get along well with anyone. In the hospital she was for a time a "good" patient and was liked by the nurses and other hospital workers. But she refused to cooperate with the social worker assigned to the task of working out with her plans for future care, and she left the hospital to attend a teen-age dance. The visiting nurse, who stops by occasionally to see how Linda is getting along and to urge her to take better care of herself, is annoyed by the girl's apparent lack of concern about her illness and by her unwillingness to follow medical advice. The nurse feels that "something ought to be done" about the case, and, like the physician, is inclined to blame Pedro for what seems to be his indifference to his daughter's state of health.

Since her mother's death, Rosalie has been the female head of the household. She buys the food, does the cooking and washing, and makes decisions about the household budget. She has had only four years of schooling, having dropped out to accompany the family on one of their excursions to the beet fields. She was then in the third grade.[7] When she was fifteen, she worked for awhile as a clerk in a dime store. She quit after a few weeks because her father demanded that she stay home and take care of the house and look after her younger sister. Rosalie rather enjoyed her brief work experience and would like to go out to work again. She mildly resents being tied down by the household chores and is occasionally angry at Linda, whose illness prevents her from assuming a fair share of the household responsibility.

In her relations with people outside the family, Rosalie is more circumspect than Linda and has not run into any open conflict with her father. She spends a good deal of time with a small group of girls her own age who live in the neighborhood and through them has met a number of boys. About a year ago she consulted one of the community *médicas*[8] about a possible pregnancy, but there proved to be no basis for her alarm. Two months ago she was treated at the city's V.D. clinic for gonorrhea. Her family know nothing about either of these events.

Larry, who is now twenty-three years old, enlisted in the Army when he was sixteen and spent three years in service. He was a freshman in high school when he enlisted, having managed to stay in school in spite of the family's moving from place to place. After his discharge he completed his high-school work and is now a sophomore at Arcadia University. He wants to be an engineer. But his GI scholarship time has run out, and he is finding it difficult to remain in college. He works weekends and during the summer at a filling station, but his earnings are not enough to pay for tuition, books, and clothes. He is considering dropping out of school and working full time for a year or so to save enough money to permit him to finish. Also, he would like to get married.

Aside from an attack of measles at the age of five, Larry has never been ill. He was a little underweight at the time he joined the armed forces, but soon gained on the Army diet. He has had some trouble with his eyes since entering the University, but does not feel that he can afford an examination. He spends little time at home and has no particular awareness of or interest in the health of any other member of the family.

Alessandro Flores is a former coal miner who has been living with the Treviños for about two years. He pays his way with part of an $80-a-month old-age pension which he receives from the state. Flores was brought into the family through the efforts of the visiting nurse in the district and a medical social worker at the Arcadia public hospital. He had been admitted to the hospital suffering from the effects of silicosis and from a benign prostatic hypertrophy. Flores considered himself perfectly well and felt that his hospitalization was silly. Since he had been living alone —his wife had died about five years before, and his five children were living in other states—an attempt was made once to have him placed in a sanitarium or a convalescent home so that he could receive medical care, but he refused to go. Although he did not tell anyone the reason for his refusal, he was afraid of being cut off from other Spanish-speaking people and of being stranded among Anglos. Flores speaks almost no English and does not feel at ease in the company of Anglos. He was lonely in the hospital and was threatening to leave when the social worker and the visiting nurse seized upon the idea of boarding him with the Treviños. In spite of the crowded conditions there, he is comfortable, and the family benefit from the regular income he brings. The somewhat limited menu that Rosalie provides is one that he is accustomed to and he has no complaint. He enjoys talking to Pedro and spends considerable time sitting on the porch and exchanging greetings and comments with friends who pass by. In bad weather he listens to radio programs from Arcadia's only Spanish language station. Having never gone to school, Flores cannot read, nor can he write anything but his name. He laboriously inscribes it on the back of his pension check, and that is the extent of his literary abilities. He has no contact with his children, all of whom have families of their own, and receives no financial help from them.

The Gurules

The apartment at the back of the house is occupied by the Gurules, Virginia and Rafael, their six children, a son-in-law, and an eighteen-month-old grandson. Like the Treviños they have only three rooms, one of which, serving as a combined kitchen, living-room and dining-room, includes among its furnishings a cold water sink, a coal range, and an icebox that seldom contains ice but serves as a storage space for food.

Virginia, who, like her husband, is forty, was born on a ranch in southern Colorado, where her father worked as a ranch hand. She is dark and stocky, has an unhurried, calm disposition, and is quite competent in the management of her household. Her ankles occasionally swell and she suffers from shortness of breath even after mild exertion and finds that she has to rest several times during the day. But these symptoms cause her no particular concern. She is pregnant again and is a little apprehensive about this because of her experience two years ago. At that time she made her first visit to a hospital to have a baby delivered. Her other eight children—three of whom are dead—had all been born at home, the first five delivered by a *partera*, or midwife, and the last three by a physician. At the physician's insistence she had gone to the hospital for the birth of her ninth child. The hospital atmosphere was strange to her, and she was not particularly comfortable there. Her real concern began when, soon after her arrival at the hospital, she was taken by a friendly nurse to see the delivery room. For some reason the delivery table frightened her, and she began to be apprehensive about her forthcoming experience with it. Throughout the day her apprehension grew. Twice she slipped out of bed and went down the hall for another look and each time became more frightened. By nightfall she was terrified. Her first five children were born, as she had been, with their mother kneeling on the floor; the next three were delivered in bed, but it was a familiar bed in a familiar room. The delivery table with its shiny metal and leather straps was not like anything she had ever known and she was afraid of it. She tried to explain this to the nurse, but to her the idea that anyone who already had eight children could be afraid of a delivery room was so improbable that Virginia was not taken seriously. The nurse merely patted her on the shoulder, assured her that there was nothing to fear and that she would be all right, and left her.

During the night Virginia's labor began. She climbed out of bed and, taking a blanket from her bed, went into one of the corners of the ward. There on the floor, alone and unassisted, she gave birth to her baby. Only after the baby had been born and she was certain that it was too late to be taken to the delivery room, did she awaken one of the other patients in the ward and ask her to call the nurse. The nurse was thoroughly puzzled by Virginia's action; the resident in charge of the ward was bewildered and resentful that such an irrational, irresponsible act could occur on his ward. Both questioned Virginia to learn what had prompted her to do such a thing; both lectured her for having done it. Virginia took the questions and the scolding with a penitent but amiable grace. Actually she was a little pleased with herself and considerably relieved at having escaped the delivery room.

Virginia's present pregnancy, which still has a couple of months to go, is beginning to weigh on her mind. She has consulted her physician and he again insists that she be delivered in the hospital. She does not want to go, but cannot think of any reasons that would be convincing to him. Besides, she dislikes having to disagree with anyone so kind and helpful, and therefore does not state her reasons very forcefully. She has agreed to go to the hospital, but actually she has no intention of going. And when her labor begins she will either remain at home alone or will call in the *partera* who helped her with her first five babies. She knows the *partera* will say nothing to her about a hospital.

Rafael Gurule was born on a small farm in the western part of Hidalgo County, Texas. The farm was sold following the death of his father from tuberculosis in the middle 1920's, and Rafael went to make his home with an aunt in El Paso. There he lived in a tenement near the international bridge, spent a good deal of his time on the Mexican side of the Rio Grande, and worked during the summers on farms a few miles down the river. He had attended school irregularly in south Texas, but never bothered to go after moving to El Paso. When he was eighteen he got a job on a railroad section gang working out of El Paso. He quit after a few months and, with a little money in his pocket, drifted northward to see the country and to look for more congenial surroundings. At a dance at a little town in southern Colorado he met Virginia Velasquez. Within a short time they were married. A month later they were living in Arcadia and Virginia was carrying her first child.

Throughout his married life, Rafael has had a varied employment history. He has never moved out of the unskilled classification, and consequently his earnings have always been low. Sometimes he has been unemployed. He worked on a WPA project for more than a year during the 1930's and on several occasions has received general assistance from the State Welfare Department. He has been employed as a carpenter's helper, a construction laborer, a warehouseman, a dishwasher, and a boxmaker. His present job in a slaughtering and meat packing plant pays the most he has ever earned, $48 a week.

On the whole, Rafael's health has been good. He has had infrequent attacks of what he calls rheumatism, one of which was severe enough to cause him to see a chiropractor whom a friend had recommended. Twice he went to the outpatient clinic of the public hospital because he thought he had kidney trouble, but no one was able quickly to find anything wrong with him and after the two visits he became discouraged and never returned. Sometimes he is plagued by a rather sharp, burning sensation in his stomach that awakens him in the middle of the night, but he can usually get relief from a remedy suggested by the corner druggist. He also takes regularly a preparation which the druggist has assured him will help to maintain his sexual vigor. Only once during the past twenty years has Rafael been sick enough to miss work. On that occasion he had a high fever, with some vomiting, that persisted for three days. Virginia called a *médica* who recommended a tea made of *flor de sauz* (elderberry) leaves to reduce the fever and a few leaves of *alhucema* (lavender) to relieve the vomiting. Fortunately, both were available in the *médica's* stock and Rafael promptly recovered.

The Gurules' six living children are all still at home. The eldest daughter, Ramona, worked for a time in an airplane factory in California, but she became lonesome for her family and returned home bringing a husband, David Bustamante. While at the factory she slipped one day and fell from a low platform on which she was working. She was not injured, but from that time on she felt that work made her nervous and has stayed at home since returning to Arcadia. Ramona is looked upon as the educated one in the family, having been graduated from the eighth grade, but neither she nor any other member of the family feels that her knowledge has been of any particular advantage to her or to them. David, her husband, who works as a plumber's helper, finished the sixth grade, but failed to make the transition to junior high school. He considers his $1.25 an hour "good money," since it enables him to feed and clothe himself, his wife, and their eighteen-month-old son, to maintain in a fair state of repair a 1947 Dodge, and to purchase once or twice a week admission to a drive-in theater. Like all the other tenants of 1407

Felicity Street, Ramona and David have no savings, no insurance, and no very definite plans for the future.

Of the Gurule children, only nine-year-old Ernest attends school. Roseann, the youngest daughter, is only two, and therefore too young to go. Lucy is six and could have entered school this year, but her mother did not get around to taking her on the first day. Then she decided that since the child was late already she might as well wait another year. Lucy, who did not care one way or the other, made no objection and has continued to play happily with her toys and her friends. The eldest son, Frank, sixteen, is subject to epileptic seizures which, fortunately, occur only rarely. He lost one job as a car washer in a filling station as a result of a grand mal seizure. At present he is employed as a stock boy in a chain grocery. His employers do not know of his illness. Nothing is being done for him. His family regard it as unfortunate that he is afflicted, but do not feel that there is much they should or can do about it. Louis, aged fourteen, has just been discharged from the state reformatory for boys, where he spent a year following his apprehension on a charge of car stealing. He does not go to school nor does he work; he spends much of his time with a group of teen-age boys at a hangout on a sandbar near the river. The three older children were each vaccinated once for smallpox. As a result of herculean efforts by the school nurse, Ernest has been immunized against smallpox, diphtheria, and whooping cough; has had one chest x-ray; and has had a dental examination and one extraction by the school clinic. None of the younger children has been immunized. Virginia is not opposed to immunizations; she just does not seem to find time to get herself and the children dressed and over to the child health clinics on the days that the visiting nurse suggests.

Since there are not enough dishes or other tableware, to say nothing of table space, the Gurule family eat in shifts, first the four adults and then the six children. Frank sometimes eats with the adults. The food is usually plentiful but lacks variety. Wheat tortillas, coffee, beans, bread, and macaroni appear frequently. Sometimes there is canned fruit. Fresh fruits, vegetables, and milk are rare. The visiting nurse has talked to Virginia at times about the seven basic foods and the necessity for eating green and leafy vegetables. Virginia is interested, appreciative of the nurse's efforts to help her, and pleased to be the object of so much friendly attention. But the menus seldom change. Cod liver oil, vitamin supplements, fresh fruit juice, and milk have been urged as essential to the health of the children. But the infant grandson, like Roseann and Lucy, has been eating at the family table since he was weaned. He likes coffee, and eats tortillas and beans. On drive-in nights he gets a special treat, a bag of popcorn or a candy bar.

The Gurules are a reasonably happy family. Their apartment is crowded and friendly. The adults have time to talk to each other and to the children. Rafael and his son-in-law like their jobs and get along well with their fellow workers. Occasionally on payday they stop at a *cantina* for a few beers with their friends. They like to talk in the evening with Mr. Flores, the old man who boards with the Treviños in the front apartment. Virginia and Ramona enjoy each other's society. They also have a small circle of friends whom they see and chat with before and after Mass, which they attend regularly. The children play with each other and with the neighbors. There is for them never any lack of companionship. Virginia and Rafael know quite a bit of English, but never feel at home in the language and prefer to talk in Spanish. The older children are bilingual, and switch from one language to another in their conversation. The young ones know some Spanish but prefer to speak English, the language of the comic strip characters, the movie comedians, and the radio cowboys.

Simoneta Roybal

If the Gurules are happy, their neighbor Simoneta Roybal certainly is not. Simoneta and her infant daughter Josie live in a single room that opens off the hall connecting the apartments of the Treviños and the Gurules. The room has an unvented two-burner gas plate which serves both as cookstove and furnace. In addition, there are a cold water sink, a table, two chairs, a bed, and a curtained-off corner that is used as a closet. Simoneta is a poor housekeeper, and the place is always cluttered with papers, clothes, empty cartons, comic books, and dirty dishes. There is no crib for the baby, so the little one sleeps in her mother's bed.

At twenty-two Simoneta finds herself with an arrested case of pulmonary tuberculosis, a toxic goiter for which surgery has been recommended, and an illegitimate daughter. The child, now six months of age, was born prematurely and was kept in Arcadia Hospital three weeks before being released to the mother. Three months later, at the insistence of the visiting nurse, the child was brought back to the hospital, where a diagnosis of malnutrition was made. During the month the baby was hospitalized she was not visited by her mother, and it was only after some prodding that the hospital authorities succeeded in getting Simoneta to come for the child when it was time for her to be discharged. Now, after another month at home, Josie is already beginning to show the same symptoms for which she had been hospitalized. Instruction in proper methods of preparing a formula and feeding a baby were given Simoneta in the hospital and by the visiting nurse after she returned home. But she was not much interested and has never made any effort to follow the instructions. When Josie shows signs of being hungry, which is often, her mother gives her a mixture of canned evaporated milk and tap water. Bottle and nipple are rinsed under the tap between feedings and then, still wet, are placed on the table to await the next meal. Occasionally Simoneta will give Josie a scrap from her plate when she is eating, a piece of bread, a bite of meat or a bone, a spoonful of canned fruit. There are only half a dozen diapers and Simoneta does not like to wash, so that Josie is not changed frequently, nor is she bathed regularly. As a result her back, from her knees to her shoulders, is raw and blistered. The bed, for which there is no rubber blanket, is wet much of the time.

Simoneta is short and dumpy and not very attractive. Her disposition does nothing to draw people to her. She is sullen much of the time and gives the impression of being either hostile or apathetic. She is not liked by the other tenants on her floor, and the agency personnel—the visiting nurse, the welfare workers—who work with her are about ready to give her up as a hopeless case.

Simoneta was born in San Rafael. Before her first birthday she was given to another family, Juan and Consuelo Gutierrez, with whom she continued to live until she was sixteen. Juan, a distant relative of her father, had no children of his own and so, as a friendly gesture, Simoneta was given to him and his wife to help fill the gap in their childless lives. There was no formal adoption. The Gutierrez couple were a highly mobile pair, and while Simoneta lived with them she was constantly on the move. She never attended school, and the family never stayed long enough in any one locality for her to form any close friendships with other children. She did much of the housework, and from the time she was ten also worked in the fields with her foster parents. Although she moved in and through Anglo communities in four southwestern states, she never learned more than a few words of English.

Simoneta was sixteen when she had her first hemorrhage. After a brief period of hospitalization during which a diagnosis of pulmonary tuberculosis was made, she was sent to a sanitarium in Arizona. She was lonely and unhappy there. Cut off from other patients and members of the staff by her inability to speak English and restless as a result of the change from a mobile to a sedentary life, she left the sanitarium against medical advice and joined Juan and Consuelo in Colorado. Within a few months she broke down again and, after some difficulty, was admitted to another sanitarium. Here she stayed for two years, not liking the place, but afraid to leave. A short time before she left, Juan and Consuelo were killed in a truck-train collision in Texas. Thus, at the time of her discharge Simoneta had no education, no particular skills, no knowledge of English, and no place to go. Her brothers and sisters were scattered; her mother and father both were dead. For a time she hoped to be able to live with a married sister in Chama, New Mexico, but her husband's work was seasonal and both felt that they could not afford to keep Simoneta.

For want of a better place to go, Simoneta came to Arcadia. She worked for four months as a waitress in a hole-in-the-wall café on Aragon Street in the "Mexican" part of town and then moved up to a job in Pete's Place, a combination bar and restaurant, near the center of the district. While working here she met and became fond of Johnnie Dominguez, a truck driver on the Arcadia-Los Angeles run. Together they rented the one-room apartment at 1407 Felicity Street. Two months after Simoneta became certain that she was pregnant, Johnnie disappeared. She has had no word from him since.

It was while she was in the hospital for the birth of her child that Simoneta first learned she had a goiter. She had previously noted a small swelling on her neck but had not thought much about it. Just before she was released from the hospital, an intern tried to explain her thyroid condition to her and to persuade her to have the goiter removed. Simoneta never did fully understand what it was he was trying to say, but she did catch the implication of surgery and would have none of it. She is afraid of surgery, feels that she might die during the operation, and much prefers to live with her goiter which she does not understand than to submit to the unknown dangers of an operation.

For the past four months Simoneta has been receiving a monthly grant of $78 from the welfare department under its aid to dependent children program. With that she pays her rent and buys food for herself and canned milk for Josie. She feels tied down by the baby and resents the fact that she can no longer participate in the Saturday night excitement at Pete's Place. Occasionally the swelling on her neck causes her concern but she has no intention of doing anything about it. She has no plans for the future, either for herself or for Josie.

The upper floor of 1407 Felicity Street is, like the ground floor, the home of three households, Fermín and Rachel Atencio in the front apartment, Miguel and Concepción Rubio, his parents, and eight children in the back, and Antonio and María Vigil, with their five children, in the middle two rooms. The one bathroom on this floor is in the apartment of the Atencios and is used exclusively by them. The other two households share the one downstairs with the three families living on that floor.

The second floor is reached by a rather steep stairway that begins just inside the front door of the house, rises sharply to a landing, turns back upon itself and leads to a railed platform off which open the doors of the three apartments. An unshaded 25-watt bulb hangs on a long cord down the stairwell to a point just above the upper floor and thus provides a feeble illumination for the stairs and both the upper and lower halls.

The Atencios

The Atencios are the aristocrats of Felicity Street. Fermín, a high-school graduate, who has lived in Arcadia all of his twenty-two years, is steadily employed. A foreman in the canning plant once owned by the Thompsons, he earns more than $300 a month, which enables him and his wife to have three rooms and a bath all to themselves, with a gas range, vented gas heaters, a seven-cubic-foot electric refrigerator, overstuffed furniture, and a console radio. They are thinking of buying a television set if they can find someone who will take the radio off their hands as a trade-in. The Atencios could afford to live in a better apartment, but they are reluctant to pay more than the $62 a month they now pay; also they feel they are receiving good value here. They have a savings account which they hope will someday include enough to cover a down payment on a house of their own, but their bank deposits are not made regularly.

A childless couple, the Atencios have relatively little to do with the other families in the building. They go out frequently in the evenings to movies and commercial dances. Fermín, who earned something of a reputation as an athlete in his high-school days, plays baseball and basketball in an industrial league during a good part of the year, and they frequently attend commercial and collegiate sports events. Rachel, who was employed as a typist before her marriage, does not visit much with the other wives in the building, but does have a group of girl friends with whom she spends many afternoons. Neither Fermín nor Rachel attends church regularly. Both understand Spanish but speak English most of the time.

The Atencios are a bit more self-conscious about their health than are most of the other occupants of the apartment house. Fermín frequently takes laxatives, and both he and Rachel regularly supplement their diet with vitamin tablets. Rachel is taking a reducing preparation which she read about in a movie magazine. Since antihistamines became popular a few years ago, the Atencios have kept a supply of them on hand and use them frequently during the winter months.

Some weeks ago Rachel became ill and, on the advice of a physician whom Fermín persuaded her to consult, was hospitalized. The diagnosis was kidney infection. She spent a week in the hospital and then left against medical advice. While there she complained constantly about the food and the service she received. Both she and Fermín felt that the soft diet she was getting was not suited to her and he frequently slipped other food to her during visiting hours. They both felt that the doctors did not tell them enough. The reason given for leaving the hospital was that Rachel's uncle who lived in Dallas was seriously ill and needed them. The real reason was that Rachel was afraid that the doctors were planning an operation.

For a few days after returning home, Rachel was quite uncomfortable and was given some symptomatic treatment, aspirin tablets, kidney pills, hot water bottles, by Fermín. When her condition did not improve, they decided to consult a *médica*, a Negro woman who lives alone in a small house a few miles north of Arcadia. They drove out to see her and felt much reassured by the visit. She began by saying that she did not want them to tell her what was wrong, that she would tell them. She then proceeded to relate a few incidents which Rachel was able to identify as having once happened to her and described some of the more general symptoms Rachel was then experiencing. The Atencios were much impressed by this display of ability, and particularly by the contrast between the approach of the *médica* and that of the physician who had recommended hospitalization. He had asked many questions about Rachel's past life and her symptoms, and had been exceedingly noncommittal about both diagnosis and prognosis. The *médica* asked no questions and was quite definite both as to what was wrong with Rachel and the prospects for a cure. For a flat $150 she offered to undertake treatment and to guarantee a cure, promising to refund the

money if that was not achieved. The Atencios accepted her terms and treatment was begun immediately. The first step was a long, very hot bath which Rachel took in an oversized tub in a back-room of the *médica's* house. She was then sent home with two bottles of medicine, one a strong-tasting greenish liquid which was to be taken internally at four-hour intervals and the other a thick, oily, very astringent preparation which periodically was to be rubbed into her back until all signs of the lotion had disap-peared. Rachel has continued with these medications, has had both bottles renewed once, has visited the *médica* twice, and has also continued her own symptomatic treatments. She is feeling better and both she and Fermín are satisfied with the treatment given by the *médica*. They are glad that she did not remain in the hospital.

The Vigils

Antonio and María Vigil and their five children live in the two-room apartment just behind the Atencios. Antonio, twenty-five years old, is a construction laborer whose employment is somewhat irregular, so that the family is never far above the bare subsistence level. Both Antonio and María were born in Texas. Soon after their marriage eight years ago, they moved to Arcadia in the hope of finding better employment. María has active pulmonary tuberculosis and was for a time a bed patient in a sanitarium located in a little town 40 miles from Arcadia. She left against medical advice because she felt all right and was lone-some for her husband and children. She has an inadequate knowledge of her disease. Nor does she understand its progressive nature, or realize that it is infectious and that she may be en-dangering the health of her children as well as that of other people with whom she comes in contact.

The two-room apartment is crowded with the seven people and their belongings. As in some of the other apartments in the build-ing, a two-burner open gas plate is used for cooking and in cold weather heat is provided by a single unvented gas heater. María is afraid of night air and keeps the windows closed most of the time. The family all sleep in the same room, on two beds and a crib.

María, who has never been to school, speaks almost no English. Antonio has some knowledge of it because of his contacts with English-speaking workers, but is uneasy with the language and much prefers to speak Spanish. Consuelo, seven years old and enrolled in the second grade at a parochial school, is the most fluent member of the family and frequently acts as interpreter for her mother. Sylvia, five, has picked up some English from her playmates. Mike, three, and Jerry, two, know only a few Spanish words. The family are Catholics, and although Antonio rarely goes to church, María is a faithful communicant, health permitting. María hopes that next year Sylvia can enter the school Consuelo attends.

All the children have frequent upper-respiratory infections. Consuelo has been vaccinated and last year was given a rather superficial examination by a school physician who looked at some 30 children in a single afternoon. About a year ago María took Sylvia, Mike, and Jerry to a well-baby clinic for immunizations. They all experienced mild reactions from their first shots, and the mother never took them again. None of the children has ever had a chest x-ray, nor has Antonio; all except Jerry and Ruby, the baby, have dental caries. Consuelo has been recommended by the school nurse for dental treatment in a clinic maintained by the parochial school system, but María has never taken her there. At nine months of age Ruby has slightly bowed legs, but María feels that they will straighten themselves out in time. The children are dirty much of the time, but they are reasonably happy, with the possible exception of Consuelo who is beginning to notice differences between herself and some of her classmates. During the past year she has been having occasional episodes of nocturnal enuresis, which María regards as normal and likely to disappear as the child grows older.

Consuelo, who is considered a very bright child by her teachers, is conscious of the fact that her clothes are not so pretty and certainly not so clean as those of many of her classmates. She felt quite humiliated when, in the first grade, she was sent home from school with a note—which her mother could not read—saying that she had head lice and would not be permitted to return until she was free from this condition. She stayed out of school two days and then returned, still with the lice. She was admitted along with the half-dozen or so other children who had followed the same procedure. The school nurse plans to call on María and talk the situation over, but so far has not got around to it.

The Rubios

The most crowded apartment in 1407 Felicity is that of the Rubios. In its three rooms live Miguel Rubio and his wife Concepción, their eight children, and Miguel's parents, Enrique and Josefina. Miguel is a serious-minded, industrious man of forty-four who works as a laborer for the city sanitation department. His income is not large and it has been necessary to supplement it on several occasions with general assistance grants from the department of welfare. Both Miguel and his wife, as well as his parents, are devout Catholics and all attend services regularly. Although Miguel and Concepción know English, Miguel's parents do not, so that most of the time Spanish is spoken in their home. The children who are old enough to talk are all bilingual, although the two older ones, Reuben, twenty, and Esperanza, eighteen, do not like to speak Spanish and use English on every possible occasion.

Like most of the other families in the building, the Rubios have no refrigeration. Perishable foods are either not used or are consumed immediately after purchase. The diet consists largely of such staples as macaroni, flour, dried beans, coffee, dried or smoked meats, and corn, all of which keep well without refrigeration. Cooking is done, winter and summer, on a wood-burning range. A small iron coal-burning heating stove is set up in one of the rooms during the winter months. There is, as in the other apartments, a cold water sink.

Josefina and Enrique were both born on a ranch near Santa Catarina in the state of Nuevo León, Mexico. With Miguel and three other children they came to the United States in 1916, drawn by what they had heard about opportunities for well-paid work. They crossed the border illegally by wading the Rio Grande and found shelter and work on a sheep ranch in southwest Texas. The entry was never legitimized, and neither the elder Rubios nor their children were ever naturalized. In 1921 they moved to El Paso, where Enrique found work as a section hand on the Southern Pacific Railway. He continued with the company until 1940 when, as the result of an accident while at work, his right leg was amputated just above the knee. With the small amount of compensation they received from the railroad, he and Josefina bought and, until 1946, operated a small store in Pharr, Texas. Business was never good, and by 1946 their resources had dwindled to the point where they could no longer keep the store going. They then moved to Arcadia to live with their son Miguel. Enrique found occasional work during the first three years of their stay and contributed something to the maintenance of the household, but for the past three years he has been unable to find work and, much of the time, would have been unable to work had anyone offered him a job. He is prematurely feeble, suffers from chronic arthritic pains, and has a persistent cough. A wooden peg, fastened to the stump by straps, enables him to get around without crutches, but he cannot walk far without experiencing pain and considerable fatigue. When his joints are particularly painful, his wife prepares and has him drink *cañutillo*[9] tea, and for his cough she frequently gives him the water in which *orégano*[10] has been boiled.

Josefina at sixty-seven is small and wizened, but very energetic. Always wearing the same black dress, with her head wrapped in a *rebozo*, or shawl, she is a familiar sight in the neighborhood as she hurries to and from early Mass. She insists on proper respect from her grandchildren for both her husband and herself, advises her daughter-in-law concerning the management of household affairs, and worries about the short hair, short skirts, and informal ways of Esperanza. She knows practically everything that goes on, not only in her own household but in the others in the building and neighborhood as well, and expresses opinions freely. She firmly believes in witchcraft, is certain that baby Cleo's latest attack of diarrhea was a symptom of *mal ojo*,[11] resulting from the strong glance of a visiting nurse, and has frequently acted as *partera* in the delivery of neighborhood babies. She has a wide store of knowledge about folk and household remedies and is frequently consulted by neighbor women as to the proper treatment for minor—and sometimes major—illness of themselves and their families. She treats herself on the few occasions when she does not feel well and has never thought it necessary to call in an Anglo doctor to care for any member of her family. Her husband did receive medical care from a railway physician at the time of his accident, but, following the amputation of his leg, Josefina treated the stump with ointments and fluids which she herself prepared.

Miguel was eight years old when his parents brought him to the United States. On the ranch he herded sheep, and after the family moved to El Paso he, like Rafael Gurule, worked in the fields on the farms down the river from that city. He left El Paso and his parents' home when he was seventeen and for eight years thereafter worked in the mines in and around Globe, Arizona. Between 1933 and 1937 he had various WPA jobs in Arizona. Early in 1938 he went out to California and found work in a foundry, which he kept until the summer of 1940. He then came to Arcadia, and within a month obtained the job with the city sanitation department which he has held since. In 1943—over his mother's objections—Miguel was hospitalized with pneumonia, and off and on throughout his adult life he has had bouts of indigestion. Aside from these and the usual run of colds and other minor respiratory infections, he has been fairly healthy.

Concepción was born and grew up in Tucson, Arizona, where her father, a naturalized Mexican, operated a small café. She was working as a waitress in Globe when, in 1930, she met and married Miguel. She is a congenial, easy-going, talkative woman who is largely unperturbed by the clamorous demands of her household and holds her own against the dominating threat of her mother-in-law. Toward her children she is affectionate, tolerant, and permissive. She accepts things as they happen and easily handles situations that less secure people might regard as crises or emergencies. Whatever happens she sees as the will of God against which one should neither fight nor protest. Her children are frequently dirty, sometimes ill, and seldom well fed.

She is not unconcerned about them; she is unexcited. On the rare occasions when school nurses, visiting nurses, or welfare department social workers have visited her home, she has listened politely, agreed with everything they suggested, and continued her own way after they had gone. During her numerous pregnancies she was repeatedly urged to see a doctor for an antepartum and postpartum checkup, but she never did. Nor has she ever been delivered by anyone except a midwife—her mother-in-law in the case of the three youngest children—and at no place except in her home. For a number of years the district nurse has tried to persuade her to take her young children to the well-baby clinic for a checkup and immunizations, but, although she has been polite to the nurse and has agreed that undoubtedly the advice was good, she has never got around to taking any of the children there.

Like her husband, Concepción has enjoyed fairly good health. She had no trouble while carrying any of the children and all her deliveries were uncomplicated. She shares the minor infections that run through the family, particularly in the winter months, and not infrequently has headaches, especially after a period of sewing, but these do not bother her much. About two years ago she slipped on the top step of the stairs and fell to the landing, but the only damage was a sprained wrist, which Josefina treated.

The two older children, Reuben and Esperanza, spend a good deal of time away from home. Reuben completed two years of high school and is a stock clerk in Arcadia's largest department store. He is doing well on the job and is liked by his employers and fellow workers. A year ago he was asked to report to Selective Service for examination but was rejected because of an old elbow injury which prevents him from entirely straightening his right arm. He intends to marry soon, a plan that is supported enthusiastically by his grandmother, Josefina, but treated with amiable indifference by his mother. Esperanza is a car hop at a drive-in food stand, a job which keeps her out late at night and brings her the outspoken disapproval of Josefina. The old lady particularly objects to the abbreviated shorts and blouse which are the working costume of her granddaughter and to the free and easy semi-joking relations which Esperanza has with the young male customers of the drive-in.

Arturo, aged fourteen, is in the seventh grade at a public school. He has very poor eyesight but he does not wear glasses. Although his eye condition has often been called to the attention of his mother, she has done nothing about it. He is a slow pupil, is not well liked by his classmates, and prefers playing with children several years younger than himself. Helen, who is ten, is shy and underdeveloped. Like her mother she is very amiable and placid. Helen is not very bright and has spent two years in each of the first two grades in school. Christine, eight, is in the same grade as Helen. She is a thin, anemic child who suffers from frequent earache, occasional sore throat, and a chronic cough, with a tendency toward asthmatic wheezing. Rosalie, five, is a well-developed child, apparently normal, except for her right foot which is turned inward. She has never received any medical attention for it. The two babies, Cleo, three, and Tommy, two, have coughs and runny noses six months of the year, diaper rash about a third of the time, and a series of scratches, cuts, and bruises as a result of unsupervised play in the yard during the warm weather. Both they and Rosalie have had measles and chicken pox within the past year. The other children had them long ago.

These, then, are the residents of 1407 Felicity Street: Six more or less ordinary low-income households in an ordinary tenement apartment building on a street that might be found in almost any sizable southwestern city. Six households, each of which has some elements of uniqueness and all of which share many characteristics with one another and with thousands of other households in the region.

One such characteristic is that these family groups are what we might, for want of a better term, call Spanish-speaking households, which means that their members have, to a greater or lesser extent, participated in a somewhat different cultural heritage from that of the bulk of the natively English-speaking people among whom they live. Thus, to some degree, varying from family to family, and depending upon the specific life experiences of the family group, their ways of thinking, acting, and believing are different from those of the numerically dominant Anglo population. In some Spanish-speaking families the differences are small, and in behavior and point of view the families are almost indistinguishable from Anglo families on the same social level. In others the differences are great, and there are many elements in the behavior, beliefs, and preferences of the Spanish-speaking family members that distinguish them from comparable Anglo families.[12]

It is with these differences in ways of thinking, acting, and believing and some of their implications for the work of persons professionally interested in illness and its treatment among the Spanish-speaking group that this book is largely concerned. Such differences, insofar as they are not unique to an individual or family group, but may be seen to derive from and be related to cultural or subcultural membership, are believed to reflect important variables in the maintenance of health and the treatment of illness. The point of view to be presented here is that the practice of the healing arts is to a considerable extent a social activity in which the course of the relationship is determined not only by the knowledge, skills, feelings, and attitudes of the professional practitioner, whether physician, nurse, psychiatrist, or social worker, but also to a considerable extent by the knowledge, feelings, and attitudes of the patient, his relatives, and friends. And one highly important, but frequently overlooked, determining variable in everybody's knowledge, attitudes, and feelings is membership in and identification with cultural and subcultural groups.

The knowledge and skills of a professional practitioner of any of the healing arts are of little value unless they are used. They may be a source of intellectual or emotional satisfaction to the practitioner himself, but they serve no further purpose unless, directly or indirectly, they are used for the benefit of patients or clients. And they can only be used in and through a social relationship, or an interlocking series of such relationships involving certainly the practitioner and his patient or client and usually other professional or subprofessional workers and other people affectively related to the patient or client. In these relationships many variables besides the knowledge and skills of the practitioner and the physiological or psychological states of the patient are operative. Both practitioner and patient have personalities, and these influence the course of the relationship. Both have conceptions of what their proper role should be and of what role the other should assume. Both have ends or goals that they are seeking in the relationship. Each has a set of attitudes and feelings about members of the various social categories into which the other can be placed. The practitioner, for example, may have notions about patients, about women, about persons of lower-class status, or about Spanish-speaking people which influence his behavior in the relationship when the patient conforms to any of these categories. The patient may have feelings and preconceptions about physicians, about professional groups, about upper-class people, about men, about Anglos which similarly may affect his or her performance in the relationship. Both patient and practitioner have sets of values which establish limits to what each can and will do in the relationship. These and many other types of variables which might be listed all influence the course of the patient-practitioner relationship.

Much more than the knowledge and skill of the practitioner and the physical or emotional condition of the patient thus enters into the practice of the healing arts. The knowledge, feelings, and evaluative judgments of all persons involved in the interaction have a bearing on its course and outcome. Where the knowledge, feelings, and evaluations are largely complementary and mutually reinforcing, the relationship and its outcome may be highly satisfactory to everyone. Where they are largely antithetical or antagonistic or simply incongruent, no one may be happy about the relationship or get much satisfaction from it. If, for example, practitioner and patient have roughly the same concept of disease, its cause, and its treatment; if the patient has confidence in the skill of the practitioner and in the practitioner's interest in him and the practitioner likes the patient and feels assured of his trust and cooperation; and if both are agreed on the relative seriousness of the illness and the necessity of doing certain things about it, then the relationship may be pleasant and gratifying for both. On the other hand, if the patient mistrusts either the motives or the abilities of the practitioner or the practitioner is ignorant of, has hostility toward, or lacks respect for the point of view of the patient, or if the patient and practitioner disagree about the importance of the illness or the desirability or necessity of any given procedure, then neither is likely to benefit much from the relationship.

One constant source of disparity in knowledge about and attitudes toward illness and its treatment is a difference in cultural orientation such as exists between English-speaking and Spanish-speaking people in the American Southwest. There are, of course, wide ranges of variation in both knowledge and attitudes within each of these population groups, variations that are to some extent correlated with such variables as age, sex, class status, education, and occupation. There is also a considerable overlap between the two groups, since each has for a number of years been influenced by its contact with the other. But even allowing for these facts, there is still an observable difference in the approach of each of these groups to illness and its treatment. Spanish-speaking people, in general, tend to have somewhat different concepts of disease, its cause, and what should be done about it, from those of Anglos. They have had historically, and to some extent continue to have, different patterns of relationships between patient and healer and different conceptions of what is the proper role of each in the therapeutic relationship. They have a different pharmacopoeia. They have, perhaps, a somewhat different basic personality structure and a different set of patterns of response to the stresses resulting from illness and incapacity. They have different notions of the proper roles of relatives and friends in the healing process. They have, in brief, an institutional complex somewhat different from that of the Anglos for dealing with such potentially disruptive conditions as disease, injuries, mental disorders or deficiencies, birth, death, and old age, a complex that largely determines what a person shall think, feel, and do when he, or persons with whom he has affective relationships, experiences any of these conditions.

Some of these differences will be described and discussed in later chapters. Here it is enough to point out that such differences do exist, and that they have an effect on practitioner-patient relationships when the cultural—or subcultural—backgrounds of the two are dissimilar. And in the Southwest they frequently are dissimilar. The Spanish-speaking people of the Southwest are, for reasons which will be discussed later, probably more subject to certain types of illness than the larger population among whom they live. They thus require more medical attention. To their reliance on their own cultural ways of dealing with disease and on their own types of "professional" healers has been added an increasing tendency toward the acceptance of Anglo healing ways and, consequently, of Anglo healers. There are among the Spanish-speaking population relatively few persons with the training, knowledge, and skills to enable them to practice the Anglo form of any of the healing arts, so that the Spanish-speaking person who wishes any kind of Anglo medical care must, much of the time, seek it from an Anglo. Anglo practitioners in the Southwest thus frequently number among their patients Spanish-speaking persons who bring to the relationship attitudes, values, and a point of view that are different from theirs and that sometimes interfere with the giving of what they consider to be good professional care.

It is this situation that provides the focal point for the present study. Its purpose is to provide factual information and enough additional references to enable the Anglo practitioner to know something about the demographic, cultural, and historical backgrounds of his Spanish-speaking patients. It will indicate areas wherein differences in knowledge, beliefs, values, and attitudes between Spanish-speaking patients and Anglo practitioners may interpose barriers to effective interaction. It will describe some of the healing ways historically and currently used by Spanish-speaking people and attempts to assess the meaning of these for the work of various types of Anglo professional or subprofessional workers in the field of health and illness. And, finally, it will attempt some generalized statement of the difficulties inherent in giving medical care to groups culturally or subculturally different from those by whom the care is given and seek to state some possible implications for medical education.

The people of 1407 Felicity have been introduced and briefly described. The task now is to relate them to the larger population group of which they are a part so that we may have a basis for understanding who they are, where they came from, and how they acquired some of their characteristics.

Chapter II

LA GENTE DE LA RAZA

THE SPANISH-SPEAKING PEOPLE OF THE SOUTHWEST are not an easy group to delimit or define. It is almost impossible to find any single criterion by which they can be distinguished from the larger population among whom they live. They are not exactly a racial group, although they frequently refer to themselves as *la raza*[1] and, in moments of impassioned oratory, have been known to make glowing reference to the qualities of the "Mexican race." They are certainly not a nationality group. Many are United States citizens by birth and have never had any political allegiance to Mexico. Others, who once were Mexican nationals, have become naturalized citizens of the United States. And still others think of themselves as Mexicans and continue to be legal subjects of Mexico. Nor can the group be said to be culturally homogeneous. Some include among their cultural equipment traits that can be traced back to pre-Spanish Indians. Some retain the folkways of isolated Rio Grande villages. Some exhibit many of the characteristics of urban-industrial populations. Even the term "Spanish-speaking" is misleading, since some do not speak Spanish at all, and others, fluent in both English and Spanish, prefer to speak the former.

Although it is difficult to find a set of criteria for precisely defining them, the Spanish-speaking people, viewed as a group, do have characteristics that distinguish them from the Anglo population. Physically, they are easily identifiable because of their common, but by no means uniform, genetic inheritance from the populations of sixteenth- and seventeenth-century Spain and various North American Indian tribal groups. Socially, they possess a variety of combinations of cultural traits that can be traced to Spain or Mexico and that are not generally shared by

Anglos. Psychologically, they tend to identify themselves as members of a distinct group and to be so identified by Anglos.[2] Subjectively defined, the Spanish-speaking people are those who think of themselves as "we" in response to the labels "Spanish-speaking," "Mexican," "*mexicano*," "Latin-American," "Spanish-American," and similar terms and are thought of by Anglos in terms of "they" in response to these identifying symbols. The criteria used on both sides in making these subjective identifications are usually multiple rather than single and include such characteristics as physical appearance, name, language, dress, place of residence, and general deportment, most of which convey cultural or subcultural meanings to everybody.

Although some Anglos tend to think of Spanish-speaking people in terms of a few oversimplified stereotypes, there is as wide a range of both physical and social characteristics among them as in any large population aggregation. There are many persons with light-colored skin, hair, and eyes among the Spanish-speaking as well as those whose darker coloring has been the basis for one of our popular stereotypes.[3]

While there are common physical and cultural factors that serve to draw together the Spanish-speaking people and give them a basis for a feeling of identity with one another, other factors operate to lessen their cohesion, weaken their sense of identification, and split the larger group into smaller fragments. Differing historical traditions, differing political alignments and allegiances, and differing social and economic circumstances are powerful forces for reducing their sense of unity and for developing in some of them characteristics that set them apart. Thus, while at times there are strong feelings of identity and solidarity among all factions within the larger group, there are also times when a part of the group will react with bitterness and hostility against another part.[4] Spanish-speaking New Mexicans, for example, have been known to show antagonism toward recent comers from Mexico. In one New Mexican town some years ago, citizens of Spanish-speaking descent actually threatened Mexican nationals who had been brought there for railroad work. Wetbacks, Mexican citizens who have illegally entered this country, are resented by residents, who regard them as an economic threat. The somewhat turbulent history of such a "national" organization as the League of United Latin American Citizens reveals the extent to which disagreements, differences in point of view, and lack of effective cooperation are possible within the larger group of Spanish-speaking people.

SUBGROUPS AMONG THE SPANISH-SPEAKING POPULATION

Within the total Spanish-speaking population there are at least three major subgroups, each of which has somewhat distinctive genetic and cultural characteristics. Like the larger group, these subgroups are far from homogeneous in terms of any single characteristic, but members do tend toward certain similarities in appearance, behavior, point of view, and place of origin that serve to differentiate them from one another, both from the standpoint of the subjective feelings of members of all three subgroups and from that of an outside observer. Although they have much in common, each subgroup has had a somewhat different history and is more or less closely identified with a definite geographic area. No studies have been made to confirm the impression, but it is probable that, even where members of different subgroups live in close physical proximity, they tend to associate more frequently and more intimately with members of their own subgroup than with those of another.

The three subgroups that we shall examine in some detail are the Spanish-Americans, the Mexican-Americans, and the Mexicans. It is because of the need to distinguish between these groups, and yet at the same time have some inclusive term, that it is necessary to use the awkward phrase "Spanish-speaking people." The terms "Spanish-American," "Mexican-American," and "Mexican" are not precise and all three are loosely used throughout the Southwest. In much of Texas, for example, any natively Spanish-speaking person is likely to be thought of as a "Mexican," although on formal occasions what is considered a more flattering term, "Latin-American," may often be used. In New Mexico and parts of Colorado, natively Spanish-speaking persons are referred to as "Spanish-Americans" regardless of their origin, citizenship, or subjective identification. In formal writings the term "Hispano" is sometimes used to designate either the entire Spanish-speaking group or one of the subgroups. But in spite of the imprecise way they are used, the terms do have descriptive value and some usefulness.

The Spanish-Americans were never legally Mexicans, except for the brief period between the time Mexico won its independence from Spain (1821) and the signing of the Treaty of Guadalupe-Hidalgo (1848), a period during which there was relatively little contact between the isolated Spanish-American communities and Mexico. Spanish-Americans do not think of themselves as Mexican and tend to resent being so designated. Mexican-Americans, on the other hand, having been born in Mexico themselves or being the children of parents or grandparents born in Mexico tend to have a sense of identification with that country which may be expressed, at the one extreme, through a vigorous and self-conscious championing of all things Mexican, or, at the other, through a relatively mild form of participation in the celebration of Mexican national holidays. Recent comers to the United States, the Mexican group are legally Mexican citizens and consider themselves Mexicans. They, and to some extent the Mexican-American group as well, want to be referred to as Mexicans and at times may resent being called Spanish-American or Latin-American.

Spanish-Americans

The Spanish-Americans[5] are descendants of colonists who began to come into the Middle and Upper Rio Grande valleys with Juan de Oñate in 1598, moving in behind the priests and soldiers of earlier expeditions. In the river valleys where the presence of water made settlement possible, small, precariously rooted communities were established—San Gabriel, Santa Cruz, Santa Fe. For the first few generations, growth of the communities was small, and the number of communities increased scarcely at all. The first colonizing effort was ended in 1680 by an Indian uprising and the subsequent retreat of the colonists to El Paso. A new effort at settling the area began with the reconquest by Diego de

Vargas in 1692. Old communities were reestablished and new ones founded, both to the north and south of the area of original settlement.[6]

Throughout the eighteenth century and during the first half of the nineteenth, a slow trickle of settlers moved up the Rio Grande. But the number was never large and 250 years after the founding of the first community at San Gabriel, there were only about 60,000 Spanish-speaking people in the area, living mainly in small, highly self-sufficient, agricultural communities. The proportion of women to men among the incoming colonists was low, so that, particularly in the early years of settlement, wives were sought among the indigenous Indian populations of the region. As communities increased in number and population, it became possible to obtain a wife either within one's own community or in a similar one, and the practice of taking wives from among the Indians gradually diminished.

Since the early 1800's there has been practically no intermarriage between Spanish-Americans and Indians, and the Spanish-Americans have been a highly endogamous group. From the time of their earliest contacts there has been some intermarriage between Anglos and Spanish-Americans, but, even though neither group has had any strong pattern of disapproval, the proportion of cross-cultural marriages always has been small. Thus, the Spanish-American of today is the genetic descendant of at least two population stocks: the people of sixteenth- and seventeenth-century Spain and New Spain, themselves already people of diverse genetic background, and the Indian inhabitants, both sedentary and nomadic, of the areas into which the Spaniards came.[7] Inasmuch as immigrants from New Spain and Mexico who came into the Southwest in the seventeenth, eighteenth, and nineteenth centuries were in part descendants of Indians living in what is now Mexico, the proportion of Indian genetic characteristics in the present Spanish-American population is fairly large. However, because of the endogamy practiced in Spanish-American villages since at least the early nineteenth century, the Indian genetic inheritance of the Spanish-Americans is probably less than that of Mexican-Americans and Mexicans.

The Spanish-Americans of today, even when living in Anglo urban environments, still retain some of the cultural characteristics developed in the villages of New Mexico and southern Colorado and to understand them one must know something of village life.

Probably the outstanding characteristic of the village communities was that of isolation.[8] Largely cut off from contacts with the outside world because of the difficulties of transportation and their own unimportance, the villagers worked out an adaptation to their semi-arid environment that enabled them to live, if not abundantly, at least securely. The pattern of settlement, brought from Spain, included a central plaza on which stood the church, other public buildings, if any, and the houses of some of the families. On streets leading from the plaza were the remainder of the homes. Surrounding them were storage sheds and corrals for animals; beyond lay the agricultural plots in which villagers grew their squash, corn, wheat, beans, chiles, fruit, and, sometimes, cotton. And beyond the fields were common lands used for grazing, for recreation, and as a source of building materials and fuel. Title to land derived from grants made by the government of Spain, sometimes to individuals, sometimes to colonizers, sometimes to communities. Some of the lands of New Mexico are still held under community ownership.[9]

From the first the villages were economically self-sufficient. They had to be, since the only convenient source from which anything might have been obtained was the Indian population, and they, living under much the same circumstances, had little to give.[10] The basis of the economy was agriculture, supplemented by a little cattle- and sheep-raising. What surplus there was above the immediate needs of the villagers was sent with infrequent expeditions to Mexico to be traded for metal utensils and implements, glass, guns, coffee, and other necessary items that could not be produced locally. Houses, churches, and other buildings were made from the soil as they are today, the roofs supported by *vigas* or roof beams made from unsquared pine logs cut from the mountain slopes. Trade within and between communities was small, and most of it was conducted on a barter basis. Money and commercial enterprise played little part in the lives of the people. There was no tax on land. The products of the land were taxable, but the tax was payable in kind rather than money and, on community grants, responsibility for payment devolved upon the community rather than on the individual. Few people had any money; virtually nobody needed it. In the village the economy was semi-communal. Land was cultivated by family groups and since, in a given village, nearly everyone was related, the fortunes of all tended to ebb and flow together. Tools and equipment were freely borrowed; both labor and products were shared. And thus, although the village community was highly self-sufficient, the individuals in it were not. The economic unit was the community, not the individual.

Generations of isolation enabled the villages to develop a social compactness and strong social organization which, until very recently, made them highly resistant to change. The family and the church were the basic institutions around which village life was centered.[11] The family unit was the large, extended family made up of several generations. Authority was vested in the older males; respect in word and deed was expected from and given by females to males and by the young to the elderly. Young men brought their brides into the family group, frequently building an apartment-like extension on the family dwelling as quarters for themselves. Marriage within the community was frequent; marriage outside was less common and when it occurred it was nearly always between members of communities situated fairly close together. The family and the village came to be almost synonymous,[12] and individuals were identified as much by the community in which they lived as by family name.

The religion was a simple and devout Catholicism which, like the family relationship, permeated all aspects of village life. To many of the villages priests came only infrequently, so that the construction and care of the church, the conduct of services, and the organizing of ceremonial observances became the function of laymen.[13] Each village had its special patron saint whose image, usually the creation of a village craftsman, had a place of prominence in the church. Saints' days were observed with appropriate ceremonies, including both religious and secular activities. Religion provided sanction for the affairs of the villagers and solace for their misfortunes. Since the religious congregation and the secular community were synonymous, the church provided an additional integrative influence in the community. And since religion was not a thing apart but an omnipresent component of each activity, it also served to unify and integrate the total life of the community. Planting and harvest; birth, death, and marriage; sickness and health; recreation; leadership and authority patterns were all invested with religious significance and associated with religious ritual, so that religion formed the core of all institutional activity.

A third institution, probably somewhat less significant than family and church as an integrative influence in the Spanish-American community, but one that has had a considerable effect on the ability of Spanish-Americans to adjust to the demands of Anglo culture, was the *patrón* system.[14] The *patrón* was a person with whom the villagers assumed a reciprocal relationship of mutual assistance and dependency. A large landowner, a person of wealth, an influential politician—anyone with prestige, power, resources, and a sense of obligation toward a given community might become a *patrón*. From him the villagers expected favors in time of misfortune; to him they gave such evidences of loyalty and support as he might demand. In a sense the *patrón* was the secular counterpart of the patron saint. His position conferred certain privileges, but it also entailed obligations. He lent money, gave advice, served as godfather to children, and performed other services. While he behaved in accordance with what was expected of him, his position was secure. But the relationship was essentially a reciprocal one, and if he failed to live up to his institutional role, he did not long remain as *patrón*.[15]

Leadership in the Spanish-American villages was institutional rather than personal. A person became a leader because of who he was, not because of what his personal characteristics were. Family position, age, and the ability to speak well in public—the last named an almost universal characteristic in the villages— were the chief determinants of leadership. Actually there was very little for any leader to do. For most contingencies that arose there was already a well-established pattern of response, and the necessity for making major decisions was small. Deviant behavior was not common; hence, there was almost no need for specialized law-enforcing agencies. Since the family and the community were frequently almost coterminous, the informal controls by which order and continuity were maintained in the family served for the community as well, and there was little need for any formal governmental organization. Conformity and obedience to custom were the rule. Having found a way of life with survival value, the Spanish-American villages continued it generation after generation. The old ways worked; innovation might not. It was better to be safe. And so change of any sort came to be feared and mistrusted. In the culture there was little place for personal initiative or private aggressiveness. One acquired status, prestige, and esteem by conforming to community expectations. In time, if one were of the right sex and belonged to the right family, one might attain a formal or semi-formal position of leadership. If not, it was of no great concern. The privileges were few, but so were the responsibilities. Leadership was nothing to aspire to; neither was it anything to shun. Certainly there was not, as there is among Anglos, particular emphasis on leadership or any pressure on the individual to develop and exercise leadership characteristics.[16]

Education was largely a matter of informal indoctrination. There was no emphasized concept of progress and hence no need for the acquisition of new knowledge. All that a person needed to know to live successfully in the village could be acquired through the informal processes of socialization. The child listened, observed, and asked questions. From the conversations of adults, from the common store of group knowledge, and from observing the behavior of his family and friends in all kinds of situations, the child learned the essentials. There was no literary tradition and virtually no knowledge of reading or writing. Very rarely, and then only in the larger communities, were there schools, and what few existed taught little that was of value to a person living in a village.

A point of strength in the social organization of the villages lay in the range of relationships everyone in the community had with almost everyone else. To the basic fact of family kinship was added joint participation in religious, economic, recreational, and other types of activities, so that everyone had an opportunity to know his community fellows in many roles. Privacy was almost impossible; the incidents of each individual's life, his feeling about them, and his activities were open to everybody. Since all shared the same general knowledge and the same philosophy, communication was easy and opportunities for misunderstanding few. Each person had not one but several relationships with every other person, so that the whole village was tightly knit together by a series of interlocking roles.

The rhythm of life was slow. The pattern of activity was governed by seasonal rather than daily changes. Nothing in the daily routine was very compelling as long as the seasonal activities of planting, crop-tending, and harvesting were carried on. The rate of social change was also slow. One year was much like another year, and there was no need to be much concerned about time. The focus of attention was the present. There was nothing very memorable in the past to be recalled. There was no particular expectation of the future. Villagers lived in the present and did what needed to be done or what was pleasant to do at the time they were necessary or pleasant.

The crises of life were familiar to all—birth, death, marriage, disease, poor harvests, storms—and the patterns for meeting them were also familiar. Around one in time of crisis were the family, the community, the church, and, if necessary, the *patrón* to give comfort, support, and assistance. No one faced a crisis alone. No one ever needed to feel uncertain about what should be done to handle a crisis situation.

In many respects, the Spanish-American villages conformed to the ideal-type folk culture as formulated by Robert Redfield.[17] Among the characteristics of a folk society, as described by Redfield, were these, which are highly descriptive of the Spanish-American village as it existed throughout much of the nineteenth century: a small population aggregation in which, typically, everyone knows everyone else; a high degree of isolation from other cultures; communication by oral rather than by written symbols and little communication of any kind outside the immediate group; a homogeneous population with relatively little division of labor; a slow rate of social change; the predominance of sacred rather than secular symbols and values; a simple technology; economic independence based on a subsistence economy; and a strong sense of group identification.

For nearly 150 years after the founding of the first settlements little or nothing happened to break the isolation of the Spanish-American villages. For another hundred years the villages remained relatively unaffected by outside events, although things were happening that eventually were to have tremendous consequences for their way of life. Independence from Spain and the Mexican rule that followed went almost unnoticed in the Rio Grande villages. The change from Mexican to United States citizenship caused little excitement, except in a few of the larger communities that were immediately thrown into contact with Anglos. Political changes in the past had meant only new administrators and had not significantly affected the status of village, family, or individual. There was little reason for the villagers to feel that the new changes were any more important than those already experienced.

But they were soon to learn differently. The acquisition of the Southwest by the United States brought powerful forces to bear upon the isolated and stabilized villages of the Spanish-Americans.[18] Economic competition of a nature and scope far beyond the experience of the villagers was introduced. New concepts, new values, and a new language appeared. Money taxes were instituted; business relationships changed in nature and became more pervasive. Sharp practices and legal technicalities, based on an entirely new system of law that was perplexing to the villagers, began to take their toll of the economic resources. One after another of the land grants was lost and village resources consequently were reduced. Grazing lands passed into the hands of the Anglos and were fenced. Forest lands were placed on a restricted use basis. The free public range disappeared. Unfortunately, these changes came at a time when the Spanish-American population was expanding and more rather than fewer resources were needed. Faced with a declining resource base and a growing need for money, the villagers were forced into wage work to supplement the income from their land. In increasing numbers the men left their villages to become sheepherders in Utah and Wyoming, beet workers and miners in Colorado, railroad laborers wherever they could be used. The depression of the 1930's ended these job opportunities for a time, and the Spanish-Americans were forced back into their villages which by then had sufficient resources to care adequately for only about a quarter of the population. Through the depression years, governmental relief funds kept the villages going. In the Upper Rio Grande Valley, 60 per cent of the rural families received relief in some form during the years 1935 and 1936.[19] World War II, with the draft of young men for military service and the opening of employment opportunities in war industries, relieved the pressure of population on resources. At one time during the early years of the war it was estimated that two out of every three of the adult males from the villages of the Rio Grande were either serving in the armed forces or working outside the state.[20] The end of hostilities brought a continuation of both the draft and the opportunities for well-paying work. Vast governmental projects at Albuquerque, Los Alamos, and White Sands have made it possible for many villagers to have good jobs and continue to live in the communities where they were born.

But the communities are not the same as they once were. The changes begun in the middle of the nineteenth century and intensified somewhat in the early years of the twentieth have been accelerated enormously during the past twenty years. The depression of the 1930's first sharply focused attention on the economic and other problems of the Spanish-Americans, brought realization of the fact that little assistance had been given them in the difficult process of adjusting to an entirely new culture,[21] and introduced a pattern of dependency on governmental agencies that to an extent still plagues welfare administrators. World War II, through the draft and increased work opportunities, again took large numbers of persons out of the villages and into areas, where, cut off from village influences, they could have new types of experiences and learn new ways and new values. The G.I. Bill of Rights at the end of the war, for the first time, enabled Spanish-American boys and girls in large numbers to attend college.[22] In addition to their influence on the villages, these forces, together with others that could be mentioned, are combining to bring Spanish-Americans, historically a rural people, into urban areas in large numbers and consequently into new situations involving increased contacts with Anglos.[23]

The changes that have occurred in villages and villagers are tremendous. They have taken place in a relatively short time and in an uneven fashion. Some of the more remote villages have managed to retain a good proportion of the old way of living. Some that are close to Anglo-dominated urban centers have lost practically all of their old culture. But culture is a hardy plant that does not wither easily, even in a hostile environment. And a couple of generations is a short time for a people to lose all its cultural heritage, even under the most adverse conditions. So it is not surprising that many of the characteristics of the Spanish-American village culture still survive in some form in the villagers and their children, even though they may live on Felicity Street in the middle of Arcadia.

Mexican-Americans

Mexican-Americans[24] are culturally similar to Spanish-Americans, although there are some noticeable differences. Both groups have virtually the same genetic background, but the Mexican-Americans probably derive a larger proportion of their physical characteristics from Indians than do the Spanish-Americans. Both are cultural descendants of a village way of life in which characteristics of aggression, competition, individual responsibility, and initiative were not highly developed and in which acceptance, resignation, cooperation, and the subordination of the individual to the community group were emphasized. Both, historically, have lived in an agricultural economy and under a semi-feudal type of social and economic organization.

For both, the extended family, the church, and the *patrón* system were the institutions around which life was organized. But the Spanish-Americans became citizens of the United States by military conquest, which involved no initiative on their part, no immediate necessity to change their way of living, and no break with their cultural tradition or change in their place of residence, whereas the Mexican-Americans are people who left their familiar surroundings on their individual volition and have come to live in an alien land.[25]

The Spanish-Americans, even though they live in Anglo cities far from the villages where they or their parents were born, tend to have ties with their cultural past that give them some degree of stability, some security, and a feeling that there is a familiar world to which they can return if the need arises. Many, individually or through their immediate families, retain title to their ancestral lands. Many have relatives in the extended family group who continue to live in their village and with whom they can maintain contact. Between jobs in Anglo cities, many return to live for a time in familiar surroundings and renew ties. And many have, among their neighbors or friends in the city environment, family members or acquaintances with whom they can feel culturally at ease.

For the immigrant generation of Mexican-Americans few of these stabilizing influences exist. They are cut off from their place of origin by distance, by the costs of travel and the difficulties of communicating across an international boundary, by their own frequent inability to read or write, and by the new ties they have established and the new ways learned here. Having come individually or in small, immediate family groups from a broad area in Mexico and being more widely dispersed throughout the Southwest than the Spanish-Americans, the Mexican-Americans have not the same opportunity for close contact with the familiar elements of their culture that the Spanish-Americans enjoy and, consequently, are subjected to a greater degree to the impact of Anglo acculturating forces. At least two factors, however, operate to cushion the cultural shock. One is that Mexican-Americans tend to live reasonably close to the border and are thus able to maintain, through contact with newcomers and through Mexican movies, radio programs, newspapers, comic books, picture magazines, foods, manufactured or handcraft products, and other cultural elements, some touch with the broad culture of Mexico, if not always with the unique elements of their own particular place of origin. A second factor is the tendency of Mexican-Americans to seek their own kind and to live together in separate, distinguishable neighborhood and community groups, in which the opportunity for interaction with other Mexican-Americans is multiplied and the necessity for mingling with Anglos considerably reduced.

The Mexican-Americans are for the most part former Mexicans—and their descendants—who came to the United States between 1900 and the early 1930's. They came for a number of reasons. Some were motivated by the disturbances of the Mexican revolution which began in 1910 and caused unsettled conditions for many years. Some were attracted by what seemed to be better job opportunities in the United States. Some were recruited to help produce food and maintain the railways during World War I. Some came to join their families. They came slowly at first, fewer than a thousand in the entire ten years before 1900. In 1910, some 20,000 came. In 1924, a hundred thousand crossed the border. By 1930 more than a million Mexicans had come to the United States legally or illegally.[26]

And then, in the 1930's, the stream reversed itself. The emergency had passed; jobs were scarce; the Mexicans were no longer needed. The workers who had picked cotton around Las Cruces and Phoenix; who had topped beets in Weld County, Colorado; who had picked grapes near Fresno, oranges in Los Angeles County, melons in the Imperial Valley, loaded their belongings and their families into jalopies and wagons and headed back for Mexico. About 300,000 of those who had come so hopefully, went or were sent back.[27] But the majority stayed. They stayed because they wanted to; because their children had been born here and were citizens; because they still wanted for themselves and their children the advantages of living in the United States; and, in many instances, because they were inconspicuous enough or skillful enough to escape the attention of the Immigration and Naturalization Service.

Many who stayed moved into cities and remained there. Some opened business enterprises and acquired Anglo skills. Some joined unions and became skilled workers. Some went to school and received professional training. Some became prosperous. But these did not constitute a great proportion of the total group. Most of those who went into cities have continued to live in *colonias* or *barrios*, segregated slum and near-slum areas. Many have remained relatively unskilled, unfamiliar with Anglo ways, uneducated, unhealthy. Among them are the slum dwellers of El Paso, San Antonio, Dallas, Denver, Tucson, Phoenix, Los Angeles, and other cities where there is a concentration of Mexican-American population.

The children and grandchildren of the original migrants have inherited some of the cultural characteristics of their parents and grandparents, and of the largely Spanish-speaking communities in which they live. They have also been exposed, in varying degree, to many Anglo cultural elements. They are thus caught between two cultures whose values and ways are sometimes contradictory. They see their parents and grandparents behaving in one way and Anglos in the community behaving in another. They are taught one set of values and practices at home and quite a different set at school. And so they are frequently disorganized and confused, not quite knowing what they want or how they might get it if they did, unable to understand fully or follow the ways of their parents, but equally unable to break away from them entirely. Many of the parents, particularly those who grew up in the semi-feudal environment of rural Mexico, speak Spanish at home, feel uncomfortable when they have to use English—if they can use it at all—and tend to cling to the customs and ways of living associated with the Mexican pattern. They believe in strong, closely unified families and in the exercise of parental authority and its unquestioning acceptance by the children, and they wish to perpetuate these and other patterns that to them represent security, familiarity, and satisfaction. The children, on the other hand, learn to speak English and to recognize the advantages of using that language in the United States. They learn also much about the Anglo way of living—the freedom of children from close supervision by the home, the kinds of satisfaction to be found outside home life, the dependence on money and commercialized entertainments, the freedom allowed adolescent girls. They become impatient with and scornful of the ways of their parents, seeing them as outmoded. They are resistant to the institutional controls of the old culture, but have not yet internalized or become subject to the controls of the new. Carrying as they do the burden of the transition from one culture to another, they need more guidance, more supervision, more help from Anglo agencies and institutions than do Anglo children of comparable age. But this, except in rare instances, they do not get.[28]

Many Mexican-Americans remained in agriculture, partly because that was all they knew when they came and partly because we did not provide them with much opportunity to learn anything else. This group still includes among its numbers many migrants for whom mobility has been a powerful factor in retarding acculturation. They still pick cotton in Texas and Arizona and New Mexico; still harvest fruit and lettuce and melons in California; still tend sugar beets in Colorado. And they are still strangers, even though some of them have resided in the United States for many years. They live in shacks on or near the land which they work, isolated from the communities through which they pass.[29] Their children often toil beside them in the fields. State and federal laws prescribe that the children cannot work, that they must be in schools, but few communities enforce the law for children of migrant workers. In winter, when the crops are in, many of the migrants return to familiar communities in the border areas or move into cities to live with others of their kind in slums and shacktowns, still largely isolated from the life of the community. Their children, like those of the city-dwelling group, also live between two worlds. They know nothing of Mexico, since most of them have never been there. They know almost as little of the United States, since, except in a narrow physical sense, few have ever been there either.

Like the Spanish-Americans, the Mexican-Americans are faced with a double problem of acculturation.[30] If they are to fit easily into Anglo culture and participate fully in both the privileges and responsibilities of that culture, they must make the transition from a way of life derived from a south European tradition of several hundred years ago, strengthened and stabilized in isolation and enriched with elements from various North American Indian groups, to one stemming from a northwestern European tradition but which has developed unique elements as a result of more than two centuries of borrowing and adaptation from many cultural streams. At the same time they must make the transition from a rural folk way of life with its own peculiar set of values and relationships to that of an urban-industrial society in which nearly everything from the rhythms of life to the relationships between parents and children is very different. And those changes are not easy to make.[31]

Some among both Spanish-Americans and Mexican-Americans have made the transition exceedingly well and are almost indistinguishable from the Anglos among whom they live. Others have barely begun to change and still retain virtually all the characteristics of their old culture. But even the most fully acculturated of the Spanish-speaking group retain some residual elements of their "Spanish" cultural heritage and even the least acculturated Spanish-American or Mexican-American has already taken on some Anglo characteristics. There has been among both groups a tendency for the most acculturated to withdraw from contacts with the group from which they came. They tend to live apart, cultivate Anglo friends, speak only English, minimize family relationships, and pursue the Anglo type of goals. Others who are able to move freely in the Anglo culture deliberately hold onto some elements of their Spanish-American or Mexican-American culture—the use of the Spanish language on certain formal or ceremonial occasions, the teaching of it to their children, the use of Spanish-American or Mexican house decorations, a style of dress, the use of certain foods or certain ways of cooking, special pride in family or group history, or similar characteristics. A few who are almost fully acculturated try earnestly to improve conditions for the less acculturated. A worry common to many of the latter is that in the transition all of their "Spanish" culture will be lost and that they will, consequently, become "like those gringos." That this fear is unwarranted can be seen in the experiences and present status of the small but growing group who are at ease in both cultures. Although largely Anglo in their way of living, their values, and their relationships, these individuals use both Spanish and English fluently, know the cultural ways of both groups, and maintain an identification with their Spanish heritage while effectively participating in Anglo culture.

Mexicans

Biologically and culturally the group we shall call Mexicans[32] is similar to the Mexican-Americans. The principal points of difference are that the Mexicans are more recent comers; that most of them are in the United States illegally[33] or, as in the case of agricultural contract workers, on temporary permits; and in general that they expect to return to Mexico.

Probably the largest proportion of the Mexican group are wetbacks, illegal aliens who have crossed the border to seek work in the United States and to take advantage of the relatively high wages paid here. Members of this group are found in large numbers in the tier of counties bordering Mexico and in areas reasonably near the border that require seasonal agricultural labor. An undetermined number move out of the border area to seek work elsewhere in the Southwest and throughout the United States. Once away from the border the chances of being picked up by the Immigration Service are not great, and it is probable that a sizable proportion of the group we have called Mexican-American are former wetbacks who elected to remain in the United States. *Braceros*, or contract workers who are brought in legally and temporarily under the terms of international agreements between the United States and Mexico, are guaranteed a stated amount of work at a specified place and at a specified rate of pay. Their employer obligates himself to furnish transportation, food, and lodging that must meet standards specified in the international agreement, and also to post a bond for each worker contracted for, guaranteeing that at the end of the contract period the worker will be returned to Mexico. A small proportion of the contract workers leave their places of employment without the knowledge or consent of their employers. Some of these may remain in the United States, if they are not picked up by the Immigration Service. Others return to Mexico voluntarily.

Like the first generation Mexican-Americans, the Mexicans, whether wetbacks, *braceros*, or legal entrants, tend to come from the interior of Mexico.[34] In addition, there is a commuting group, who live on the Mexican side of the border but regularly cross over—usually with official permission—to work in the border cities on this side. The migrants from the interior are mostly young adult males; a good proportion of them are married, but only a small number bring their wives and children along. Although the majority come in search of agricultural work in the United States, some are able to find employment both as skilled and unskilled workers in a variety of occupations. No penalties are assessed against employers hiring wetbacks, the only inconvenience being that of having their workers picked up at any moment and sent back across the border. Nor, except in rare instances, is the wetback himself subjected to any penalty. If apprehended, he is usually given the option of leaving the United States "voluntarily," which means that he is taken to the border by the Border Patrol and started across an international bridge. Once on the other side he can, if he wishes, promptly return to his job here, running only the risk of again being picked up and given a free ride to the border.

Relatively few of the group we shall call Mexicans[35] have had more than two or three years' schooling and most of them are functionally illiterate in the sense that they cannot effectively read or write, although they may be able to write their names and read very simple materials. Few can speak English well, but those who repeatedly cross the border acquire some understanding of the language. They come largely from isolated *ranchos*, *haciendas* or *ejidos*, small agricultural settlements located on an area of cultivated land, or from small agricultural and service communities of three thousand persons or fewer.[36] They come largely from portions of Mexico that have been relatively little affected by the industrial revolution that has for some years been transforming that country. As a consequence, they have little familiarity with the type of urban-dominated industrial culture they enter. With scarcely any education, no command of English, few resources, and limited occupational skills, their prospects for improving their economic and social status in this country are not good. They are hired for the least skilled, lowest-paying jobs, frequently seasonal in nature. Their housing, particularly if they are agricultural workers, is usually bad, frequently being no more than a brush hut on the banks of an irrigation ditch or a shack thrown together out of odds and ends of old lumber. With the protection of an international agreement and a contract supervised by two governments, *braceros* fare better than wetbacks, who are protected by no one. Being here illegally, the wetback has no rights and is fair game for exploitation. He is not entitled to welfare, health, or educational services; he cannot claim compensation in case of injury on the job; he cannot seek the protection of the police or the courts if his person or property is violated.

Even to a greater extent than either Spanish-Americans or Mexican-Americans, the Mexican in the United States is deprived of opportunities for an extensive range of contacts with Anglos. Wetbacks have few relationships with Anglos other than their limited dealings with Anglo employers and Immigration Service officials. They live in camps located near the fields in which they work or in towns, in small shacks built at the rear end of lots in sections inhabited by Mexican-Americans. Whenever possible they patronize stores owned and operated by Mexican-Americans. Frequently even their employer-employee relationship is with a Mexican-American in those areas where the practice of using crew chiefs to recruit labor is common. They work in groups with other Spanish-speaking people and spend their leisure time with them. If they attend religious services, it is usually as part of a congregation made up entirely of Spanish-speaking people and with the services conducted in Spanish. If they are ill, they treat themselves or seek advice from relatives or friends. If the illness is thought to be serious, a *médica* or *curandera*[37] may be sought. On the rare occasions when a physician is consulted, the natively Spanish-speaking is preferred to the Anglo.

Braceros, too, have only limited opportunities to acquire Anglo culture traits. They are brought into the country in groups and taken directly to their places of employment. They live for the most part on the farm or ranch where they work. What leisure time they have is usually spent in the Spanish-speaking section of a nearby town. At the end of their employment period they are returned to Mexico. They may have brief contacts with their employer, with a few Anglo workers, with some officials of the United States Employment Service, and with Anglo dealers in supplies and services. Beyond those they seldom enter into any relationship with Anglos.

The Mexicans thus live under conditions that include relatively few pressures toward acculturation. Many of them keep in touch with their country by moving back and forth across the border.[38] They live under circumstances that make it possible to satisfy their needs without extensive contacts with Anglos. Their attitudes and feelings and their educational level are such that they rarely make much effort to acquire elements of the Anglo culture. If, however, through their own inclination and their good fortune in avoiding the Border Patrol, they remain on this side of the border for extended periods of time, pressures to acculturate do begin to build up. For those who leave the Southwest and seek employment elsewhere such pressures may become very strong, since in every community to which they migrate, except a relatively small number of cities and agricultural areas, they are forced into relationships with Anglos and the Anglo culture. For those who remain in the Southwest, or who move to such cities as Chicago, Detroit, or New York, or who work in agriculture in such states as Minnesota, Michigan, or Colorado, it is possible to continue to live in what is largely a familiar culture. Thus, the pressures toward change are minimized.

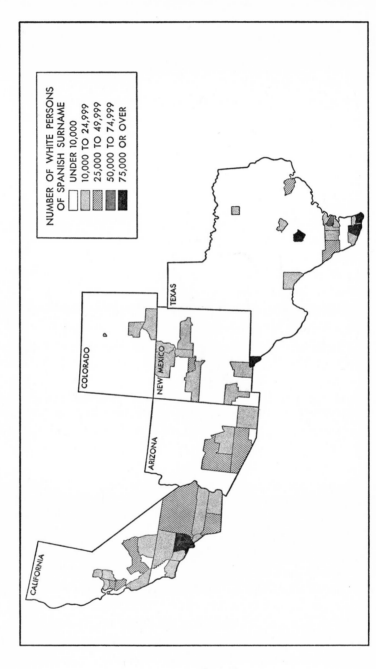

NUMBER OF WHITE PERSONS
OF SPANISH SURNAME

UNDER 10,000
10,000 TO 24,999
25,000 TO 49,999
50,000 TO 74,999
75,000 OR OVER

CONCENTRATION OF WHITE SPANISH-SURNAME POPULATION IN FIVE SOUTHWESTERN STATES
IN 1950—NUMBER OF PERSONS BY COUNTIES

GENERAL CHARACTERISTICS OF THE SPANISH-SPEAKING
POPULATION

Number and Distribution

The Spanish-speaking population of the five southwestern states includes from two and a half to three million persons, who together make up about a tenth of the total population of those states. Approximately two million are Mexican-Americans, who form the largest part of the substantial Spanish-speaking populations of Arizona, California, and Texas. About 400,000 are Spanish-Americans, living largely in New Mexico and Colorado. The remainder are Mexicans, located mainly in the commercial agricultural areas of California and Texas, whose numbers change considerably from day to day. Detailed information on the number, distribution, and other demographic characteristics of the Spanish-speaking population will be found in Appendix A. The two maps on pages 64 and 66 illustrate graphically the distribution of this population group by counties in the five states.

If one looks at the distribution of Spanish-speaking people in the Southwest, two characteristics immediately become apparent: (1) a tendency toward a general distribution of the population over the whole area, and (2) a seemingly contradictory tendency toward concentration in certain areas. Of the more than 400 counties in the five southwestern states, only 93 had no Spanish-name persons recorded in the 1950 Census, and 76 of these were in the northern and eastern sections of Texas which, properly speaking, are not a part of the Southwest.[39] All counties in Arizona and New Mexico, all but four of those in California, and 50 of the 63 in Colorado were found to contain some Spanish-name persons. In only one county, Zapata in Texas, was the proportion of Spanish-name persons reported by the Census Bureau greater than 90 per cent of the total population, but in several—all of which are in New Mexico and Texas—the concentration was greater than 80 per cent. Thirty-six counties had more than 50 per cent Spanish-name population, 45 were found to have between 25 and 49 per cent, and more than a hundred counties had a Spanish-name population of from 5 to 24 per cent

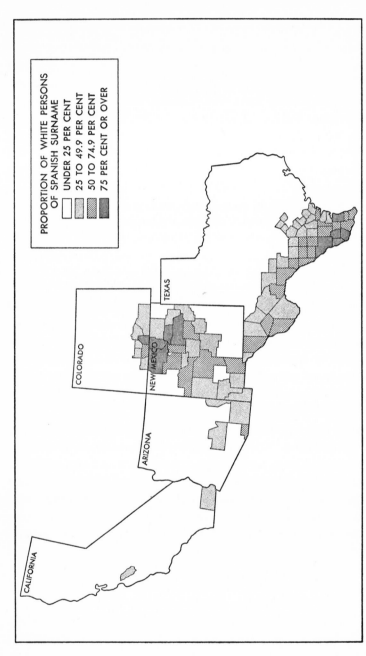

CONCENTRATION OF WHITE SPANISH-SURNAME POPULATION IN FIVE SOUTHWESTERN STATES
IN 1950—PROPORTION OF TOTAL POPULATION BY COUNTIES

of the total. The largest numbers of Spanish-name persons were found in Los Angeles County, California (287,614), Bexar County, Texas, which includes the city of San Antonio (176,877), and Hidalgo County, Texas (112,422). Two other Texas counties, Cameron and El Paso, each had more than 80,000 Spanish-name persons, and 12, of which six are in California, had more than 25,000 each.

In general, the proportion of Spanish-name persons in the total population is greatest in counties nearest the Mexican border and tends to diminish as one moves northward into the United States. Conspicuous exceptions are those in northern New Mexico and southern Colorado that are largely inhabited by Spanish-Americans, and other counties such as Weld in Colorado and San Benito in California, where specialized employment conditions have resulted in a heavy concentration of Spanish-speaking people. The greatest numerical concentrations of Spanish-name persons are in the counties where the large cities of the Southwest are located. More than 800,000 Spanish-name persons live in the six counties containing more than 50,000 Spanish-name persons each, and only one of these, Hidalgo in Texas, does not include a large city. Only one of the larger southwestern cities, Fort Worth, contains fewer than 10,000 Spanish-name persons. Most of them have 20,000 or more.

In some respects the Spanish-speaking people are a highly mobile population. Not only do they move into the Southwest from Mexico in large numbers, but they also move around in the area and out of it to a considerable extent. Spanish-American villagers from the Rio Grande and San Luis valleys move into Denver, Pueblo, and Albuquerque. During World War II great numbers of them migrated to the West Coast to work in war industries. Thousands of Mexican-American residents of south Texas annually follow the cotton harvest northward. Other thousands journey west and northwest for the vegetable and fruit harvests. Still others go to work the crops in Mississippi, Arkansas, Michigan, Wisconsin, Colorado, and even more distant places. Most of these migrants return to their homes in the Southwest; many choose to remain in the areas to which they migrate. Rural people move into cities in search of industrial employment. So great has been this movement that in some areas the proportion of urban residents among the Spanish-speaking is actually higher than that of Anglos.

The Spanish-speaking people are thus scattered throughout the Southwest and, at the same time, are concentrated in certain areas. The tendency toward concentration extends down to local residential arrangements, so that in the main, the Spanish-speaking, wherever they are found in the Southwest, tend to live together in separate communities or to inhabit separate and distinct parts of larger communities. The "Mexican part of town" or the "Mexican section" is a familiar sight to anyone traveling in the Southwest. Whether it is a *colonia* in California, a *corral* in San Antonio, Martineztown in Albuquerque, a wetback camp in the Lower Rio Grande Valley, the "East Side" in Austin, an isolated mountain village in northern New Mexico, or a "Mexican town" in northwest Texas, the picture is much the same: an area with somewhat substandard housing, facilities, and services, inhabited largely or entirely by a Spanish-speaking population, and to some extent cut off from the surrounding Anglo population by some combination of physical, psychological, and social barriers.

The "Mexican section" generally includes some of the least desirable residential areas of the community, and the inhabitants, by virtually any criterion that one might use, generally occupy a disadvantageous position. Their houses are more likely to be substandard than those of the rest of the community. There are fewer paved streets and sidewalks and more houses without sewer connections. The people are poorer than the average for the community. They own less property, and what they do own is in general less valuable, less desirable than that of people in other parts of the community. A higher proportion of them have low-paying, unskilled jobs than do the Anglos among whom they live. The educational level, as measured by number of school years completed, averages lower than that of the community as a whole. It is particularly low for persons forty years of age or older. The schools lose more children by drop-out. Attendance is less regular. A smaller proportion of the children finish elementary school and enter junior and senior high schools. The general health level is lower, with the result that proportionately more public health and welfare work is required here than in the community as a whole. Malnutrition, dysentery, tuberculosis, and infectious and contagious diseases in general are more prevalent. The proportion of people receiving public and private agency services is higher than in the total community. Political participation is likely to be low. Active interest in community programs and civic affairs is not great.

This generalized description of the "Mexican section" of almost any southwestern town or city should not be accepted as representative of conditions among all Spanish-speaking people. Many do not live in the "Mexican section" of their communities; and of those who do, many occupy dwellings and have economic, educational, and other advantages equal to or better than those of the majority of Anglos. But a large proportion of the Spanish-speaking population of the Southwest do occupy a position of lesser advantage relative to the rest of the population, and areas with conditions such as those just described can be found in almost any urban community in the region.

Spanish-speaking people who live in the country are not noticeably better off than the urban residents. If they own land, as do many of the relatively stable Spanish-American families of northern New Mexico and southern Colorado, they are likely to have too little of it to produce an adequate living. Those who have no land can live as tenants, sharecroppers, or hired hands on the farms of people who do own land; or they can, as many Spanish-speaking families do, join one of the many streams of migrant agricultural laborers, in which case their living conditions are likely to be almost indescribably bad and opportunities for improving their condition practically nonexistent.[40]

Economic Status

Judged by Anglo standards, the Spanish-American villagers have never been prosperous. The land they settled was not bountiful, and their technical skills were not such as to make it produce much more than a bare subsistence. While it is true that there have been, throughout the history of the Southwest, wealthy individuals and families in the area, for most of the people the conditions of living have been hard and the economic rewards meager.

Before the coming of the Anglos the economy of the villages was a semi-communal, subsistence one based on the cultivation of small irrigated patches near the communities and the common use of surrounding pasture and range lands on which cattle and sheep grazed. The precarious economic balance of the Spanish-American villages would have been seriously threatened by the encroachment of Anglos were it not for the fact that their arrival shifted the economic base, made possible the development of new skills and new types of economic relationships, and provided a source of wage-work opportunities through which the villages, if not able to improve their economic status much, were at least able to hold their own.

In the early 1930's conditions abruptly changed for the worse. Job opportunities were drastically reduced and, almost overnight, the villagers were thrown back onto a reliance on depleted land resources that were no longer sufficient to provide even a bare subsistence for the increased population. The crisis was met, in part, as already indicated, by a program of government relief so extensive that in one area, the Upper Rio Grande Valley, some 60 per cent of the rural families received relief in one form or another during the years 1935 and 1936.[41]

Economic conditions for Spanish-American villagers improved considerably in the late 1930's and throughout the 1940's largely as the result of income derived from nonvillage sources. Selective Service took many young men into the armed forces and allotment checks began to flow back to the villages. Agricultural jobs again became available. Industrial expansion and the high wages paid by war-stimulated industries drew many Spanish-Americans out of their villages and into Anglo communities. Individuals and families alike began the long climb to Anglo middle-class status.

Since the end of the war, the economic gains of the 1940's have been continued. High prices for agricultural products and a somewhat decreased pressure of population on land resources have enabled those who remained in the villages to improve their economic condition. The atomic energy installation at Los Alamos, the atomic project at Sandia Base in Albuquerque, and extensive governmental activities at the White Sands Proving Grounds near Alamogordo, New Mexico, in Denver, and elsewhere in the Southwest have provided employment for villagers living within a 40 to 50 mile radius of any of these projects and have made it possible for many to have a higher level of living than was possible at any time in the past. Where a few years ago agriculture was the mainstay of the economy and most families used wage work to supplement the living they gained from agricultural activity, now, in the areas around the huge governmental projects, wage and salary work is the principal source of livelihood, and for many families such agricultural activity as is carried on is merely for the purpose of providing fresh foods for family use. Even persons who do not work directly on one of the projects benefit from the increased economic activity in the area made possible by the demands of project workers for goods and services.

Although present conditions are relatively good, the economic situation of the Spanish-American villages remains somewhat precarious. There are still far too many people in the village areas of New Mexico and southern Colorado to be supported by the depleted land resources. Any considerable reduction in the appropriations for government projects in New Mexico would have one or more of the following results: (1) a marked decrease in the level of living of many Spanish-speaking people; (2) the necessity for a revitalization of some kind of federal relief program for the area; (3) an exodus of population, both Spanish-speaking and Anglo; and (4) the movement into urban areas of many Spanish-speaking people not equipped by temperament, education, or the possession of occupational skills, to compete effectively in an Anglo environment. On the other hand, if the government projects are continued for a number of years, not only will it be possible for the Spanish-Americans to maintain their present level of living, but they may also gradually acquire the necessary Anglo traits and skills.

Unlike that of the Spanish-American villagers, the economic position of the Mexican-American and Mexican rural population has not improved much in recent years. In the great commercial agricultural areas like the Imperial Valley of California and Lower Rio Grande Valley of Texas, and in places where the production of cotton, vegetables, and fruit is made possible by the periodic appearance of great numbers of migrant workers, wages have remained low and the level of living of the agricultural workers has shown little change. The poor working conditions and the low financial rewards received for their efforts have impeded the Spanish-speaking agricultural workers in acquiring the skills, knowledge, and attitudes that would enable them to function effectively in the Anglo cultural environment.

No especially good studies have been made of the incomes of the Spanish-speaking urban population, but in general it can be said that there are proportionately more persons in unskilled, low-paying jobs among them than is true of the Anglos. Lack of skills, poor educational background, unfamiliarity with Anglo ways, and, at times, discrimination by Anglos, all operate to keep many urban Spanish-speaking persons at the bottom of the economic ladder. In parts of the Southwest, even those with craft or other skills are referred by employment agencies to unskilled jobs only, and in some few areas there are differential wage rates for Anglo and Spanish-speaking doing the same kind of work. Until recently, laundry work and domestic service were about the only kinds of occupation open to Spanish-speaking women, and there still exists in some areas a prejudice against hiring Spanish-speaking people for jobs on any but the lowest levels.[42]

Housing

The low economic status of the Spanish-speaking population is related in complex ways to other conditions, many of which influence the relationships Spanish-speaking persons have with individuals and agencies whose task it is to provide health, welfare, and other services to members of the group. One such condition is housing.

Whether Spanish-speaking southwesterners live in city or country, their housing is likely to be poor. Houses are generally small and old. Sanitary facilities are frequently substandard or are lacking entirely. Overcrowding is common. At one extreme is the brush hut of the wetback in the border counties, providing little more than an overhead shelter. Almost as bad and perhaps in some ways worse are the tenements of El Paso, where a dozen or more families may share a water tap and a single indoor toilet. Much better are the small but neat frame houses that one sees on driving through the towns of south Texas, and the solid, square adobe homes of the Spanish-Americans of New Mexico and southern Colorado. Better still are the well-furnished, comfortable Anglo type of homes of Spanish-speaking professional and business persons with good incomes. And perhaps, if anything, a little above the average, there is our familiar dwelling at 1407 Felicity Street.

The dwellings of Spanish-American villagers, although small and often poorly furnished by urban Anglo standards, provide housing that compares favorably with that available to persons on the same economic level anywhere else in the country. Adobe has many advantages, other than cheapness, as a building material, and often village houses are beautiful as well as comfortable. The use of electricity has become common, and many of the houses are screened. Water supplies have been much improved in recent years, and although the people of many communities still depend for their water on streams, irrigation ditches, or open wells, the efforts of interested citizens and public health personnel have done much to make safe water more widely available. Some overcrowding does exist, but this is partly compensated for by the opportunity to spend much time out of doors.

The housing of Mexican-American agricultural workers, whether migrant or not, is probably not so good as that of the Spanish-American villagers. Many nonmigrants or part-time migrants who live in small towns occupy houses that are adequate, although frequently small. Electricity and, more rarely, refrigeration are available. Running water is piped into many of the homes that are located near a city supply. Sewer connections are more likely to be the exception than the rule. Overcrowding is common. Houses are frequently built close together on small lots, and often, particularly in south Texas, two or more houses occupy the same lot. Dwellings occupied by migrants at or near their places of work are almost always substandard. At best, they will be no more than clean, sparsely furnished frame buildings with a safe water supply and only minimum sanitary facilities, including community toilets, showers, and laundry. At worst, they range from no shelters at all through tents to dilapidated shacks with no provision for water or sanitation.

There is, of course, considerable variety in dwelling types for urban Spanish-speaking people. But in general the group will be found to occupy buildings in the oldest and most neglected parts of town, where rents and ownership costs are low and community conveniences, services, and facilities at a minimum. Stated simply, a disproportionate number of urban Spanish-speaking families live in slums.

The relation between the quality of housing of many of the Spanish-speaking people and their needs for health services is easy to see. Overcrowding, uncertain or unsafe water supplies,[43] lack of sewer connections, screens, and refrigeration, and many of the other conditions that are included in the concept "poor housing" contribute to the prevalence of disease and make difficult the maintenance of health. Any population living under the circumstances of many of the Spanish-speaking people would be expected to have health problems; it is, therefore, not surprising to find that the Spanish-speaking group have many.[44]

Education

The poor quality of the housing of many Spanish-speaking families is less a matter of choice—although choice does enter to some extent in the desire to live among other Spanish-speaking people—than a reflection of their low economic status and of the fact that only recently have large numbers of them begun to move rapidly toward the acquisition of Anglo ways and values. Impressive evidence of that movement is what has recently been happening in education.

In the culture of the Spanish-American villagers and in that of the particular group of Mexicans who migrated in large numbers to the United States, formal education, as we have seen, was not highly valued. One learned what he needed to know not from a separate group of specialists, but from his elders in ordinary day-by-day relationships. There were few schools in the Southwest before 1846, and those introduced by Anglos soon after that date were not strongly accepted because of the unsuitability of curricula, teaching methods, and language of instruction. Although a small proportion of Spanish-American parents have long seen in the schools an opportunity for their children to learn English and to acquire other attributes that would enable them to move more freely in the Anglo society, until recently parents in general have not insisted that their children either attend school regularly or continue their education. Eight years of schooling have been thought by many fathers and mothers to be enough and if a child failed to complete even that small amount of formal education they have shown no great concern. Consequently, the level of educational achievement of Spanish-Americans, as measured by years of school completed has remained fairly low,[45] and school administrators in some areas still have to cope with problems of irregular attendance and early dropping out among the Spanish-speaking children.

The children of Mexican-Americans, too, have been at a disadvantage educationally as a result of parental indifference, low incomes, and the influence of such factors as high mobility, discrimination by Anglos, and, in some instances, the requirement that they attend segregated schools.

In recent years, however, many changes have taken place which together are resulting in improvement of the educational level of Spanish-speaking people. Urbanization is bringing more of them into the cities where educational facilities are accessible, community pressures strong, educational achievements suitably rewarded, and there is less expectation that children of school age will work to help maintain the family. Educational administrators have become increasingly concerned with the problem and have made great effort to get Spanish-speaking children enrolled in school. The educational benefits to veterans have made it possible for large numbers of Spanish-speaking students to obtain college training, and considerable numbers have taken advantage of the opportunity. The rise in economic status of many Spanish-speaking parents has been accompanied by a general change in attitude toward education and the development of an interest in seeing their children finish high school. These and other changes are bringing about a rapid improvement in the educational status of the Spanish-speaking population as they move toward a level of accomplishment approximating that of the Anglos.

Health

There are no satisfactory sources of information on the health of the total Spanish-speaking population. However, studies that have been made of one or another small group within the larger population indicate that the level of health is lower and the prevalence of some types of disease probably higher among Spanish-speaking people than among the total population of the Southwest.[46] Undernourishment, a high infant mortality rate, and a greater prevalence of some infectious and contagious diseases, notably tuberculosis and dysentery, are conditions frequently reported among the Spanish-speaking populations that have been studied. Age-specific birth and death rates are both somewhat higher for the Spanish-speaking than for the population as a whole, although the death rates have been coming down rather rapidly in recent years and the birth rates are beginning to reflect the increasing urbanization of the Spanish-speaking population.

The health of the Spanish-Americans who have remained in their native villages is probably not greatly different now from what it has been in the past quarter-century although a somewhat improved economic status has contributed to a more nearly adequate diet, and the influence of such organizations and agencies as the New Mexico Health Council, the Catholic Maternity Institute, and the state and local health departments of Colorado and New Mexico have made medical personnel and facilities more available and have brought about improvements in water supply and sanitation in some areas. Spanish-Americans who have moved into cities share in general the health status of other city dwellers of their socioeconomic level. This means, as compared with the total population, proportionately more diseases of infancy and childhood, more communicable disease in all age-groups, more deficiency disease conditions, and a generally lower level of health and well-being.

The health status of Mexican-Americans is roughly comparable to that of Spanish-Americans. A recent study of migrant families in Colorado, most of whom were Mexican-Americans, reported serious health problems, but very little health care; a diet lacking in meat, vegetables, and milk; little contact with medical personnel during the previous year; a low level of immunization against smallpox, diphtheria, and whooping cough; and an infant mortality rate about twice as high as that for the state of Colorado as a whole.[47] Urban Mexican-Americans, like Spanish-Americans, have about the same level of health and the same needs for more adequate health information and care as do others on their social and economic levels.

Political Participation

In a democratic society, such as ours, one of the most certain ways for any group to improve its position is to participate effectively in politics. Such participation, of course, requires informed and vigorous leadership, a fairly high level of group self-consciousness, and a wide knowledge of what the democratic political process is and how it operates, qualities for which the Spanish-speaking group have not in the past been noted. Political participation by the group has been somewhat spotty, ranging from almost complete indifference in some areas to highly effective participation in others. On the one hand, the political effectiveness of the group has been minimized at various times and places because of failure to register and vote, the selling of votes, support of paternalistic bosses, intragroup splits over candidates, lack of qualified candidates from within the group, and inability to win the support of other population groups. On the other hand, there is evidence that in some areas Spanish-speaking persons are acquiring political skill and are beginning to make their weight felt in the political arena.[48]

New Mexico, a state in which the Spanish-Americans until recently made up more than half the total population, is unique among the five southwestern states in the degree to which the Spanish-speaking have exercised political influence on all levels of government. Even in the most isolated of the villages, politics is a subject of considerable interest, and partisan rivalries frequently are bitter and intense. Spanish-speaking candidates have sought and won the highest offices in the state. They have represented their state in the United States Senate and House of Representatives and their nation in diplomatic and consular services abroad. When local, state, and national slates are made up and platforms adopted by political parties, the potential vote of the Spanish-speaking population is taken into consideration.

Although they do not vote as a unit and are as likely to support an Anglo as a Spanish-speaking candidate, the Spanish-Americans are a political force to be reckoned with in New Mexico. In the state as a whole, however, it is likely that their influence is waning. And there is the possibility that, as they become a smaller proportion of the state's population and increasingly acquire the social, educational, and economic attributes of the Anglo population, the political influence of the Spanish-Americans, as a separate group and on the state level, will continue to decline.

In contrast to the Spanish-Americans, Mexican-Americans have until recently had almost no effective participation in political activity and little or no political influence. Many never bothered to become citizens of the United States and therefore legally could not vote or hold public office. Others were prevented from political activity by migratory status, discrimination, lack of knowledge of how to participate in politics, and by feelings of apathy and indifference toward political affairs. In Texas, where the largest Mexican-American population lives and where the group makes up a substantial proportion of the total population and a majority in some counties, no member of the group has ever held any of the higher elected state offices, and even in counties where the Spanish-speaking people form a high proportion of the population Anglos generally are in control of the political machinery and monopolize the public offices. The winning of the Democratic nomination for county clerk in El Paso county in 1948 was sufficiently newsworthy to justify a story in *Newsweek*, pointing out that it was the first time in more than thirty years that a Spanish-name person had won a major office in that county, which is nearly 50 per cent Spanish-speaking.

As their economic, educational, and general social status improves, Spanish-speaking people may be expected to take an increasing part in the political life of their respective communities and states. The amount and quality of participation will certainly continue to depend, as it has in the past, on such factors as the historical background of the particular group, numbers and proportion of Spanish-speaking in the total population, the presence or absence of discrimination or other hindering influences, the proportion of persons among the Spanish-speaking who are legally eligible to vote, and the amount and kind of encouragement given by Anglos to the political development of Spanish-speaking groups.

CLASS DIFFERENCES WITHIN SPANISH-SPEAKING GROUPS

Just as there are differences within the Spanish-speaking population of the Southwest that enable us to distinguish between Spanish-Americans, Mexican-Americans, and Mexicans, so are there noticeable differences within each of these groups that enable us to separate them into subgroups on the basis of certain observable uniformities of attitudes, attributes, achievements, and associations. These differences can probably best be described in terms of social class.[49] The basis of class distinctions lies in the tendency of persons with certain combinations of personal and social characteristics to associate more frequently and more intimately with those of similar characteristics than with those whose characteristics are considerably different, and to develop feelings of identification with those whom they perceive to be like themselves. Class differentiations to some extent cut across ethnic group lines, so that, on some levels at least, Spanish-speaking persons may feel a closer identification with some Anglos than with others of the Spanish-speaking group. In general, however, the awareness of cultural group distinctions is only minimized but not entirely superseded by social class identification. Hence, even though an upper-class Mexican-American, for example, may feel more at ease with an upper-class or upper-middle-class Anglo than with a lower-class Mexican-American in a situation involving some degree of intimacy, the Anglo and the Mexican-American probably would each retain in the relationship awareness of the cultural group affiliation of himself and the other.

The few studies that have been made of class structure within the Spanish-speaking group tend to confirm the notion that class differences do exist within each of the subgroups in the larger Spanish-speaking population and that the differences to some degree both determine and reflect the extent of acculturation. In other words, there are differences of attitude and behavior within the various subgroups in the Spanish-speaking population that correlate roughly with subjective identifications individuals make of their own status and the status of others. Recognition of these differences is one basis for the subjective identification which, in turn, by discouraging association between persons of unlike characteristics, fosters further difference.

Among the Spanish-American group there are characteristics —occupational, economic, educational, residential, religious— that are frequently found together and that, in their totality, are important indices of class status.[50] *From the standpoint of the Anglo value system*, the lowest social class is that of the still isolated villagers who, as a group, are likely to have varying combinations of the following characteristics, many of which have previously been mentioned: a social system relatively little affected by contact with that of the Anglos and still maintaining the old traditional emphasis on family, church, *patrón*, and community; a low economic status, still basically dependent on agriculture, with heavy reliance on small, inadequate land holdings and supplemental welfare funds; generalized rather than specialized occupational skills; a high proportion of illiteracy among old people and a high rate of drop-outs among school children after the third grade; a fair amount of hostility toward outsiders, particularly Anglos; a tendency to live largely in the present; strong beliefs in witchcraft and magic, and considerable reliance on folk medicine for diagnosing and treating illness; devout Catholicism, with a large membership among the adult males in the *penitente* order; relatively little knowledge of the English language.

For many reasons, mostly related to the breakdown of isolation, this is a rapidly changing group. Recent changes have included an improvement in economic status as a result of generally improved economic conditions and the opportunities now available for employment at Los Alamos, Sandia Base, and similar projects, both governmental and private, keyed to national defense; the beginnings of occupational specialization; changes in family relationships, with a trend away from the extended family pattern and toward lessened feelings of responsibility for aged parents, adult siblings, and cousins; extended use of English; more interest in education and in the possibility of social mobility; a greatly increased amount of contact with Anglos and Anglo ways, resulting in lessened hostility and the adoption of many elements of the Anglo material culture—for example, automobiles, electricity, packaged and processed foods, patent medicines, mail order clothes, and canned beer.

Very close to the villagers in the Spanish-American class structure, *as viewed by Anglos,* are the lower class of the urban and suburban areas, composed largely of former villagers who have moved into cities and towns, or fringe areas, in the hope of improving their condition. A number of the inhabitants of 1407 Felicity Street belong to this group. Members of this class still cling to some of the values and customs of the old culture, but have also taken on many Anglo characteristics. They still live, like the villagers, mainly in adobe houses—except in areas like central and northern Colorado where adobe is not widely used— but the house is likely to have electric lights, sometimes running water, and other Anglo services and conveniences. Members of the group are still Catholics, but the church does not occupy the place in their lives that it did in the villages, and the men, although nominally members, frequently do not attend services except on holidays or other important occasions. Membership in the *penitente* organization is not common. Incomes are low and are mainly derived from unskilled or semi-skilled types of jobs. Married women rarely work outside the home, although unmarried girls and sometimes married women with few children do take domestic service and other low-paying jobs. Older people are not always functionally literate, and children, although some finish high school, rarely are encouraged to go beyond the sixth or eighth grade. There is little admitted belief in witchcraft or magic, but still considerable reliance on home remedies and folk medicines. There is, as among the villagers, a tendency to live in the present and to let the dim, distant, nebulous future take care of itself.

The attitude toward Anglos is likely to be a mixture of envy and resentment, envy of the Anglos' possession of material things and skills which the Spanish-Americans of this class have come to want but only rarely can have, and resentment at what seems to be a lack of acceptance of Spanish-Americans by Anglos, which in many instances may be a real rejection and in others no more than a manifestation of the impersonal quality that Anglos bring to nearly all their relationships. English is used outside the home and is understood by children and young adults. Spanish is likely to be the language used in the home and in informal communication with relatives and friends. In some areas the extended family pattern remains fairly strong, although somewhat weakened by a tendency toward separate residence for family units of parents and minor children and decreased feelings of responsibility for aged parents and other relatives. In other areas the extended family pattern has broken down, resulting in serious problems of illegitimacy, desertion, broken homes, and unattached individuals. Conflicts and misunderstandings between generations are not uncommon among this group as a result of the fact that the younger people tend to take on Anglo ways faster than their parents.

The lower-middle class of urban or suburban residence is similar to the lower class in many characteristics. Differences can be noted in a less close tie with the church among the lower-middle class, and a tendency toward the acceptance of the Protestant religion among a small proportion of the group; a wider use of English; a somewhat higher economic status; a tendency toward the Anglo family pattern; a greater emphasis on the benefits of education, which results in children finishing high school and in some few attending college; an occasional over-zealous championing of Anglo values and ways by young adult males; and the use of Anglo folk medical practices along with a reliance on Anglo medical personnel and institutions.

The urban-suburban upper-middle class, which would include most of the proportionately few professionally trained people among the Spanish-Americans and a good proportion of the businessmen and state-level politicians, is noticeably different in a number of respects from the lower-middle and lower classes. The proportion that are Protestants, although still relatively small, is higher than among either of the other two classes. Family rela-tionships and social relations in general tend to follow Anglo pat-terns, with young people generally accepting many Anglo middle-class ideals and values. English is the language most frequently used, even in the home, but Spanish is usually known by the adults. Economic status is likely to be good, and many members of this class have moved out into Anglo sections of the towns and cities in which they live. The educational level is high as com-pared with that of the two lower groups, and young people fre-quently attend and are graduated from colleges. Members of this class receive varying degrees of acceptance by Anglos, depending on the area in which they live, and, on the whole, associate to a considerable extent with Anglos. There is relatively little associa-tion with or concern for lower- and lower-middle-class Spanish-Americans, except insofar as such association or concern is neces-sitated by professional, political, or business interests. There is considerable emphasis among the men on the Anglo values of success, getting ahead, providing for the future, making progress. Wives generally do not work, although young married women without children may continue to work outside the home during the early years of their marriage. Anglo health knowledge and practices are accepted and used.

The small urban upper class enjoys a status based mainly on old family tradition. Members of the group are likely to be strongly Catholic. The social relationships and family system are much like those of the Anglos, except that there is a tendency to emphasize kinship and to maintain to some degree vestiges of old male-female relationships within the family group in which the activity of the female was largely restricted to the home and immediate family. English is spoken and is used both within and outside the family group; it is a matter of pride that all members of the family know Spanish well and use it on ceremonial occasions. The level of formal education is high, and in most families the children are sent to college as a matter of course. There is some feeling of superiority toward Anglos, particularly those of a lower-class status, but a wide adoption of Anglo ways and values, including those of medicine. The Spanish cultural heritage is a matter of pride, and deliberate and sophisticated attempts are made to preserve elements of that culture. There is some glorification of the past and a tendency to remember and revere particularly notable ancestors.

Among Mexican-Americans, as among Spanish-Americans, class differences can be noted. Here two categories probably will be sufficient to delimit somewhat homogeneous groups, with the distinguishing characteristics being occupation, family background, education, wealth or income, and command of Anglo ways.[51] What we may call the lower class is composed of persons with unskilled or semi-skilled occupations, whose incomes are low and whose property holdings are not great.[52] They are highly mobile physically, but not socially, and their children usually do not receive training in the skills that would enable them to rise above the social level of their parents. Emphasis on education is not great and almost none of the children gets beyond the elementary grades. Because of lack of occupational skills and the seasonal nature of much agricultural work, income is not large and the level of living is low. As among the lower-class Spanish-Americans, Spanish is preferred to English as the language of the home, and Anglo ways, except for those involving the acquisition, possession, and use of material objects, are not well understood or widely practiced. Association is mainly with other Spanish-speaking people, rather than with Anglos.

The middle class among Mexican-Americans is made up of those with enough command of Anglo cultural ways to have moved up the socioeconomic ladder. Included in this class are businessmen of many types and a wide income range, professional people, politicians, and some white-collar workers who, even though they may have less income than some persons in the lower class—for example, truck-owners and crew chiefs, mechanics, skilled craftsmen, railway workers—have other attributes that separate them from the class below.

This middle class may be thought of as two groups rather than one. A part of the group is still clearly oriented toward Mexico and things Mexican. Its members speak Spanish by preference, even though able to use English, continue the kinds of social relationships characteristic of their class in Mexico, maintain an interest in events in Mexico, and observe Mexican holidays with appropriate ceremonies. Another part is as clearly oriented toward the United States and things Anglo. Members of this part prefer to use English, have adopted or are rapidly adopting Anglo patterns of social relationships, are relatively little interested in what happens in Mexico, and actively and vigorously pursue Anglo goals.

Both groups are much more acculturated than the lower class and more at ease in Anglo culture. Both, however, probably associate more with other Spanish-speaking people than with Anglos, although this is probably not true of those who moved out of the Spanish-speaking group and live as more or less isolated small family groups among Anglos. In some areas, notably along the border, middle-class Mexican-Americans, particularly those distinguished by long residence in an area and a long family background plus the possession of wealth or influence among the Spanish-speaking group, may be admitted to full participation by socially exclusive upper-middle-class Anglos. While lower-class Mexican-Americans, like Spanish-Americans on the same class level, are likely to believe in magic and to rely heavily for medical knowledge and treatment on folk medical

beliefs and practices, middle-class members generally accept Anglo medical ways.

The Mexican group, as here defined, is made up only of one class. There are some persons who cross the border legally and who have characteristics that might place them in the middle or upper classes, but their number is relatively small. As has been pointed out, the Mexican group is largely made up of wetbacks and contract agricultural workers whose lack of skills, low incomes, poor education, and relative lack of command of Anglo ways are such as to justify their inclusion in the lower class. In general their characteristics are those of the lower-class Mexican-Americans, with a little more emphasis on those cultural characteristics deriving from Mexico and a bit less on those acquired in the United States.

One further statement may be made about the attitude of Spanish-speaking people toward intermarriage with Anglos. In some areas of the Southwest there is active opposition to such a practice on the part of both groups. In other areas neither group has any particular feeling about it. In no part of the Southwest is intermarriage extensive but it does occur.[53] Although there is little information available on the subject, the prevailing patterns may be somewhat as follows: Mexicans of both sexes tend to marry within the Spanish-speaking group. So do lower-class Mexican-Americans and Spanish-Americans. Marriages across cultural lines occur, although not extensively, among middle- and upper-class Spanish-speaking people, and are probably relatively more prevalent among those of upper-middle-class status than among lower-middle-class or upper-class people.

These brief descriptions of social classes among the Spanish-American group are not intended to be accurate in any strict scientific sense. They are merely another attempt to illustrate the point that the Spanish-speaking group is not a homogeneous population, but rather one in which there are many varieties and combinations of characteristics, ranging from an almost complete acceptance of the Anglo culture to a relatively small degree of change from the old village culture. In general a low position on the socioeconomic ladder is associated with the clusters of characteristics most closely resembling those of the village culture; increasing socioeconomic status is accompanied by the progressive adoption of elements from Anglo culture. Spanish-speaking people of low-class status are likely to be more at ease with other Spanish-speaking persons than with Anglos. They often behave in ways that are difficult for Anglos to understand, particularly middle- or upper-class Anglos. Middle- and upper-class Spanish-speaking people, on the other hand, have generally internalized many Anglo values and practice many Anglo ways. They are likely to be at home in the Anglo culture and to be able to associate freely with Anglos. And their behavior in a given situation is likely to be such that it can be easily understood by Anglos.

FACTORS THAT RETARD ACCULTURATION

One question frequently asked by Anglos whose work brings them into contact with Spanish-speaking people in the Southwest is "Why do they remain different?"—a question that sometimes seems to imply a lack of good intent on the part of the Spanish-speaking. One answer, of course, might be that they do not remain different, but that they are rapidly changing in the direction of adopting Anglo characteristics. Another might be that Spanish-speaking people are not so different as they might seem at first glance, and that much of what is interpreted as cultural difference may well be a subcultural class difference which is simply more conspicuous when exhibited by Spanish-speaking people than it is among Anglos who share that particular characteristic or cluster of characteristics. However, there still remains the fact that in some respects the Spanish-speaking people are culturally different from Anglos and that some of these differences are remarkably persistent.

Proximity to Mexico

For all groups among the Spanish-speaking people there are, of course, powerful pressures both for and against the adoption of Anglo ways. One hindering factor is the proximity to Mexico of many Spanish-speaking southwesterners, which makes possible a constant reinforcement of their culture. More than 50 million people cross the Mexican border into the United States each year.[54] Approximately the same number cross in the other direction. This enormous traffic provides a continuing link between the Spanish-speaking people of the border states and Mexico. And not only people move across the border. Printed materials, motion picture films, material goods, and radio programs also come into the United States, and all function to retard the acquisition of Anglo cultural traits. The need to learn English is lessened when one can satisfy nearly all his needs in an environment in which mainly Spanish is spoken. The pressure to conform to Anglo ways is minimized when one is surrounded by people who follow other ways. As individuals and families acquire Anglo characteristics and move toward becoming culturally indistinguishable from the Anglo population, their places are taken by newcomers from Mexico who have few, if any, Anglo cultural traits. Furthermore, these newcomers have interests in Mexico and continuing contacts of one sort or another with people there that help to make them resistant to changes in the direction of adopting more than a minimum of the Anglo culture.[55]

Segregation

A second strong factor retarding the acculturation of Spanish-speaking people is segregation. Wherever they are found in the Southwest, whether in a New Mexican village, agricultural community, small town, or city, Spanish-speaking people tend to live by themselves in separate communities or neighborhoods. In some areas this segregation is the result of discriminatory policies adopted by Anglos. In others—for example, in migratory labor camps—it results from the concentration of Spanish-speaking people in certain types of occupation. Mostly though, it is a manifestation of the free choice of Spanish-speaking people— "free," that is, within the limits set by the fact that poor people do not have a wide range of choice with respect to where they will live. It is more comfortable to live among people like oneself than among those who are in many respects culturally alien and possibly hostile.

Whatever the reasons, segregation is a common phenomenon among the Spanish-speaking people of the Southwest. And segregation, whether enforced or voluntary, definitely retards acculturation. The Spanish-speaking people who live in separate neighborhoods, or communities, or counties, have restricted opportunities to associate with persons outside their own group. In large areas of high concentration of Spanish-speaking population, such as parts of Rio Arriba County in New Mexico (80 per cent Spanish-speaking in 1950) and Starr County in Texas (89 per cent Spanish-speaking), it was until recently and to some extent still is possible for a person to live a whole lifetime with no direct association with Anglos other than occasional official, commercial, or casual contacts. Even in cities where population concentration forces extensive contacts on streets, in public transportation vehicles, and in commercial and recreational establishments, the Spanish-speaking people still tend to confine their meaningful associations to those with other Spanish-speaking persons.

On Felicity Street, for example, the inhabitants of our apartment house at 1407 have a minimum of contacts with Anglos other than those that are official—for example, a visit by a school nurse—commercial, or exceedingly casual, such as contact between two persons who happen to be passengers on the same bus. Some of the children are born in their own homes on Felicity Street without the intervention of any Anglo. In the case of those delivered in hospitals the mothers maintain a partial isolation because of the impersonal nature of the relationships established. The playmates of Felicity Street children are Spanish-speaking; they go to schools, either public or parochial, in which the majority of their classmates are Spanish-speaking. When, as adolescents or young adults, they venture into the Anglo community outside their neighborhood, they often go in pairs or groups and thus carry a part of their familiar world with them. Obtaining and holding jobs require association with Anglos, but the relationship is a commercial one, and such personal informal relations as are established on the job are largely with other Spanish-speaking employees. Courtship and marriage are likely to be within the group; and the new family finds living quarters in the same community or in a similar one elsewhere. Religious and recreational activities require minimal associations with Anglos. The church membership is likely to be a segregated one, whether Catholic or Protestant. Spanish language movies are usually available; if not, one attends English language movies, but often in company with other Spanish-speaking persons. Spanish language radio programs can be heard in almost any part of the Southwest, and their number is increasing as Anglo advertisers come to appreciate the extent of the purchasing power of Spanish-speaking listeners. Illness can frequently be handled within the community or neighborhood group, for almost everyone knows something about efficacious remedies, and where common knowledge does not suffice, there are still *médicas, curanderas,* druggists, and, occasionally, physicians within the group to whom one can turn. Death, too, is often a segregated affair, with the funeral conducted from a segregated church, by a Spanish-speaking undertaker and with interment of the deceased among his kind in a segregated cemetery or section of a cemetery.[56]

Segregation is thus both a cause and an effect of retarded assimilation. Spanish-speaking people tend to live among their own kind in separate communities because they are aware of cultural differences between themselves and those they sometimes refer to as "gringos." Separate communities minimize the opportunities for cross-cultural contacts and thus delay the acquisition of Anglo cultural traits. Lack of Anglo traits makes for continued awareness of difference and a continuation of the tendency to live apart. And so the circle continues.

Lack of Leaders

A third important factor in the slow rate of acculturation of Spanish-speaking people is the failure of the group to develop within itself leaders who can help bridge the gap between the two cultures. In the whole Southwest there are relatively few persons who, because of exceptional talent or strong motivation or fortunate circumstances, or a combination of all three, are able to give effective leadership to any considerable part of the Spanish-speaking population.[57] Aside from these few, such leadership as is available is institutional in that it comes from persons who exercise it because of their position, not because of ability, leadership skills, or other personal qualities; it tends to be opportunistic and individualistic in that leaders seek to satisfy their own self-interest rather than promote the welfare of the group; or it is sometimes unrealistic in that it stresses opposition and resistance to Anglo culture and an attempted glorification of old traditional ways.

Basic to the observed inability of the group to develop adequate leadership is undoubtedly a cultural tradition in which there was no great necessity for personal leadership and little opportunity to practice the art. Basic also, and for the same reason, is the lack of any tradition of what might be called "followership." In the Spanish-American culture, as exemplified in the Rio Grande villages, few problems arose that called for any decision-making or policy-forming and those few could be handled by institutional leaders—priests, *patróns*, older males—who exercised this privilege because of who they were rather than their fitness as to personal characteristics or abilities. Owing to this cultural arrangement and the fact that existence was precarious and any experimentation might have devastating results, the qualities that make for leadership in an Anglo world—initiative, imagination, daring, orientation toward change—were given a low value by the group. In one sense the whole community was a single organization set up to ensure the necessities of economic and social life to its members, a function that it performed well. Since the community provided for all areas of living, there was little need to set up separate special organizations to carry on particular functions.[58] Thus, there was no tradition among the Spanish-Americans, and scarcely any among Mexican-Americans and Mexicans, of deliberate, self-conscious organization for the purpose of achieving specific ends. What tendency there is toward organization is largely the result of contact with Anglos and is itself an evidence of some degree of acculturation.

Many attempts have been made to organize Spanish-speaking people in the Southwest for various purposes. But until recently, with one or two exceptions, they have been failures. Two regional organizations, the Alianza Hispano-Americana and the League of United Latin American Citizens, have been in existence for a fairly long time, but one is largely a fraternal insurance group and the other a loosely organized series of local councils that have had no consistent regional program and only sporadic success in some local communities. Neither has exercised any long-range influence among the Spanish-speaking group. In 1952 the most vigorous organizations among the Spanish-speaking people were the American G.I. Forum and the Community Service Organization. The Forum is a group of young Spanish-speaking veterans who were organized under the dynamic leadership of a Corpus Christi physician, and who, largely in south Texas,[59] were meeting with some success in their fight to eliminate discrimination against Spanish-speaking people, improve health and educational conditions, and make their influence felt in local and state politics. The Community Service Organization, working largely with urban people in Los Angeles and other parts of southern California, was moving toward virtually the same objectives. Both undoubtedly owe much of their success to the fact that they have been active among people who have come to know and appreciate the necessity for and effectiveness of organization in the Anglo culture.

Attitude of Suspicion and Mistrust

A final factor that may be mentioned as a retarding influence in acculturation is an attitude of suspicion and mistrust that operates primarily against Anglos but in some areas, as already suggested, is also directed by some Spanish-speaking people against others of the same group. The result is the undermining of sincere efforts at leadership and organization from within the Spanish group and an unwillingness to cooperate with Anglo individuals, agencies, or organizations in programs intended to benefit the Spanish-speaking people. Anyone familiar with the history of contact between Anglos and Spanish-Americans can understand how this attitude might have developed. Its persistence, however, is a definite detriment to the acculturation of the Spanish-speaking people, since it tends to reduce both the amount and the range of association with Anglos.

FACTORS THAT PROMOTE ACCULTURATION

Of course, not all of the forces operating on the Spanish-speaking people are working in the direction of retarding acculturation. There are some very powerful influences that tend to promote acculturation and, in the long run, they will be decisive.

Population Size

One such influence is that resulting from the difference in the size of Anglo and Spanish-speaking populations. There are only a few million Spanish-speaking and more than 150 million Anglos. Each group will influence and be influenced by the other, with the extent being, in part, related to the size of the groups. The smaller group is certain to be attracted toward the ways of the larger, since contacts and association cannot be entirely avoided and since the adoption of Anglo ways is usually psychologically or materially rewarding. The larger group is not likely to be so much affected by cultural borrowing as the smaller. Some Anglos, particularly those living in the Southwest, will adopt a few elements of the Spanish cultural heritage—the language, some food tastes and preferences, styles in clothing or decoration—but most Anglos will be unaffected, since they have little or no contact with Spanish-speaking persons. Some Spanish cultural elements will become relatively stable parts of the Anglo culture on regional or national levels—as, for example, the use of such words as *canyon*, *arroyo*, and *mesa* and the architectural use of the corner fireplace in southwestern buildings—but these will be few in number and not very important in the totality of Anglo culture.

To oversimplify the process, acculturation may be thought of as a function of the proportion of contacts or associations with persons outside one's culture to the total number of associations or contacts one has. A good proportion of the contacts of the Spanish-speaking people in the Southwest are with Anglos and the number will continue to increase. In the case of the Anglos, except possibly those living in areas where there are large concentrations of Spanish-speaking people, the proportion of contacts with the

Spanish-speaking is fairly low and is likely to continue so. The opportunities and pressures for acculturation are thus going to be greater for the Spanish-speaking than for the Anglos, if for no other reason than the relative sizes of the two groups.

Urbanization

But there are other reasons, too. One of them is urbanization. The Spanish-Americans and Mexicans come from rural areas and a long tradition of rural living. Their culture is adapted to the conditions of rural life; it is not equally well adapted to urban conditions. Urbanization is fairly new to the Southwest and to those areas of Mexico from which the Mexican-Americans and Mexicans come. A hundred years ago, for example, there was not a single town in the Southwest with a population as large as 5,000 and not more than 20,000 persons in the area lived in settlements as large as 2,500. Los Angeles in 1850 was a village of 1,600. San Antonio had not yet reached a population of 3,500. Today nearly three-quarters of the Spanish-speaking population of California live in or near Los Angeles; there are 100,000 or more in or about San Antonio; and considerable numbers live in Houston, Dallas, Denver, San Diego, El Paso, Albuquerque, Tucson, and other cities of the Southwest.

The implications of this shift for the culture of the Spanish-speaking people are many and profound. A few can be mentioned here to illustrate the point that urbanization is a powerful force toward acculturation. New family and community relations have developed. There are more divorces, more marriages outside the group. New economic relations and activities have appeared, as have new patterns in recreation. The use of Spanish has declined[60] and the language itself has changed as new concepts have been added and English words borrowed or adapted. There are more intragroup and intergroup tensions and conflicts. Class divisions have grown sharper and the various subgroups within the Spanish-speaking group are not so homogeneous as they once were. Old holidays have been lost; new ones have been added. Increasingly the focus of attention of children is away from the home. These and the many other changes that have resulted from the shift from rural living to city living have been disruptive of old ways and have brought new pressures.

Urban living, in contrast to rural life, brings many changes in patterns of association. A given individual comes into contact with greater numbers and more diverse types of persons in the city than in a rural community. A higher proportion of his contacts are with people he does not know and who do not know him. A greater proportion of his relationships are thus contractual; a lesser proportion are personal. This shift in type of relationships has important implications for the Spanish-speaking person who comes from a cultural background in which nearly all relationships were personal and where the only contacts were with well-known people. He is likely to leave a situation involving association with an official or professional Anglo—for example, a visit to a doctor or a state employment agency—feeling unsatisfied, puzzled, and perhaps resentful because he does not know how to evaluate or respond to impersonal relationships and does not feel at ease with them.

The Anglo official or professional person who deals with Spanish-speaking people is frequently likely to feel that they are too ready to become dependent, that they seem to want him to make decisions for them, that they do not come up to his expectations of what their part of the relationship should be. He is accustomed to impersonal relationships and to a separation of business and personal relationships. The Spanish-speaking person comes from a culture in which there is little or no separation of what is personal or private from what is public or a matter of business. Anglo and Spanish-speaking people thus approach their relationships with different expectations of what is proper behavior; and when the behavior of other people does not conform to their expectations either is likely to be dissatisfied with the outcome of the association. But impersonal, contractual relations are characteristic of urban life, and however unsatisfactory they may be, the Spanish-speaking person who lives in a southwestern city must enter into them. And in so doing and in learning to be at ease with them, he loses a part of his own cultural heritage and acquires a part of that of the Anglos.

Mobility

Another factor that operates to facilitate acculturation is mobility. The cultural tradition of the Spanish-Americans and Mexican-Americans has been one in which individuals did not move around much either physically or socially. Individuals were born, grew up, and died in or near a single community, and the status of the family into which they were born was the status they held throughout their lifetime. In contrast to that pattern, the Spanish-speaking people of the Southwest today move about freely and, in increasing numbers, are within a lifetime able to change their social status. Few of the adults living at 1407 Felicity Street were born in Arcadia. The heads of most of the families moved a number of times before coming to their present residence and will undoubtedly move again.[61] Most of the men, and some of the women, have held more than one job. None of this particular group has moved very far up the social or economic scale, but at least the possibility of so doing has been present.

There is, in addition to the movement of Spanish-speaking people themselves, another way in which mobility affects the acculturation of the group. It is the movement of Anglos into areas previously occupied by the Spanish-speaking. The first contacts between the two groups resulted from the westward expansion of Anglo culture, and during the past hundred years there has been a continuous movement of Anglos into the Southwest. They and the elements of their culture have penetrated everywhere, so that it is no longer possible for many Spanish-speaking persons to avoid extensive contact with either. The plaza in the village of Trampas, New Mexico, for example, has not moved. It still stands where it has stood for more than a century. But now there is a gasoline pump on one side of the plaza, a symbol of the encroachment of Anglo culture. The pump and the canned and packaged foods on the shelves of the store behind it, and the electric wires that come in across the fields and join each of the houses to the outside world are evidence that the native of Trampas does not have to go outside his village to be affected by Anglo culture. Whether one goes out to meet it or remains at home to await its coming, Anglo culture intrudes, bringing changes that are not always foreseen and not always welcome, but that are inescapable.

Education

Another important factor in fostering acculturation is formal education, which we have already discussed in other sections of this chapter. The school, as Anglos know it, was not an important part of the early culture of the Spanish-Americans or Mexican-Americans.[62] Until recently almost no one in the villages of the Middle or Upper Rio Grande valleys or in the small towns and remote communities on the central plateau of Mexico had much interest in or opportunity for formal education, and no one suffered any particular disadvantage for not having gone a number of years to school. Anglo culture, on the other hand, places a high value on formal education, and individuals who fail to win a diploma of some kind frequently feel regret at their lost opportunity.

Although their education deficiencies are still the subject of much concern among professional educators,[63] the Spanish-speaking people are participating more and more in formal education, and are thus subjecting themselves and their children to a powerful acculturative experience. The official language of the schools everywhere in the Southwest is English and, although there are some Spanish-speaking villages in which teachers use Spanish in the classrooms, the schools in general provide an atmosphere in which there is both an incentive and an opportunity to learn and use English. The schools are also means whereby Anglo concepts, ways, and values can be communicated to natively Spanish-speaking children, so that the child who finishes eight or twelve grades of school has been long exposed to Anglo cultural elements. Parents, too, are affected by the school experiences of their children. There is contact between parents and teachers and school administrators, and pressure is exerted on parents to participate in such Anglo organizations as the Parent-Teachers Association. In urban areas Spanish-speaking children are increasingly finishing high school, and considerable numbers of them have attended college through availing them-

selves of veterans' benefits. In high school and to an even greater extent in college, Spanish-speaking students are thrown into frequent and intimate association with Anglos. Outside of certain special courses, the Spanish language cannot be used. Highschool and college students are thus subjected to three strong acculturative forces in the English language, the curricula they study, and their close association with English-speaking students. The result in most cases is the acquisition of a good many Anglo cultural traits.

The few factors that could be mentioned here are by no means all that influence the acculturation of Spanish-speaking people. Any member of the group is subject to these and to many other influences in varying intensity, and the degree of acculturation that he attains is a function of his total experience in both cultures. The influence of a particular kind of experience will vary according to such factors as the emotional state of the person at the time of the experience, the age at which the experience began, the extent to which it could be related to other experiences, and the number of times it is repeated. Thus, while it is possible and useful to make broad generalizations about the entire Spanishspeaking group and the subgroups within it, these generalizations do not necessarily provide any basis for understanding or predicting the behavior or attitude of a given individual in a particular situation.

IMPORTANCE OF AN UNDERSTANDING OF CULTURAL OR SUBCULTURAL DIFFERENCES

Medical personnel and others whose occupation or position brings them into association with members of the Spanishspeaking population—or of any other group exhibiting cultural or subcultural differences—can probably develop more satisfactory relationships and give more effective service if they are sensitive to the implications of cultural differences and know something of the specific culture of the group with whom they are working and of the possible range of differences within the group. A relationship with any particular Spanish-speaking individual could possibly be made more satisfactory to both participants if the Anglo professional person or official could know the particular subgroup to which the Spanish-speaking person belonged and something about the extent of his participation in the Anglo culture—specifically where he was born, where he has lived, how much schooling he has had and where he received it, where he has worked and at what jobs, how well he knows English, to what social class he belongs, what religion he professes, and similar types of information. Such knowledge, although not of absolute predictive value for an individual, might help to explain such behavior as nonattendance at clinics, failure to have children immunized, the use of laymen or marginal professionals in the treatment of illness, reluctance to enter or remain in a tuberculosis sanitarium, leaving a hospital against medical advice, the use of folk remedies—for example, the wearing of amulets or copper bracelets to ward off disease—even during hospital confinement, and similar actions and attitudes that are puzzling from an Anglo point of view. If such behavior can be seen and interpreted as an expression of cultural conditioning rather than as simply the whimsical result of individual deviance, it becomes possible to anticipate it and to devise effective ways of changing it or of adapting to it.

Stated in more general terms, a knowledge of the cultural and subcultural orientation of his patient and of its possible bearing on the behavior of the patient in the clinical situation is an important instrument in the complex of knowledge and skills that the professional medical practitioner brings to his work. This is not to say that he must have the detailed knowledge of the social scientist. What he does need is an awareness of the extent to which cultural and subcultural orientation can influence behavior and some general knowledge about the particular attitudes, points of view, values, beliefs, and behavior patterns of the cultural group from which his patient comes. So equipped, he is able to see uniformities in and reasons for kinds of behavior that otherwise might be ascribed to individual perversity, indifference, apathy, or ignorance and to so direct his own behavior as to obtain the desired patient response.[64]

Some of the diverse backgrounds possible to Spanish-speaking southwesterners are reflected in the inhabitants of 1407 Felicity Street. Pedro Treviño and his boarder Alessandro Flores are both Spanish-Americans. Both were born in small rural villages and have come by devious routes to be residents of an Anglo city. Their attitudes and behavior still reflect much of their village origin. Rafael Gurule is a Mexican-American, born in a rural area, but brought up along the Mexican border where the cultural influence of Mexico was strong. He has lived much of his life in cities and has acquired many Anglo characteristics. His wife, Virginia, is Spanish-American. She grew up on a ranch and in a small town in southern Colorado and, until her marriage, had never been farther than a few miles away from her birthplace and had had no extensive contacts with English-speaking people. When soon after their marriage the Gurules moved to Arcadia, Virginia took with her a kind of rigid adaptiveness that has enabled her to adjust to the imperatives of city life and at the same time keep much of her rural and Spanish-American heritage.

Simoneta Roybal is also Spanish-American, but she lacks the stability that could come from a childhood spent in a village environment. Having moved almost constantly during her early childhood and having spent much of the past five years either alone or as a patient in an institution, Simoneta occupies a limbo somewhere between two cultures and is not really a part of either. With foster parents and parents both dead, and brothers and sisters long since out of touch with her, and with no husband and no close friends, Simoneta can move neither toward a closer identification with the Anglo ways she has never had an opportunity to learn nor back toward the Spanish-American ways of her parents from which she was separated almost at birth. She is cut off from the institutional ties of family and church and lacks the necessary social skills to develop ties in the Anglo culture. Thus, she is an agency problem.

The Atencios are Spanish-American, but were both born in Arcadia, so that their Spanish heritage has been relatively weak and their exposure to Anglo culture relatively strong. Consequently they are the most acculturated of the Felicity Street residents, and many of their behavior patterns and attitudes are indistinguishable from those of Anglos. They are fluent in the use of English and have enough command of Anglo skills and ways to give them a relatively good income, which enables them to live more comfortably than their neighbors. Although they have been married several years, they have no children, a fact that has caused interested comment among some of the other wives in the building. They have an eye to the future and intend to improve their economic position. For them the influence of family and church are weak, but this is not particularly detrimental since they find satisfaction and stability in the Anglo pattern of husband-wife relationship, clique participation, and the expectation of upward social mobility.

The Vigils are Mexican-Americans, both born in a rural area, and both relatively little affected by their exposure to Anglo culture and city ways. Antonio has changed jobs occasionally, but has remained always within the area of unskilled labor. He has had the opportunity for no more than a bare minimum of contact with Anglos, having always lived and worked among other Spanish-speaking people. His wife María is traditionally concerned with her home and her children and has not formed many associations other than the old family and church relationships.

The influence of Mexico is still strong among the Rubios, although no member of the family has been in that country for more than thirty years. Miguel and his parents were born there, and Concepción, Miguel's wife, although a native of Tucson, was much exposed to Mexican cultural influence through her parents and her nonfamily associations in the border region in which she grew up. Josefina, the grandmother, is a strong stabilizing influence in the family. She has made few concessions herself to Anglo culture and serves as a strong focal point of resistance for other members of the family.

In behavior, belief, and attitude the inhabitants of 1407 Felicity Street reflect the various cultural and subcultural heritages and the differing personal experiences each has had. In this respect, and in educational, social, economic, and political attainments, they are like a good proportion of the Spanish-speaking population of the Southwest. They are not, as has been pointed out, entirely representative of the large group. Nor could they be. But they do illustrate, in their persons and problems, the types of cultural and subcultural difference that can be stumbling blocks for those who seek to give health, welfare, educational, or other social services to a population group different from that from which they themselves come.

The Arcadian physicians, social workers, nurses, teachers, ministers, and priests have been sometimes quite successful and sometimes conspicuously unsuccessful in attaining their professional objectives with the individuals and families they work with at 1407 Felicity Street. Linda Treviño's life will be cut short because neither physician nor visiting nurse has been able to get her to cooperate in restricting her activity to the amount that she can do safely. Alessandro Flores refused to enter a convalescent home where he could get good care, but, fortunately for him, a visiting nurse was able to find a substitute course of action that took care of his problem almost as well as if he had entered a home. Virginia Gurule might have been spared the need to have her baby born on the floor of a hospital and the resident physician might have avoided some bewilderment and embarrassment had there been a little better understanding and communication between Virginia and the hospital staff. Louis Gurule has been in the state reformatory for boys once and may well go there again and possibly later to the state prison unless he gets some effective guidance. Simoneta Roybal suffers needlessly from goiter and her baby daughter is undernourished. Fermín and Rachel Atencio might have saved the $150 they paid a *médica* for what they believed would be a cure for Rachel's kidney condition. María Vigil could be persuaded to reduce the danger of infecting her children with tuberculosis if she were properly approached. The bowed legs of Ruby Vigil and the twisted foot of Rosalie Rubio could be straightened if their parents could be brought to see the relative ease with which something might be done about these conditions and the serious psychological and social consequences of allowing them to go untreated.

A knowledge of their culture is no magic talisman which will enable the professional person to solve all the problems that may beset him in his dealings with Spanish-speaking persons or others who are culturally or subculturally different. But a knowledge of culture can be a useful asset which, while possibly of little utility by itself, may have the property of making other knowledge and skills more effective in their application. Between the members of one cultural group and those of another there is frequently a cultural chasm that is difficult to bridge. Each tends to see his ways of thinking, believing, and behaving as right and natural and proper and any deviation from those ways as strange, bizarre, and incomprehensible. And each evaluates his own behavior and that of the other in terms of a cultural yardstick which, understandably perhaps, almost always shows his behavior to be admirable and sensible and that of the other, to the extent that it deviates from his, to be less so.

The chasm that separates Spanish-speaking and Anglos in the Southwest is in some areas of their relationship both wide and deep and in others hardly perceptible. Its full course cannot be traced here, but some parts can be briefly observed and perhaps indication given of how it may in places be bridged.

Chapter III

THE CULTURAL CHASM

ONE WHO LOOKS CASUALLY at the English-speaking and Spanish-speaking populations in the Southwest is more likely to be impressed with their similarities than with their differences. The behavior of Spanish-speaking people, particularly in its more obvious aspects, does not differ greatly from that of the Anglos among whom they live. Both wear the same kinds of clothing and eat about the same kinds of foods at about the same intervals. Both drive automobiles if they can afford them, listen to radio and television sets, and patronize motion picture theaters. In both groups the husband characteristically goes out to work and the wife stays home to care for the children and the house. The practice of middle-class wives working outside the home is probably less prevalent among Spanish-speaking than among Anglo families, but some Spanish-speaking wives do go out to work. Both populations send their children to public or parochial schools with the belief that they will assure the children an easier and more abundant life than their parents had. Both treat their ailments with preparations from the drugstore and if these fail seek professional advice and help. In all such practices, the variations between the groups are matters of degree rather than kind and the range of variation within either of the groups is greater than the range of difference between them.

Despite these similarities, there are, however, differences in points of view and ways of behaving that occasionally make it difficult for members of one group to understand the behavior of the other. No member of the hospital staff, for example, is certain as to why it was necessary for Virginia Gurule to have her baby born on the hospital floor. Visiting nurses in Arcadia are sometimes baffled by what seems to be a complete indifference of Spanish-speaking mothers to the health of their children. A staff member of the Texas Employment Service who went to some trouble to get well-paying, out-of-state jobs for a group of young Mexican-Americans cannot quite understand why a number of them soon quit their jobs and returned to their home communities where there were no comparable economic opportunities. School teachers and employers often feel frustrated at their inability to get school children and employees to report at the appointed time. Social workers are frequently exasperated at the purchase by relief clients of a late-model car, an expensive radio or television set, or some other "luxury." Sometimes, of course, these instances of what seems to be aberrant behavior are traceable to individual idiosyncrasies. More often they are due to culturally derived differences in values, attitudes, preferences, tastes, and patterns of perception.

When cultural differences are wide, it is fairly easy to take them into account in attempting to understand the behavior of a member of a different culture. Where they are not very great and the resulting variations in behavior are somewhat subtle, as between the English-speaking and Spanish-speaking of the Southwest, it is easy to forget that they exist and to expect that persons possessing the attributes of a slightly different culture will behave as we do. When they do not, the tendency is strong to react with moral disapproval and the application of various kinds of sanctions in order to bring about the expected behavior. Anglo school officials, for example, frequently feel that some Spanish-speaking parents ought to be more concerned about the school attendance and progress of their children, and a common topic in discussions of the "problem" of educating Spanish-speaking children is how much coercion should be used to assure the interest and support of parents. There is also a further tendency, when members of the culturally different group have highly visible biological characteristics, to see their behavior differences as somehow due to innate genetic factors that, through some unexplained mechanism, produce the questionable behavior.

BELIEFS OF ANGLOS ABOUT SPANISH-SPEAKING PEOPLE

One is not surprised, therefore, to find among Anglos of the Southwest a great body of opinion and belief about the characteristics and abilities of the Spanish-speaking people, some of which is fairly sound but much of which is sheer nonsense.[1] But whether fact or fancy, these beliefs and opinions can be and are used to determine, justify, and explain the behavior of Anglos with respect to members of the Spanish-speaking group. They enabled, for example, a south Texas employer of "Mexican" labor, in testifying before a congressional committee, to speak of "a thing that is very typical of the race. It used to be if they got $3, they would lay off for maybe a day, because at that time they could get a bottle of vino for probably four bits, and Mama would make them kick through with the rest of it, and they would get drunk on that bottle, and they would not come back. Now, they get more money and unfortunately a lot of them lay off longer after pay day."[2] The same gentleman, a few minutes later, was also able to say that "as far as the race is concerned, they are the finest people to be around. They are a happy race; they are very congenial. They try to please to the best of their ability."[3]

If the Mexican-Americans migrate periodically to follow the cotton harvest, as they do in some parts of the Southwest, their wanderings are ascribed to their possession of a gypsy spirit that predisposes them to a peripatetic life. If Spanish-speaking children are retarded in school, as many of them are, the reason is said to be that they are slow-witted and not natively endowed for academic pursuits. If Mexican-Americans and Mexicans are found in large numbers in stoop-labor jobs in agriculture, it is believed they are naturally adapted to such work and suffer little or no physical discomfort from it. If a Spanish-speaking employee or patient or client fails to appear on time for an appointment, it is remarked that he belongs to a group that is naturally irresponsible and undependable. If Spanish-speaking families of eight or ten persons are found living in one or two rooms, it is said to be because they are very gregarious and like the crowding.

Notions such as these are quite prevalent in the Southwest wherever Spanish-speaking people are found in any considerable numbers. They have the merit, for those who accept them, of providing easily understandable reasons for the behavior and the status of Spanish-speaking persons and at the same time of showing why the behavior derives from and the status is justly proportional to the abilities and capacities of the group. They provide also an easy way to rationalize the *status quo* and to make unnecessary any attempts to improve conditions for the Spanish-speaking group. If the status of Spanish-speaking people is a direct result of the operation of innate characteristics, as many of these beliefs imply, then obviously there is no point in trying to make any changes in their condition. They are already in the positions and relationships they are best suited for, and any attempt to alter matters would only result in bringing discomfort and dissatisfactions to this "happy race."[4]

There have been a few attempts, all of doubtful quality, to validate "scientifically" some aspects of the stereotype of the "Mexican" as it is held in parts of the Southwest. One such study, written by a candidate for a Master's degree in sociology at a Texas institution of higher learning, pointed out that the "Mexicans" of the area under study were fairly docile and caused little trouble for the reason that they lacked "that inborn feeling of inferiority to the white race that causes the Negro's resentment of segregation and inequality." Among the other characteristics of the "Mexican race," this investigator noted the following: (1) laziness, as manifested in a disinclination to work, unless absolutely necessary; (2) no sense of time, a lack which was observable in the inability of "Mexican" children or their parents to get anywhere on time; (3) gregariousness, as shown in a preference for living under very crowded conditions; (4) artistic ability: "the Mexican has an intense love of color; a love of music is an animate quality of the race"; (5) contentment with conditions as they are, as revealed in a lack of ambition and the absence of efforts to improve their status; (6) "a native charm of manner and innate sense of courtesy"; (7) a disregard for the truth, which reveals itself in a type of chronic lying that is "not vicious, but comes about largely through a childlike inability to stick to the truth"; (8) a lack of thrift and tendency to spend money for pleasure rather than for necessities; (9) a strong gambling instinct; (10) honesty; (11) a tendency to be hot-tempered and vengeful; and (12) an innate ability for dancing and rhythm.

A somewhat different but overlapping set of characteristics was noted for "Mexicans" by another student who had had many years' experience teaching their children. Among the traits he found characteristic of the "Mexicans" as a group were: (1) a spirit of charity toward everyone, particularly toward other "Mexicans"; (2) a spirit of sociableness and hospitality; (3) a capacity for strong domestic affections; (4) an extreme sensitivity to insult; (5) artistic ability but no creative originality; (6) a love of any kind of music; (7) a sense of appreciation for favors; (8) respect for authority; (9) loyalty to friends; (10) fondness for sports coupled with the inability to lose gracefully; (11) a fondness for talking; (12) a tendency in children to be slow thinkers; (13) a "total lack of any worthy ambition"; and (14) a passion for gambling.[5]

Anyone who has had an opportunity to work with and observe Spanish-speaking people in the Southwest will immediately recognize that underlying *some* of these generalizations are ways of behaving that can be observed among *some* members of the Spanish-speaking group. The weakness in the two studies mentioned, and in others of a similar nature that have been made, lies less in the observation than in the inadequacy of the assumptions on which the generalizations rest; for example, that there is a "Mexican race" of which the population observed was a representative sample; or that complex social behavior is largely determined by genetic inheritance. The weakness is also due to the failure of the investigators to take into account their own cultural biases and values. Few if any of the generalizations cited above are valid as stated. Certainly none is demonstrably due to any genetic inheritance, as the investigators supposed. But many of them are based on observable behavior traits that are characteristic of *some* members of the Spanish-speaking population in *some* situations. A good many Spanish-speaking people do habitually arrive late at functions. So do a good many Anglos. A student of the history of the Spanish-American villages would certainly notice the relative absence of effort toward change or improvement during much of their existence, although if he were wise he would seek the causal factors in something other than innate lack of ambition. Anyone observing the tender devotion of many Mexican-American children toward their brothers and sisters could understandably suppose them to have an extraordinarily strong capacity for family affection. Those who have attended meetings of Spanish-speaking people and listened to a seemingly endless succession of speakers can perhaps be forgiven for believing that members of *la raza* have a fondness for talking. But these behavior characteristics, to the extent that they exist among the Spanish-speaking population, are, like all social behavior patterns, learned responses to types of recurring situations. They vary considerably from person to person and from time to time. And they are not innate.

Any generalization that is made about the behavior of any large group of people is almost certain to be a great oversimplification. When the generalization relates less to the actually observed behavior than to the motives thought to underlie it, that is, the "why" of the behavior, it is likely to be even more oversimplified. And when it is made by persons belonging to a different culture, their own cultural values and biases frequently lead to the imputing of motives and attitudes that do not exist in the persons being observed. Furthermore, the observers tend to evaluate the behavior and to make judgments of approval or disapproval about it on the basis of their ideas of what kind of behavior is appropriate in the observed situation and often fail to take into account the possibility that, as a result of their participation in a different culture, the persons observed may have quite dissimilar ideas and be acting in accordance with them.

When an Anglo, for example, either explicitly or by implication, makes the statement that "Mexicans are lazy," he is either repeating something he has heard or is drawing a conclusion from his own observations. Or, since this particular statement is frequently heard in the Southwest and opportunities for observing

"Mexicans" in work situations are not uncommon, he may be doing both. In either case the evidence on which it is based is likely to be such as to make it unacceptable to any but the most uncritical.[6] Furthermore, the statement itself is not a description of behavior, but rather an inference of an attitude that is thought to be a motivating force in eliciting certain types of behavior responses. And, since the term "lazy" is for Anglos a value-loaded symbol, the generalization carries a judgment of disapproval of the inferred attitude. Thus, what the Anglo is saying, in effect, is: "I have heard or observed that some 'Mexicans' do not work in situations or under circumstances in which I think that work is the appropriate response. I conclude, therefore, that they have an attitude toward work that is different from mine, and since mine is right and good, theirs must be wrong and bad." What such judgments disregard, of course, is the possibility that the behavior of the "Mexican," insofar as it actually is different and is not merely thought to be, may derive from another set of attitudes and values in terms of which it is "right and good" and any other kind of behavior "wrong and bad."

It is not the purpose here to undertake an exhaustive analysis of the attitudes and values underlying the behavior of Spanish-speaking persons in the Southwest. The basic research that might provide the data for such an analysis is far from complete, and, even if the information were available, the analysis would take far more space than can be given in these pages. We propose to examine a few characteristics deriving from the historical circumstances of Spanish-speaking people of the Southwest that may be influential in determining the behavior of Spanish-speaking persons in activities involving relationships with Anglos. Insofar as possible, attention will be centered on characteristics* in which

---

* It must be remembered that these are *group* characteristics that may or may not be exhibited by any given individual. Among ten thousand or a hundred thousand Spanish-speaking persons, the prevalence of any characteristic ascribed to that group would be greater than among a comparable group of Anglos. Within the Spanish-speaking population, "Spanish" characteristics can be expected to be more prevalent among the old, the rural, the poor, the recent arrivals from Mexico than among the young, the urban, the well off, or those who have been many years or many generations in the United States. Any given individual may have all or none or any combination of these characteristics, depending on his unique personal experience. So may any given Anglo.

there is considerable variation between the Anglo and Spanish-speaking ideal.

LANGUAGE DIFFERENCES

One of the most obvious differences, of course, is that of language.[7] Inability to speak a common language presents an almost insuperable barrier to communication and makes difficult the achieving of a wide range of mutually satisfactory relationships between Anglos and Spanish-speaking people. Inability to speak English, or to feel at ease with it, is a powerful factor in the tendency of many Spanish-speaking people to avoid any but the most necessary contacts with Anglos. The resulting maximizing of contacts with other Spanish-speaking people and minimizing of interaction with Anglos tend to make unnecessary the acquisition of English, since the individual can in many areas get along well without it. Thus, language difference is both a cause and an effect of isolation, and as such exerts a strong influence in the perpetuation of other cultural traits of Spanish-speaking people and in retarding their integration into the Anglo group.

A person living in the Spanish-speaking sections of such cities as San Antonio, El Paso, or Los Angeles can live fully without knowing a word of English. But, since it is almost impossible to avoid hearing English or seeing it printed, the proportion that does not know any English is probably quite small. Some knowledge of the language is both convenient and desirable, since one inevitably is drawn into relationships with such people as governmental agents, potential or actual employers, or school teachers who may not know Spanish. And, if one wishes to extend his relationships with the English-speaking community, a good command of the language is essential. Furthermore, since English is the language of the classroom in all parts of the Southwest, the schools are a channel through which its use is constantly being facilitated. Thus, there are strong forces operating to promote the acquisition and use of English by Spanish-speaking southwesterners, and the degree to which any given individual can or cannot use the language is a function of his differential exposure to the various influences that operate on members of the group.

The use of a different language, quite apart from any effect it may have on intergroup communication, is of itself something of a barrier to the establishment of good relations, particularly in an area like the Southwest where the great majority of the Anglo group are monolingual. Many Anglos are annoyed and sometimes become suspicious or angry when, in their presence, Spanish-speaking people begin to "jabber" in their own language. The irritation is likely to be particularly strong when there are observable signs of levity in the conversation. At such times the Anglos feel they are being laughed at, or at best "talked about." Feelings thus engendered occasionally find expression in retaliatory acts against the Spanish-speaking. More often they are worked off in indignant discussions with other Anglos in which the main theme of the conversation is the old, familiar one: "If they don't want to learn English why don't they go back where they came from?"

The ability of the Spanish-speaking to communicate in a language that the Anglo does not understand strengthens the subjective awareness of differences between the two groups and makes it easy to set up categories of "we" and "they" which, once established, help to obscure the tremendous similarities between the two populations and to focus attention on the relatively minor differences. To the English-speaking professional man or woman the use of Spanish by a patient, client, or student—particularly when accompanied by other actions that do not coincide with Anglo notions of behavior appropriate to the set of circumstances under consideration—can cause irritation, hostility, frustration, or other reactions that may be damaging to the professional relationship. One persistent notion in the Southwest is that many Spanish-speaking people pretend not to know English even though they actually do. There may be occasional instances where this is true, but they are not nearly so common as they are thought to be. The idea, however, whether true or not, provides a handy rationalization for the Anglo in situations where use of the Spanish language hinders or prevents establishing a good relationship. It justifies any irritation he may feel by making it possible to place the blame for the communication block on the Spanish-speaking person. This rationalization of his emotions may be good for the Anglo, but, unfortunately, it does not improve the quality of the relationship.

Another prevalent notion, but happily one not frequently encountered among professional people, is that there is a correlation between the volume of sound and the ability to comprehend a language. The belief is seldom so stated, but its existence can be inferred from observing attempts by English-speaking people to communicate with those who speak only Spanish. The Anglo begins in an ordinary tone of voice. As it becomes apparent that he is not being understood, he repeats his remarks in a louder tone. As the volume goes up—presumably along with the Anglo's blood pressure—the Spanish-speaking person makes greater and greater efforts to comprehend the significance of such vehemence, but good intentions and desires cannot be substituted for a knowledge of English, and so he understands nothing except that he is missing something of possibly great importance. Having failed to communicate even by shouting, the Anglo may be strongly tempted to conclude that his listener is stupid, particularly if he happens to have some preconceived ideas about the mental capacities of the group to which the listener belongs. But, again, neither the action nor the resulting rationalization of its failure does anything to improve communication or to bring about the kind of interaction desired.

In relations between Anglos and Spanish-speaking people in the Southwest, it is expected that the latter will make the greater effort to open channels of communication by becoming bilingual. They, it is felt, have an obligation to learn English, but there is no considerable corresponding feeling that Anglos ought to learn Spanish. Since English is the language of the country and the Spanish-speaking people came here voluntarily—the special case of the Spanish-Americans is usually ignored when this argument is being presented—it is felt that they should make an effort to conform to our ways, particularly in the matter of using our language. And the failure of some to do so is a definite source of exasperation to many Anglos.

The expectation is a reasonable one and has much to recommend it both from a moral and a practical standpoint. All persons living here should, for the sake of unity and harmony, acquire the attributes that will enable them to be included in the group designated by the term "we." To fail to do so is to perpetuate differences that are felt to be both undesirable and possibly dangerous. From a practical standpoint, the ability to use English opens doors to more opportunities and relationships than are available to persons who speak only Spanish. It is not wholly without significance that income, social acceptance, freedom from discrimination, and similar indices of desirable status are roughly correlated with ability to use English.

An awareness of these considerations makes it difficult for many Anglos to understand why the Spanish-speaking people as a group are not more strongly motivated to learn English, and allows them to interpret the inability of some Spanish-speaking people to understand or speak English as being due to stupidity or some form of hostility. Actually the reasons for the persistence of Spanish in the Southwest are many and complex. Isolation and the concentration of Spanish-speaking people in areas where they are the numerical majority are certainly factors; so is the proximity to Mexico and the ebb and flow across the border of large numbers of people from areas where English is not spoken. The failure of our school systems to enroll and hold Spanish-speaking students and to work out effective means of teaching them English cannot be ignored. Psychological considerations related to individuals' feelings of security probably enter the picture. And other reasons could be cited. But whatever the reasons, the inability of many Spanish-speaking people to speak and understand English is a differentiating factor, contributing to the persistence of feelings of disapproval, dislike, and mistrust between the dominant and minority populations in the Southwest and hindering the establishment of effective channels of communication and mutually advantageous relationships between members of the two groups.

The lack of any considerable feeling that Anglos should learn Spanish is evident from the fact that for relatively few jobs in the Southwest involving interactions with Spanish-speaking people is a knowledge of Spanish required as a qualification. Only in jobs where the work involves dealing with persons known not to speak English and where the relationship clearly involves benefit to organizations or persons other than the Spanish-speaking, is a knowledge of Spanish a requisite. To handle large numbers of Spanish-speaking agricultural workers, crew chiefs with a knowledge of their language are needed. The *bracero* program of contract labor importation uses persons on some levels who must speak Spanish. Railroad crews, construction gangs, and other types of mass employment often need supervisory personnel who know Spanish. But where the relationships are with individual Spanish-speaking persons or are primarily for the benefit of the Spanish-speaking, the Anglo worker usually is not required to speak Spanish. Municipal and county officials and employees, public health nurses, probation officers, welfare workers, and school teachers, to mention only a few categories, are not usually expected to know Spanish, even though their work may be almost entirely concerned with Spanish-speaking people. This means for them, at least to the extent that they work with people unable to speak English, some measure of ineffectiveness in their work, poor cooperation with those they work with, and much additional effort to achieve a given result. It means for the non-English-speaking person inadequate service, a poor understanding of his rights and responsibilities with respect to a given agency, and curtailment of experiences that might facilitate his acquisition of Anglo ways.

There is probably no general rule as to which language is preferable in dealing with Spanish-speaking people throughout the Southwest and in all kinds of situations. If English is not known, Spanish will have to be used or there will be no effective communication. This means that in areas where there is a heavy concentration of Spanish-speaking people some of the personnel of agencies offering public services and others who have business or professional relations with Spanish-speaking individuals or groups will need to know Spanish. For communication with persons who may know some English, but whose age, personal experience, unfamiliarity with Anglo ways, inability to hear well, or other factors may make communication in English difficult, it is probably economical in terms of both time and effectiveness of communication, as well as courteous, to use Spanish as much as possible. With individuals who know English well, it is probably better to use that language, particularly in the early stages of a relationship, and thus avoid the possibility of giving offense to persons who might resent an implication that they do not know English. Adolescents and young adults, especially those who have already taken on many of the attitudes and values of Anglo culture, frequently are sensitive about their group identification and do not like being addressed in Spanish by an Anglo stranger, although they may use that language in conversations among themselves.

One other aspect of language difference needs to be mentioned. This is the extent to which language itself both embodies and determines the thought and perception patterns of a cultural group. Language enables us to make sense out of reality. It provides for each of us a way of isolating, categorizing, and relating phenomena without which experience could be only a confused succession of sensations and impressions. Our perceptions, to the extent that they represent anything more than crude sensation, are organized around concepts, each of which is represented by one or more verbal symbols. What a person "sees," the meaning it has for him, and how it is related to other phenomena are determined by the concepts he has, and these in turn are learned from the social groups into which he was born and with which he lives. Since concepts are represented in verbal symbols, the language a person knows and uses is a good guide to the way he perceives events and objects in the world about him.

Like other elements of culture, language for most of us is so taken for granted that frequently we are not aware of the clues it provides for understanding our own behavior and that of other people. It is not without significance, for example, that, as Arthur Campa has pointed out, in English a clock runs, while in Spanish it walks (*el reloj anda*).[8] Such a simple difference as this has enormous implications for appreciating differences in the behavior of English-speaking and Spanish-speaking persons. If time is moving rapidly, as Anglo usage declares, we must hurry and make use of it before it has gone. If time walks, as the Spanish-speaking say, one can take a more leisurely attitude toward it. If an English-speaking workman arrives late at his job with the excuse that he missed the bus, the language he uses indicates that he was the active agent in his failure to make connection with the bus and he, therefore, is responsible for the lateness. A Spanish-speaking workman, in the same circumstances, would not say that he missed the bus but that the bus left him. The active, and therefore culpable, agent was the bus, not the workman, and he cannot blame himself nor does he expect to be blamed for his late arrival. The Anglo foreman, however, who knows that people miss buses, is not likely to be sympathetic to the notion that the fault lies with the bus, particularly if he also is told that the workman's clock was "walking" a bit slowly.

In the repetition and proliferation of small differences such as these lies the basis of large misunderstandings between people of different cultures. Unable to understand in terms of the concepts of his culture, that buses leave people, that objects lose themselves, that automobiles wreck themselves, that dishes break themselves by falling away from people, that diseases are the manifestation of the will of God, the English-speaking person reaches into his box of categories and brings out concepts in terms of which his experiences make sense to him. And thus the Spanish-speaking people come to be labeled as untruthful, or irresponsible, or lazy, or superstitious, or are assigned some other stereotyped characteristics. Thereafter their behavior is "understood," but not in a way that is conducive to the establishment of either deeper and more accurate levels of understanding or mutually satisfactory relationships between members of the two groups.

DIFFERENCES IN ORIENTATION TO TIME

The cultural characteristics of any people are not a haphazard, random collection of elements unrelated to each other or to the environmental situation in which that people finds itself. They are rather a closely knit, interrelated, and interdependent set of traits that have been developed, not by the application of any predetermined logical scheme, but through the slow, unplanned series of accretions resulting from trial-and-error attempts of the group to find ways of adjusting to its environment.[9] The principal function of culture is a purely utilitarian one, to enable the group to survive. Each trait has—or once had, since some traits tend to persist long after changing circumstances have made them unnecessary—some relationship to other traits and some relevance for the environment in which the particular group happens to live. Culture has its locus in the personalities of people, and personality is built up by successive layers of experience. New layers may be added; old ones cannot be taken away, although they may be greatly compressed. When people move, their culture goes with them. And, if one wishes to know the "why" of their behavior, he must look to the old environment as well as to the new.

Many of the traits that distinguish the Spanish-speaking and Anglos in the Southwest can be seen as related to the particular historical and environmental circumstances the two groups have experienced. An example is the well-known and frequently mentioned difference in their orientation to time.[10] Stated in somewhat extreme form the difference is this: The Anglo is primarily oriented toward the future; the Spanish-speaking person is oriented toward the present and, to a lesser extent, the immediate past. Anglos tend to be much preoccupied with time. They carry watches and make a point of referring to them frequently. Huge clocks are a prominent part of many public buildings. Clocks are also displayed in windows of stores and offices. Radio and television programs frequently remind their audiences of the correct time. Appointments are made for a specific hour and minute, and a high value is placed on being "on time." Days are broken up into small segments of time and certain amounts of the precious stuff are allotted to each activity. The rhythm of living is primarily a daily one, and a person tends to do the same thing at the same hour each day. "Time is money" the Anglos tell each other, and to "waste" time—that is, to fail to do something designed to influence the future in some way— while not exactly sinful is subject to disapproval.

Not only clocks but also calendars are important elements in the time orientation of Anglos. Nearly every home has at least one and most offices have several. They are consulted frequently, and most Anglos would feel a little apologetic if they were unable to give on request the date, month, and year. In fact, one test of sanity in the Anglo culture consists in asking what day and year it is. Many Anglos have their time scheduled or at least tentatively planned far in advance; they know what they are likely to be doing at a given time weeks, months, and in some cases, even years in the future, health and other factors permitting. Relatively few of the activities Anglos engage in have much significance for the moment. Many are oriented toward the future and are essentially attempts to control the future. Thus, the present is important not for itself, but because it offers an opportunity to engage in activities that can affect the future. In other words, for Anglos most activities are not ends in themselves but are rather means to ends, the attainment of which lies somewhere in the future.

Unlike the Anglo, the Spanish-American or Mexican-American is likely to be strongly oriented toward the present or the immediate past. He is not a visionary, with his eyes on the golden promise of the future. Nor is he a dreamer brooding over the glories of the past. Rather he is a realist who is concerned with the problems and rewards of the immediate present. The past, since he comes from a folk culture with no tradition of writing, was not carefully recorded, contained little that was sufficiently out of the ordinary to justify recording, and has been almost forgotten. The future, since for hundreds of years it brought almost nothing different from what he already had, offers no particular promise and is neither to be anticipated with joy nor feared. But the present cannot be ignored. Its demands must be coped with, its rewards must be enjoyed—now.

The Spanish-speaking person, whether Spanish-American, Mexican-American, or Mexican, has had in his immediate past some contact, direct or through his parents, with a village, agricultural society. In the village the rhythms of life were seasonal rather than diurnal. What one did on a particular day did not matter; what one did during the year mattered a great deal. The community was small and the division of labor not very complex, and most people did what others of their age and sex were doing and at approximately the same time. There was no need for the intricate interrelating of activities that is so necessary in an urban-industrial society. A man awoke in the morning knowing from the season what tasks he might engage in that day. But the tasks were seldom urgent, and if he chose to do them in one order or another or put them off until another day, neither he nor anyone else was inconvenienced. There being no "jobs," no first-of-the-month bills, no pressure toward competition, no formal organizations, no particular value placed on preciseness of any kind, few clocks, and no resources or skills with which more could readily be constructed, there was no pressure to develop any particular concern with time. And so the villagers, both in Mexico and along the Rio Grande, developed through many generations of almost imperceptible change cultures in which time was a matter of no particular consequence.

As Arthur Campa pointed out fifteen years ago, Anglos have developed some peculiar and erroneous notions about Spanish-speaking people's conceptions of time.[11] We have already mentioned that there is a widespread misconception among Anglos in the Southwest which holds that the "Mexican" is lazy and that he will not work unless coerced. "Mexicans" are believed to have a *mañana* attitude which leads them to put off until tomorrow many things that they should do today, and as a result little ever gets done. Actually this generalization is based on accurate, although incomplete, observations. What throws if off is the failure of the Anglos who make or accept the generalization to take into account the "Mexican" attitude toward time. The Anglo works now in order to be rewarded in the future. The Spanish-speaking person, having no very definite concept of the future, prefers immediate rewards. What the *mañana* attitude actually involves is that the Spanish-speaking person puts off for an indefinite *mañana* those things that can be put off and does today those that can be done only today. If what must be done today is work—as in the case of a harvest or the need to earn money—the work is done, not gladly perhaps or with any sense of dedication, but with an uncomplaining acceptance of the responsibility of the moment. When what must be done today is something else—participation in a fiesta, say, or in the celebration of the birthday of a patron saint, or embracing an opportunity to visit distant relatives— then what must be done now or never is done and what can be postponed until another time—work perhaps—is postponed. In a very real sense the Spanish-speaking person lives in and for the present, a fact that frequently bothers and confuses Anglos who live in today but for tomorrow.

There are many illustrations of difficulties caused by the different time orientations of Spanish-speaking and Anglos. Some are trivial, as for example the bewilderment of some Spanish-speaking people when asked by a physician, "What day would you like to come to clinic next week?" How are they to reply to this strange question? How can they know how they may feel next week or what they will be doing? What is there to make one day preferable to another? And why come next week, anyway, when they are at the clinic now? Some are more serious, as for example the irritation of employers at employees who fail to appear for work or who habitually arrive late, and the resulting closing down of employment opportunities to Spanish-speaking workers. Some have extremely serious consequences. Consider, for example, the case of the Spanish-speaking woman who is known to have tuberculosis in an early stage but refuses treatment because she feels well at the moment and sees no point in inconveniencing herself now in order to avoid a possible consequence in the nebulous future.

Like other aspects of culture our attitudes toward time are so much a part of us and seem so right and natural that it is difficult to understand how anyone could have a different point of view. That a person could have no particular concern for the future is almost inconceivable to an Anglo. That an Anglo will sacrifice the present for some possible gain in the dubious future is likely to be equally inconceivable to anyone reared in a Spanish-American or Mexican village. The difference in point of view could be well illustrated by the old story of the grasshopper and the ant were it not for the fact that the story, as told by Anglos, is already interpreted from the Anglo point of view, in that the attention throughout is focused on the ultimate fate of the improvident grasshopper and the certain—although also temporary—survival of the industrious ant. By passing lightly over the values deriving to the grasshopper during his long summer and emphasizing the tragedy that befalls him as a result of his unconcern for the future, the story seems to demonstrate beyond doubt the wisdom and rightness of the Anglo attitude toward time. (It also illustrates the value the Anglo places on the accumulation of material possessions!) But with only a slight change of emphasis it could be made to illustrate the orientation of the Spanish-speaking people. The eminently sensible grasshopper lives each day according to the imperatives of the day, enjoying what may be enjoyed, enduring what must be endured. The coming of winter brings more than he can endure, and he perishes, having lived fully and well, albeit briefly. The foolish ant, with an eye to the future, toils throughout the summer, storing up food against the coming cold. He survives the winter and is rewarded with another summer's toil. The version one prefers depends on his values. There is no way of proving that one story is better than the other, or that one point of view about the relative importance of present and future is better than the other. The most that can be expected is that one be aware of the possibility that there can be a point of view other than his own and that persons having different attitudes toward time may be expected to behave somewhat differently in given situations, at least some of the time.

DIFFERENCES IN ATTITUDES TOWARD CHANGE

Closely related to a group's attitudes toward time are the views of its members about change and progress. Anglos, of course, are highly oriented toward change. For nearly three hundred years they have been living in a period of accelerating change. Hardly a day passes that does not bring its quota of new things—new discoveries, new inventions, new products, new relationships, new perspectives, new ideologies, new problems. New automobiles are introduced with the announcement of 85 "important new improvements" over the models of only a year ago. A soap that just weeks ago was only slightly less than miraculous in its cleansing power is replaced by an "entirely new and greatly improved" formula. A new source of power—atomic energy—is bringing new promises, new worries, and new fears. Newness among the Anglos has come to be valued for its own sake, and oldness alone, quite apart from any other characteristic a person or object or event may have, is enough to make it or him somewhat undesirable.

Much of the attractiveness of new things derives from their being thought to be somehow better than the old, and thus the notion of progress becomes associated with the fact of change. To the Anglo progress is a self-evident fact. How can he doubt it when the evidence is all about him? Not only is he the recipient of a multitude of new things—but each is bigger, better, more efficient, more durable, brighter, more powerful, more convenient, more mechanized, more accurate, more comfortable, than its predecessors. Not only is this the best of all possible worlds, but by the minute it is getting better. There are problems, of course, and many imperfections, but progress is being made toward their solution and they will not exist, or will be greatly diminished, in the future. There is probably nothing the Anglo more completely accepts than the notion that change is good and progress inevitable.[12]

The Spanish-speaking person, coming from another background, has a somewhat different orientation toward change and progress. He and his ancestors have lived for many generations in an environment in which there was almost no change and in which efforts toward innovation, had they occurred, might have been seen as dangerous. Isolated from the main stream of western civilization, cut off from all but the most meager of contacts with urban centers, and living, for the most part, in a somewhat precarious equilibrium with their environment, the Spanish-speaking people had but little opportunity either to experience or initiate change. Until very recently the change that occurred within the lifetime of a man was almost unnoticeable. The village of an old man was essentially the village into which he had been born. Neither people, nor objects, nor events changed very much or very rapidly. The future, if envisioned at all, was seen as an extension of the present. There being little or no change, there could be no notion of progress. There being no conception of progress, there could be no desire for change. Security and stability lay in the old, the familiar, and the well-tested ways and techniques. Uncertainty, and possibly danger, came with the new, the unfamiliar, the untried.

The present-day Spanish-speaking person, living in an Anglo world, may be handicapped in his efforts to understand and be understood by the persistence of attitudes toward progress and change which he inherited from the village. He may mistrust and fear the changing future into which the Anglo so buoyantly rushes. He may want to hold onto whatever he can of the old and familiar rather than pursue the new. He may be confused by the effort to adjust to a constant succession of new elements and fail to grasp the principle that it is the succession, the flow, that one must adjust to and not the elements that make up the stream. His attitudes and his behavior may be such as to make Anglos impatient or exasperated at what they interpret as being lack of initiative, backwardness, unprogressiveness, or satisfaction with things as they are. Some Spanish-speaking persons, of course, have caught the Anglo point of view and, like recent converts to a religion who are more zealous in their observance than older members of the faith, have become enthusiastic devotees of change and progress. But these are likely to be the more acculturated members of the Spanish-speaking group who are rapidly becoming culturally indistinguishable from the Anglos. For the less acculturated members—older persons or those who have had relatively little contact with Anglo ways—the old attitudes persist to some degree and operate to interpose barriers to good understanding and effective interaction between them and Anglo professional people.

DIFFERENCES IN ATTITUDES TOWARD WORK AND EFFICIENCY

Closely related to a group's orientation to time and its attitudes toward change and progress are the values its members place on work, achievement and success, and on efficiency. Here again one can note wide differences between the Anglo and Spanish-speaking ideals.

Anglos are doers. They like to be busy. As a group they value activity above contemplation. As a group, too, they see industriousness as a virtue. Work for them is a value in itself, regardless of the return it may bring. It is simply better to work than not to work, and one of the worst things that can be said of an individual is that he is lazy—that is, that he does not like to work. Idleness is thought to be very close to sinfulness and those who do not work or work only with reluctance are regarded as being deficient in character. Anglos identify themselves with and are identified by their work. One of the best ways for an Anglo to answer the question "Who is he?" is to say what he does. If one Anglo asks another, "Who is that man?" and receives the reply that "he is a banker" or "he is a plumber" the question is considered adequately answered. The extent to which Anglos identify themselves with their work can be seen in the reluctance of many of them to retire, even when they could well afford to do so, and in the tremendous sense of loss of identity and purpose that came to many people in the 1930's when, as a result of the depression, they lost their jobs. Reduction of income and of the security that in our culture derives from income was psychologically traumatic, but almost equally so was the lack of "something to do."

Associated with the emphasis on work is the Anglo's preoccupation with success. Indeed, if work has any meaning beyond itself, it is that it is a road to success—which may be defined as anything from a greatly increased income to achieving notoriety or attaining an upward social and occupational mobility. Success, as the term is commonly used, refers less to a subjective satisfaction with one's performance than to an objective recognition by others that one has attained commonly esteemed goals. Success is such a valued goal that the means by which one reaches it are not always critically judged. The ideal of success extends even across generations, and parents are eager to give their children "the right kind of start" so that they will have successful careers and an easier life than their parents. The notion that they somehow ought to be a success acts as a constant incentive to Anglos to "keep their noses to the grindstone" and work for a successful—although seldom accurately envisioned—future.[13]

Minor, but nonetheless important, values of working Anglos are efficiency and practicality. As a group they pride themselves on their practicality and on the "know-how" that makes them and their products efficient. They are inclined to be a bit impatient with theoretical considerations or with the philosophical implications of their activities and want to get on with the "practical" business of "getting the job done." The statement frequently heard in discussions among Anglos, "I agree with you in theory, but it just isn't practical," illustrates their concern with practicality, which usually takes the form of action directed toward the attainment of short-run, isolated goals. It is thought "practical," for example, to pass and enforce laws providing for the capture and incarceration of tuberculous persons who refuse to go to sanitariums for treatment, since this provides an "efficient" way of removing possible sources of infection from the community. Practicality and efficiency are both high values and no "right-minded" Anglo would think of questioning the validity of such a statement as "it is better to be practical than impractical," or "it is better to be efficient than inefficient."

In attitudes toward work, success, efficiency, and practicality the ideal viewpoint of the Spanish-speaking person is far from that of the Anglos. The Spanish-speaking ideal is *to be* rather than *to do*. This may be related to the fact that in the villages it would have been almost impossible to identify a given individual by telling what he did, since there were few, if any, specialized occupations and no one did anything very different from anyone else. To place a villager one needed to know his age and sex, what family he belonged to, and what was his position in the family. Further identification was in terms of his personal characteristics. Or the emphasis on being may be related to the fact that in the villages opportunities for "doing" were quite limited, so that the only way a person could have a differentiated status was in terms of what he was. At any rate, there never developed among the Spanish-speaking any great concern for doing. Activity was not highly valued and work was looked upon as something necessary but of no particular importance in itself. Work was the lot of man, and one did what he needed to and no more. And, indeed, why do more, when it would only result in more food than one could eat or more clothes than one could wear or more houses than one could live in? When the results of one's work are products that must be immediately consumed or utilized, work beyond the ability to consume or use is meaningless. And so the Spanish-American and Mexican villagers, having few storage facilities and little opportunity for trade, developed no tradition of work either as an end in itself or as a means to a possibly more abundant life.

Circumstances that might have led to the development of a drive toward success were also absent in the villages. A person was esteemed on the basis of his possession of qualities that for the most part were the qualities of others of his sex and age and that were definitely self-limiting. Where everyone has the same characteristics and skills, it is almost impossible for anyone to be outstanding; and where esteem is based on such uncontrollable factors as sex, age, family membership and centers in such limited areas as being a good son, a just father, a good provider, a faithful wife, the ability of an individual to command very much of it through his own efforts is definitely restricted. There were simply no avenues in the village through which "success" as the Anglo knows it could be achieved, and so no cult of success and no particular awareness that one must be either a "success" or "failure" developed.

Nor was there much concern for practicality or efficiency. The one was guaranteed by the fact that familiar techniques had survived the test of time and were known to give certain fairly predictable results. Furthermore, if one spent a good portion of his time doing what he wanted to do, a certain practicality was assured by the fact that satisfactions were sure to follow the activity or it would not be continued. And, since goals were relatively few, simple, immediate, and attainable, the question of the practicality of a given action could quickly and easily be settled. A basic reason for the development of a concern for efficiency is undoubtedly that it is economical in terms of time or

effort. But in the villages there was no great concern with time, and effort was regarded as the lot of man, who was born to toil. More efficient means of crop husbandry might have produced more abundant yields. But for what? More efficient techniques of animal husbandry might have brought about a much better quality of livestock. But why?[14]

In this general area, as in many others, there are abundant opportunities for misunderstanding and misinterpretation between Anglos and Spanish-speaking. The Anglo finds it difficult to understand why Spanish-speaking people seem to have no "ambition," why they apparently have no drive for success and are seemingly or actually content to live year after year with no observable striving for upward mobility. He is likely to interpret this in his terms and in accordance with his values as due to a lack of "gumption," or as resulting from ignorance or laziness or indifference or some other characteristic which he regards as undesirable. A frequent complaint of Anglo supervisors of Spanish-speaking employees is that they sometimes lack initiative in seeking another task when they have finished one that has been assigned them. Having finished one job some sit and wait for someone to find another for them, a practice that makes considerable sense in terms of the attitudes and values of the village culture, but which is at almost complete variance with Anglo notions of how employees ought to behave.

DIFFERENCES IN ATTITUDES OF ACCEPTANCE AND RESIGNATION

A closely related trait of the Spanish-speaking people is their somewhat greater readiness toward acceptance and resignation than is characteristic of the Anglo. Whereas it is the belief of the latter that man has an obligation to struggle against and if possible to master the problems and difficulties that beset him, the Spanish-speaking person is more likely to accept and resign himself to whatever destiny brings him. With his eyes on the future, the Anglo tells himself and his friends that "while there is life there's hope." Greater difficulties mean greater obligations to struggle to surmount them, and the success stories that Anglos tell each other and their children are frequently of cultural heroes who were distinguished by the fact that against great odds and a high probability of failure they struggled and won success. The stories of the rise of President Lincoln from log cabin to White House and the numerous tales of young men who started with determination and a shoestring and rose to fame and fortune affirm not only a belief in democratic values but also the need to rebel against circumstances, to overcome environmental limitations, and by effort to reach the goals of one's own choosing. The environment is something to be manipulated, to be changed to suit his needs, and the Anglo reserves his deepest admiration for those who "never say die."

The Spanish-speaking person, by contrast, is likely to meet difficulties by adjusting to them rather than by attempting to overcome them. Fate is somewhat inexorable, and there is nothing much to be gained by struggling against it. If the lot of man is hard—and it frequently is—such is the will of God, incomprehensible but just, and it is the obligation of man to accept it. Behind the Spanish-speaking person there is no tradition of heroes who conquered against great odds—unless one goes back to the time of the Spanish *conquistadores*. In the collective recollection of village life there is only the remembrance of men and women who were born, resigned themselves to suffering and hardship along with occasional joys, and died when their time came. Great and stirring deeds were not done in the villages: no one conquered disease, or changed the face of the earth, or composed memorable music, or invented a mechanical marvel, or illustrated the heights to which a man could rise if only he had vision and courage and an indomitable will. This is not to say that there were not men of vision and valor among the ancestors of the present generation of Spanish-speaking people. There were, and there are among those now alive. But the particular kinds of valor and vision required for one to feel consistently that he not only can but should make the attempt to triumph over difficulties and obstacles, however great they may be, were not developed to any considerable degree by the kinds of experiences the Spanish-speaking villagers historically have had.

ɪe attitude of acceptance and resignation, to the extent that ɪsts, is difficult for Anglos to understand. Feeling that a per- ought to rebel against circumstances, ought to master and control them, Anglos are puzzled by the behavior of persons who apparently do not share these feelings. An Anglo who falls ill feels an obligation to "do something" about his sickness, a feeling that is generally shared with an equal or greater intensity by his family and friends. Sickness is something which one must struggle against and, if possible, overcome. So the sick Anglo, with the encouragement and assistance of his relatives and friends, treats himself or seeks professional help and generally engages in or submits to a series of activities designed to restore his health. A frequently expressed fear during illness is that something that might be done is not being done; and death, when it occurs as a result of disease, is made acceptable to the survivors by the assurance that "we did everything which could be done." When the Spanish-speaking person becomes ill, he may also treat himself or seek professional assistance, but there is not so strong a feeling that he should or must do so. If the patient is uncomfortable and the onset of the disease fairly sudden, treatment may be started quickly. If the disease comes on gradually and in the early stages involves no great discomfort, the patient and his family may feel no strong obligation to do anything about it. Or, in either case, such treatment as may be given may be abandoned if it is required over too long a period of time, or is expensive, or does not produce definitely observable results.

Spanish-speaking persons suffering from chronic diseases are sometimes so indifferent to treatment that Anglo health workers become exasperated. A county health officer recently spoke of a Spanish-American father who "contributed to the murder of his daughter" by not following medical advice and sending his daughter to an institution where she might have been treated for her tuberculosis. Both father and daughter were told what would happen if the girl were not treated, but the warnings had no effect on either. The girl remained at home and died in her early twenties. The Anglo health officer and his colleagues attributed the death to virtually criminal negligence on the part of the father and spoke bitterly of his apparent callousness and lack of love for his daughter. The father and others in the family saw the death as a regrettable but natural phenomenon and were comforted by the fact that their love for the girl was such that she could spend her last days in her own home surrounded with warmth and affection, and had not been committed to the impersonal care of Anglo strangers.

The attitude of accepting rather than fighting against circumstances is sometimes given expression by withdrawal from unpleasant or potentially difficult situations. Thus, Spanish-speaking persons who need professional services may withdraw from contact with an Anglo who could give those services if they encounter evidences of hostility, or if they are being too strongly urged to make a decision or take some course of action which they are reluctant to pursue. The withdrawal may take the extreme form of refusing the Anglo admission to the home when he or she makes a professional call. It is more likely, however, to find expression in polite reticence and a passive refusal to cooperate. One aspect of the withdrawal tendency is the frequently encountered reluctance of Spanish-speaking people to make initial contacts with Anglo agencies—clinics, employment offices, and the like—where they are uncertain as to what they may expect or what may be expected of them, and where there is always the possibility of encountering some prejudiced person who is hostile, or perhaps some employee whose bureaucratic impersonality seems to imply an indifference to their problem.

Another manifestation of a general attitude of acceptance is a kind of passivity toward persons in authority, which has led Anglo employers and supervisors to comment on the "docility" of Spanish-speaking employees, who are seen to be exceedingly responsive to orders and demands made upon them by their employers. The idea of the "docile Mexican" is particularly prevalent in areas near the border and probably derives in part from the presence of large numbers of wetbacks who have no choice but to be docile since they are here illegally, and who generally are not familiar enough with Anglo ways to know how to protest. To the extent that docility as a characteristic of Spanish-speaking persons exists elsewhere in the Southwest, it is likely to be a manifestation of the general tendency to accept circumstances rather than to rebel against them, to adjust by conforming rather than by resisting.

The tendency to accept and conform, however, does not mean that the Spanish-speaking person lacks strong feelings of individuality and is content to be an undifferentiated member of a group. On the contrary, as many Spanish-speaking people themselves have noted, there is among members of the group a need for self-assertion and to be recognized for one's personal qualities, a need that finds some fulfillment in the establishing of personal relationships; in the institution of *machismo*, an exaggerated emphasis on masculinity; in outbursts of temper and, sometimes, overt aggression; and in the practice of the art of public speaking. This is not the "rugged individualism" of the Anglos, which stresses independence and the obligation of the individual by his own efforts to wrest from a hostile environment what he wants. It is rather an individualism of being rather than doing, a need that is satisfied by recognition rather than by accomplishment. This trait of "individualism" is seen in the inability of some Spanish-speaking people to orient themselves to such an abstraction as "the job" and their seeking to establish, even in situations that by Anglo standards do not warrant them, personal relationships with employers, politicians, and other persons of influence and authority. An Anglo can be "loyal" to a job and an organization and expect no more recognition than that included in his impersonal relations to those about him in the organizational hierarchy. The Spanish-speaking person is more likely to reserve his "loyalty" for some person above him in the organizational structure with whom he can establish a personal or particularized relationship. The foreman or employer who expects his Spanish-speaking workers to respond to the same kinds of impersonal incentives that result in performance from Anglos is likely to be disappointed with their response, while the "boss" who allows the formation of personal relationships and utilizes the loyalty of Spanish-speaking workers to him as a person as a means of getting performance may have reason to be much pleased with the quality and amount of work done. Likewise, Anglo professional people who permit or even encourage a personalistic quality in their relationships with Spanish-speaking patients or clients may find that they are more successful in getting their professional help accepted than those who insist on a rather rigid impersonality in their relationships.

The village environments in which the distinctive cultures of the Spanish-speaking people were produced were such that persons in them developed an orientation to people rather than to abstract ideas, and to people whom they knew rather intimately and in many roles. Impersonality could hardly exist in a village where everyone was known to and shared experiences with everyone else, and it is to be expected that those who have been conditioned by the culture of such villages will feel easier in personal rather than impersonal relationships.

DIFFERENCES IN ATTITUDES TOWARD DEPENDENCY

Among the cherished values of the Anglo is a preference for independence and a corollary dislike and distrust of the dependent state. The ideal Anglo stands on his own two feet and, in the archaic phrase, "is beholden to no man." From the Anglo point of view, independence hardly can be overdone, while dependence, even of relatively slight degree, quickly comes to be regarded as undesirable, if not downright pathological. Anglos neither like to be dependent nor to have others dependent on them, and an implicit obligation of one who receives help is that he will at the earliest possible moment take whatever action may be necessary to make him independent again. During the depression of the 1930's, when millions of Anglos were on relief, there was much discussion of the possible damage that might be done by this wholesale dependence on the government, and there is still, among welfare workers and other Anglo professional people, considerable expression of misgiving lest their efforts somehow damage the characters of those to whom they give services by making them more dependent. Frequent expression is given to the point of view that people should be helped to help themselves and a good proportion of Anglo institutional services are deliberately designed to transfer people as rapidly as possible from a dependent to an independent state.

Underlying social casework practice is the assumption that clients are best helped, both psychologically and materially, by making it possible for them to help themselves. It is widely felt that assistance which involves no effort or participation on the part of the recipient is not only likely to be unappreciated but positively harmful, since it tends to minimize any incentive toward independence.

In the culture of the Spanish-speaking people independence is not given nearly so high a value. The unit of independence was the village community, and each village was relatively self-sufficient. Within the village, however, there was considerable interdependence, with the fortunes of individuals varying almost directly with those of the group. Between the adult individual and his family—an extended family that included three or more generations as well as uncles, aunts, cousins, nieces and nephews —was a reciprocal relationship of mutual interdependence in which each supported and was supported by the other. Intermarriages between families tied the whole community together in a network of relationships through which each individual could claim assistance from almost anyone else and was expected to give similar assistance when it was requested of him. A dependent status, when it was necessitated by misfortune or indicated by the circumstances in which an individual found himself, was not considered extraordinary. Other persons rendered whatever services or gave whatever goods were required and, in time, the individual either died or again became able to carry his share of the load. There were, of course, no agencies whose specialized function was to give material assistance of any kind—unless the *patrón* be thought of as a kind of agency—and people helped or were helped as the need arose, passing in and out of dependency relationships with each variation of their familial and individual fortunes, and with no thought that a dependent status might be wrong or dangerous or undesirable.

Dependence, thus, has one meaning for the Spanish-speaking person and quite a different meaning and significance for the

Anglo. The Anglo who accepts help from another individual or an agency is supposed to do so reluctantly and to feel obligated to exert every effort to become independent at the earliest possible time. The Spanish-speaking individual who accepts professional or institutional assistance from an Anglo individual or agency is expected to feel the same way. But to the extent that his attitudes and actions derive from the village culture, he is likely to view the giving and accepting of assistance as the normal and proper functioning of an institutional relationship in which both parties to the relationship are simply "doing what comes naturally." He needs help, so he accepts it for as long as it is available. Professional people and the agencies are expected to give help because that is their function. There is nothing in the relationship to get excited about. The Anglo, however, is likely to view the situation in moral terms and to feel that assistance should be reserved for those who deserve it or are "worthy of it"; that is, those who require assistance "through no fault of their own," who feel a bit of guilt or shame at having to accept help, and who will make an effort to change their status as rapidly as they can. The Spanish-speaking point of view is that assistance should be given to those who need it, with need being subjectively defined. Each, naturally, evaluates a given situation in terms of his own point of view. And in the difference in point of view lie the bases for many misunderstandings between members of the two groups.

DIFFERENCES IN ATTITUDES TOWARD FORMAL ORGANIZATIONS

One observation that is frequently made about the Spanish-speaking people of the Southwest is that the group has been unable to develop effective leadership from among its members or to organize successfully for the purpose of improving its status with respect to the rest of the population.[15] It is true that there are some large and fairly long-lived organizations of Spanish-speaking people and that there have come out of the group many individuals with considerable talent and ability for exercising leadership in their respective fields. But the organizations have been singularly ineffective in meeting the needs of the Spanish-speaking people, and most of the "leaders" have, at least until very recently, exercised their talents to a greater extent outside the group than within it.

A part of the failure to develop effective leadership from within the group has undoubtedly been due to the great differences within the Spanish-speaking population in the various parts of the Southwest, which have made interstate or regional organization almost impossible. A part of the failure must also be ascribed to the cultural trait of "individualism," mentioned above, which not only operates to hinder efforts to organize the group, but also has some relationship to a tendency of potential leaders to be hostile and to undermine each other's work. Probably more important than any of these is the fact that there is no strong tradition of either achieved leadership or organization within the culture.

Anglos, as many observers have noted, are great joiners, and their way of meeting a group problem is first to set up a committee to study and report on it and then to create an organization to deal with it. Rare is the Anglo who does not have membership in one or more formal organizations, and some belong to so many that they have difficulty remembering them all. Societies, clubs, associations, and other types of organization exist in abundance, and practically any specialized interest that an individual may have can be given expression by joining an existing organization made up of those with similar interests. If there is no such organization, it is usually easy to find enough other interested people to set up one. In these organizations there exist innumerable opportunities for the development and exercise of leadership skills, so that one who has talent for and interest in organizational and leadership activities can easily find opportunities to practice and perfect his skills. Thus, there is in the Anglo culture not only a well-developed tradition of organization but also a considerable body of collective experience in how to go about setting up an organization and making it effective, as well as an expectation that special interest groups will organize to promote and, if possible, attain their ends.

In the village culture of the Spanish-speaking people there were almost no formal organizations (possible exceptions being the church, the *penitente* order, and, in some Spanish-American villages, an irrigation ditch committee) and few or no opportunities for the development and exercise of the qualities of achieved leadership.[16] Whatever needed to be done could be accomplished largely through the informal relationships of the community itself, and there was little need to set up any additional organization to pursue any special interest or goal. Relationships between members of the community were such that the relatively few interests sanctioned by the culture could be expressed and satisfied within the existing patterns of association. The whole community constituted in a sense a single primary group in which each member had intimate access to every other member and each had an opportunity to know the others in nearly all of their several roles. The range of community activities and interests was limited to those in which every member of the community could, at some stage in his development, be expected to share. For each type of activity and each interest area there were well-understood preexisting patterns of relationships into which individuals were fitted on the basis of ascribed characteristics. "Leadership" was probably more nominal than actual, since in any case it consisted largely of carrying out prescribed routines in a prescribed manner and included but minimal opportunity for the exercise of judgment or invention. One was a "leader" only in the sense that a person who is at the head of a procession of people, all of whom know where they are going, is a leader, and even this restricted role was reserved for persons with requisite institutional rather than personal qualities.

Persons close to the culture of the village thus have but little understanding of formal organization, little orientation toward a type of leadership based on personal, individual characteristics, and almost no tradition of responding to leadership of this type. Spanish-speaking persons are harder to organize than comparable groups of Anglos, and many organizations that have seemed to get off to a good start have failed as soon as the initial enthusiasm wore off or the outside stimulus was removed. Individuals who develop a personal drive toward leadership and who have the necessary talents and skills for organization of one kind or another frequently move over into the Anglo group where their abilities are seemingly more appreciated and a given amount of effort is likely to produce greater results. Such persons are likely to be highly acculturated in the sense that they have taken on many of the attitudes, values, and techniques of the Anglos, and their activities frequently have little direct relationship to the needs and problems of the group from which they came.

There is at the present time no effective national or regional organization of Spanish-speaking people[17] and no more than a handful of leaders who have a command of the Anglo culture and can at the same time exercise strong leadership among the less acculturated members of the Spanish-speaking group. In some local areas, and in one or two instances on a statewide level, there are the beginnings of organized movements that may develop the specialized kind of leadership and organizational skill necessary to get results in the Anglo culture. Such organizations, to the extent that they are successful, may well become a bridge over which Spanish-speaking people can move toward the acquisition of enough Anglo culture to enable them to improve their collective status. One difficulty with the concept of organization as a bridge to the acquisition of Anglo culture elements, however, is that, since organization as a means of attaining group and individual goals is not an element of the village culture, a fairly long step toward acculturation must be taken before any given individual can set foot upon the bridge.

Many more points of difference between the Anglo culture and those of the several types of Spanish-speaking villagers could be cited, but enough have been mentioned to illustrate and provide some documentation for the generalization that when, in given situations, the behavior of members of the Spanish-speaking group is noticeably different from that which Anglos think is proper for that situation, the reason is not that the Spanish-speaking are a different kind of people subject to a different human nature, but rather that they may view the situation from a different perspective and with a different set of meanings and values. The Spanish-speaking couple who failed to report to the proper authorities the birth of a child and its death one hour later, and who themselves buried the infant in a box in their yard, were not bad or heartless people. They were, of course, picked up by the police when their deed became known. But they do not deserve punishment. Instead, they need an opportunity to acquire an understanding of our ways, a reorientation. They did what all people do in the tiny, remote Mexican community from which they came. They did what for them seemed right, what was customary, what they had learned to do from the people among whom they had lived most of their lives. But in the United States it was not right, not customary. If they remain here, this couple will have to learn different ways. But they, like other Spanish-speaking people, must have time in which to learn, help in the learning, and some understanding and acceptance during the learning period.

Pedro Treviño is not indifferent to the health of his daughter Linda. He has a different idea of what constitutes illness from that held by the doctors who attended Linda and a different attitude toward the probable future consequences of what he may do or not do today. He is more concerned about his daughter's morals than about her health, not because he thinks morality more important than health but because the improper behavior is clearly apparent to him and the poor health is not. Getting angry at Pedro will not help to solve the real problem of the doctor on the case, which is to give good medical care to Linda. If Linda is to get that care, the cultural orientation of her father and sister will have to be taken into account, understood, and somehow manipulated in such a way as to assure their cooperation in the plans of the doctor. How to obtain that understanding and succeed in that manipulation are a part of the *medical* problem that Linda presents and must be considered along with all other aspects of that problem if her illness is to be successfully treated.

Simoneta Roybal and her daughter Josie need a great deal of intelligent help if they are not to become even more of a burden to the community than they now are. With no family ties and few friends, with not much understanding of Anglo ways and no strong identification with those of the Spanish-speaking people, Simoneta is isolated, shut off from both groups and from the possible resources which closer group ties might give her. Unable to speak English, suspicious of well-intentioned offers of assistance, lacking any strong motivation to change her circumstances, she will be hard to work with, hard to help. Simoneta's problem does not arise from the fact that she is Spanish-speaking, but it is complicated by that fact, and the agency workers and others who deal with her will have to take it into account in making plans for her.

María Vigil loves her children and would not knowingly do anything to harm them. That her active tuberculosis makes her a menace to them has not occurred to her. Nor will telling her make her see it. She is not stubborn or stupid. For her the test of illness is how one feels. She feels as well as she ever has, and therefore cannot be ill. And, if she is not ill, how can she possibly transmit a disease to the children? María has not worked this out in her mind and reached a conclusion. She has not thought about it at all. In a very real sense she was not able to "hear" the words which were intended to tell her that she is seriously ill and that her illness could be communicated to her children unless she took steps to prevent it. She did not "hear" them because the concepts which would make them meaningful are not known to her. She "knows" about sickness, and in terms of her "knowledge" she is not sick. The Anglo physicians who have tried to treat her and to tell her about her condition also "know" about sickness and in terms of their "knowledge" she is ill. The problem of how to communicate with María, how to make her see the fact of her illness and its possible relationship to the future welfare of her children, is as much a medical question as will be that of how to treat her illness and protect her children, once a way to break through the communication barrier has been found. For such a problem, a knowledge of cultural variation and its possible consequences for behavior may be a useful tool.

Chapter IV

HEALING WAYS

Wᴛᴛʜ ʀᴇɢᴀʀᴅ ᴛᴏ ɪʟʟɴᴇꜱꜱ ᴀɴᴅ ɪᴛꜱ ᴛʀᴇᴀᴛᴍᴇɴᴛ, as in other aspects
of their culture, the Spanish-speaking people of the Southwest
have many traits in common with the Anglos. Like most other
people, they have minor ailments that they tend to disregard.
Like all people, they occasionally have aches and pains, chills
and fever, and other insistent symptoms that force them to seek
relief. And, as in the case of most other people, what they do,
how they do it, and when, are determined by the "knowledge"
they have of the meaning and cause of their symptoms, and of
what can or should be done about them. Such knowledge is a
product of association with other people and may be as restricted
or expansive, as consistent or contradictory, as the range of their
associations permits it to be.

MEDICAL KNOWLEDGE OF SPANISH-SPEAKING PEOPLE

In varying degree, depending on who he is, where he lives,
and what his personal experience has been, the Spanish-speaking
individual draws his knowledge of illness and its treatment from
four widely separated sources: (1) from the folk medical lore of
medieval Spain as refined in several centuries of relative isolation
from its source; (2) from the cultures of one or more American
Indian tribes; (3) from Anglo folk medicine as practiced in both
rural and urban areas; and (4) from "scientific" medical sources.
In a given instance of illness, elements from any or all of the four
sources may be utilized in any sequence that may seem appropriate to the individual or to those who may advise or otherwise
try to help him. In a case recently observed, a young Spanish-
American couple first attempted to treat the husband's digestive

141

difficulties with popular remedies purchased from an Anglo drugstore. When that failed to bring the desired results they used liberally concoctions suggested by the wife's mother, which were prepared from anise, sagebrush, and horsemint. Dissatisfied with the results of this therapy, they next consulted an Anglo physician. When, after two visits to his office, the husband's discomfort persisted, they sought the services of a *curandera* who was reputed to know a good deal about stomach disorders. Another woman, the daughter of a Pueblo Indian mother and a "full-blooded Mexican" father, who now lives in an Anglo city, prides herself in possessing considerable medical knowledge, most of which she obtained from an uncle living in one of the New Mexico pueblos. Although she has been a regular patient at an Anglo cardiac clinic, this woman feels that Anglo doctors do not really help anybody and are frequently too stubborn to take advantage of the superior wisdom of some of their patients. She treats herself, her family, and neighbors who seek her advice, from a pharmacopoeia that includes Anglo patent preparations, household remedies from both the Anglo and Spanish folk medical traditions, and herbs, the preparation and the use of which she learned from her Indian uncle.

Illness and disease, it must be remembered, are social as well as biological phenomena. On the biological level they consist of adaptations of the organism to environmental influences; on the social level they include meanings, roles, relationships, attitudes, and techniques that enable members of a cultural group to identify various types of illness and disease, to behave appropriately, and to call upon a body of knowledge for coping with the condition defined as an illness. What is recognized as disease or illness is a matter of cultural prescription, and a given biological condition may or may not be considered an "illness," depending on the particular cultural group in which it occurs.[1] Infestation by intestinal worms is generally regarded as a type of disease by people in the United States. Among other people, for example the inhabitants of the island of Yap, worms are thought to be a necessary component of the digestive process. *Mal ojo*, *susto*, and *empacho* are examples of diseases that are common in

Latin America but unknown in the United States—with the exception of the Spanish-speaking Southwest—although the symptoms which give rise to diagnoses of any or all of these are fairly common in this country. What should be done about a given condition defined culturally as "illness" and the proper relationships of a sick person to other people are also culturally prescribed. An individual thus has cultural guides that enable him to know when he or others may be regarded as sick, something about the cause and nature of the sickness, what may be done to alleviate or remedy the condition, and the behavior expected of him and of others in the situation.

The Spanish-speaking people, having drawn from many cultures their understandings of illness and disease and of the proper behavior associated with their various manifestations, have a somewhat incongruous set of notions which, in a given individual, may range from an uncritical belief in witchcraft or magic as etiological factors to complete acceptance of the latest "scientific" methods of diagnosis and therapy. It is not uncommon to find elderly Spanish-speaking patients in the most modern of Anglo hospitals wearing bracelets of copper wire to prevent rheumatism or similar painful conditions of the joints, or other amulets or charms believed to have therapeutic value. As in the case of other cultural elements, no valid generalization can be made that will be applicable to the entire Spanish-speaking population, since the range of experiences within the group is extremely wide and the opportunities for differential participation in two or more cultures varied. It is probable, however, that age and degree of participation in Anglo culture are the most important variables associated with differences in belief, knowledge, and practice with respect to illness and disease. Older persons and those having relatively little effective contact with Anglo culture can reasonably be expected to have drawn much of their knowledge and belief about sickness and its treatment from Spanish or Indian cultural sources. Younger persons and those with a relatively large degree of effective participation in the Anglo culture are more likely to share Anglo beliefs and attitudes about sickness and to utilize Anglo techniques for dealing with it.

In adopting new ideas about illness and new materials and techniques for treating it, the Spanish-speaking people have not necessarily abandoned any of their old ideas or healing methods. Some individuals may have dropped certain practices used by their parents or grandparents in treating certain disease conditions, or may have failed to learn them, but in the Spanish-speaking population viewed as a whole most of the old ways persist in some form. Drugstores in the "Mexican" sections of Anglo cities in the Southwest do a thriving business in herbs and other folk remedies. *Parteras, curanderas, médicas, albolarias,* and even *brujas*[2] still find a demand for their services in both rural and urban areas. Alternative types of medical service and methods of treatment are seldom mutually exclusive, so that the adoption of the new does not necessitate giving up the old. The new is merely added to the old body of knowledge or belief, and either or both are drawn upon, depending on the circumstances. The Spanish-speaking person who puts himself in the hands of an Anglo institution and practitioner for a surgical operation expects to receive the utmost benefit from Anglo knowledge and skill. If, subsequently, he wears a piece of *oshá* over the incision, this does not necessarily indicate any lack of faith in Anglo methods but rather his reliance on a wider range of "knowledge" than that possessed by the Anglos who are treating him. Penicillin and the other antibiotics admittedly reduce or prevent infection, but so, in his opinion, does *oshá*, and it does no harm to be doubly certain of results by using both.

FOLK MEDICINE

Three of the four sources from which the Spanish-speaking people derive their ideas about sickness and its treatment provide them with types of knowledge, belief, and practice that may be classified as folk medicine.[3] Folk medicine differs from "scientific" medicine in a number of ways. In any culture, it is generally the common possession of the group. In a folk culture, there is relatively little division of knowledge with respect to medicine, so that what one adult knows about illness and its treatment is usually known by all other adults. Although knowledge of the origins of folk medical practices and beliefs may have largely been lost, the practices and beliefs themselves are often so rooted in tradition that they seem a part of the natural order of things and are as much taken for granted as is the daily rising and setting of the sun. Folk medical lore is transmitted from person to person and generation to generation by informal methods and through what sociologists like to call unstructured situations. One learns it, much as he learns other elements of his culture, as an incidental part of his everyday associations. Folk medicine is usually well integrated with other elements of a folk culture and is reinforced by them. The expected attitude toward a given element of folk medicine is one of uncritical acceptance. Failure does not invalidate a practice or shake the belief on which it is based. A remedy is tried, and if it works no surprise is evinced, since that is what was expected. If it does not work, the failure is rationalized and something else tried. In most illnesses the patient ultimately either recovers or dies. If he gets well, the remedial technique is credited with effecting the cure. If he dies, the reason is not that the remedy was inappropriate, but that the patient was beyond help.[4] Folk medicine, like scientific medicine, undoubtedly derives much of its prestige and authority from the fact that the majority of sick persons get well regardless of what is done.

If practitioners of scientific medicine think of folk medicine at all, they are likely to regard it as mere superstition or as a somewhat curious and outdated survival, having about the same relationship to medical science that astrology has to astronomy. But folk medicine, even in cultures with a well-developed tradition of scientific medicine, is a flourishing institution, and many folk practices have survived because they undoubtedly do get results. Although they are in general uncritically accepted by those using them, folk medical practices are subjected over a period of time to a rough empirical evaluation. Those that seem successful frequently come to be more and more used and thus firmly entrench themselves in the minds and behaviors of the group using them. Those that consistently fail to do what is expected of them tend to be used less and less frequently and, in time, may be dropped altogether. There thus operates a selective process that

tends to weed out the ineffective practices and to strengthen those that prove to be effective.

Between scientific medicine and folk medicine there is a constant two-way interchange. Remedies that have been developed by scientific medicine become a part of the pharmacopoeia of folk medicine (for example, aspirin to relieve headaches or other minor aches and pains) and others with a long history of folk use are "discovered," analyzed, tested, and ultimately become a part of scientific medicine (for example, curare, quinine, cocaine). It is not the materials or procedures that determine whether a given technique represents folk or scientific medicine, but rather the way in which they are used and the body of knowledge or belief that lies behind the use. Scientific medicine is rooted in a precise knowledge of cause and effect relationships and a critical attitude toward both practices and results. Folk medicine is neither precise nor critical. It is rooted in belief, not knowledge, and it requires only occasional success to maintain its vigor.

The folk medicine of a given people, however, is usually not a random collection of beliefs and practices; rather, it constitutes a fairly well-organized and fairly consistent theory of medicine. The body of "knowledge" on which it is based often includes ideas about the nature of man and his relationships with the natural, supernatural, and human environments. Folk medicine flourishes because it is a functional and integrated part of the whole culture, and because it enables members of cultural groups to meet their health needs, as they define them, in ways that are at least minimally acceptable.

The Spanish-speaking people of the Southwest, as has been indicated, draw their medical beliefs and practices from many sources. One of these, and one that particularly influences the medical beliefs and practices of the two groups we have called Mexicans and Mexican-Americans, is the folk medicine of Mexico.

Mexican Folk Medicine

There is probably no single body of medical knowledge and practice that is common to all persons of Mexican origin. The isolation of many areas and the poor communication existing between them until recently have undoubtedly contributed to the development of somewhat different bodies of medical lore in different parts of the country. Varying degrees of contact with indigenous Indian cultures have also resulted in variations in medical knowledge and practice. But there are a few elements, common to a number of different areas in Mexico and other parts of Latin America, that have influenced the medical behavior of Spanish-speaking persons in the Southwest.

One widely dispersed body of knowledge and practice is that related to concepts of heat and cold as qualities both of disease conditions and of materials used in therapy.[5] These concepts provide a means of determining what remedy may be used for a particular illness and what the consequences are likely to be if the wrong treatment is used. Illnesses are classified as hot and cold, without respect to the presence or absence of fever, and the correct therapy is to attain a balance by treating "hot" diseases with "cold" remedies and "cold" diseases with "hot" remedies. Foods, beverages, animals, and people possess the characteristics of "heat" or "cold" in varying degree, and it is thought wise always to maintain a proper regard for the principles of balance.[6] "Hot" foods, for example, should never be combined, but rather should be taken in conjunction with something "cold," with care being used to see that extremes of heat and cold are not taken together. A person with a "cold" disease is endangered by being given "cold" remedies or foods, since these are likely to aggravate his condition. There is no general agreement on exactly what is "hot" or "cold"; therefore, the classification of a given material or condition may vary from place to place.

Another fairly common body of belief and practice in Mexico relates to the concept of the clean stomach and includes the idea that the maintenance of health requires a periodic purging of the stomach and intestinal tract. At least one disease, *empacho*, is thought to be directly due to failure to achieve a clean stomach, and the rather large number of purgatives used are evidence of the extent to which the concept is accepted.[7]

Blood is considered important in the balance of health and disease and many folk remedies serve the function of purifying the blood or otherwise improving its quality. Loss of blood for any reason, even in the small amounts necessary for laboratory tests, is thought to have a weakening effect, particularly on males, whose sexual vigor is thereby believed to be impaired.[8]

Illness is conceived primarily in terms of not feeling well. Conditions that are not accompanied by subjective feelings or discomfort are generally not classified as illness; hence, there is no obligation to do anything about them. Health is looked upon as a matter of chance, and it is felt that there is very little that a person can do to keep it. Minor discomforts usually are not sufficient motivations to seek treatment, and frequently persons are seriously ill before they begin to seek or accept help. There is a tendency to conceal illness, partly deriving from the idea that to be sick is a manifestation of weakness.

Air is considered potentially dangerous, particularly if cold or if it is blowing over one. Night air is more dangerous than day air, and persons already ill are thought to be particularly susceptible to the harm that air can bring. Consequently, sickrooms are not ventilated, and special care is taken to see that all windows and doors are closed at night.

Pregnancy requires adherence to many dietary restrictions and a reduction in the amount of water drunk, lest the head of the foetus grow too large for an easy delivery. Frequent bathing and regular exercise in the prenatal period are thought to facilitate the delivery process, which frequently takes place with the woman in a squatting or kneeling position. After the delivery the mother remains in bed for an extended period of time, and then she takes or is given a steam bath. During the first three days following delivery the diet is restricted to a small amount of "cold" foods. Thereafter, "hot" foods again may be eaten.

With respect to etiological factors, three types of causation are recognized: empirical, magical, and psychological. Empirical or "natural" diseases are those in which a known external factor operates directly on the organism to produce the illness. Any disorders resulting from exposure to bad air, invasion by microorganisms, contact with an infected person, eating improper foods, failure to keep a clean stomach, and similar hazards are considered "natural" diseases. A long list of illnesses, including pneumonia, rheumatism, diarrhea, colds, smallpox, worms, tuberculosis, and venereal disease, is placed in this category. Magical diseases are those in which the causative factors lie outside the realm of empirical knowledge and cannot be thus verified. Such a disease is *mal ojo*, or evil eye, which is produced in young children, often without intention, by persons who have a "strong glance." Some kinds of *susto*, a type of illness resulting from fright, are of magical etiology in that they are felt to be caused by the possession of an individual by an evil spirit. And there are, of course, many kinds of bewitchment in which a person with evil intent and magical power can cause illness symptoms in another. Psychological diseases are those in which a strong emotional experience causes the appearance of the disease symptoms. Examples are *susto* when it occurs in young children who have suffered a severe fright, or epilepsy, which is believed to result from strong emotional feelings.

For most illnesses there are appropriate remedies. The number and range of remedial measures are so great that only some of the major categories can be indicated here. Herbs are widely used in a variety of ways and for a large number of conditions. Tea made by boiling leaves or stems in water is a common remedy. Herbs are also taken with foods, are used in aromatic preparations whose fumes may be inhaled, are applied to external surfaces in the form of powder, and are worn in bags or cachets over parts of the body, much as the Anglos not so many years ago wore asafetida to ward off colds. Massage or some other form of manipulation of body parts is considered efficacious for some illnesses, and poultices and plasters of various kinds are used to produce both mechanical and magical effects. Salves and ointments are not uncommon; foods are both prescribed and withheld for remedial purposes; and various types of bathing are practiced. Prayer and the reciting of religious formulas are common forms of dealing with sickness, and where the illness is thought to be magical in nature, spells, charms, incantations, and other ritualistic practices may be utilized. In recent times, practices and materials have been borrowed from scientific medicine, and injections or "shots" have become a common form of treatment.[9]

Mild disorders are treated by the afflicted person or by some member of his family. More serious cases, or those that do not yield to home treatment, may require calling in someone with more specialized knowledge. Who is called and when, depends on the type and seriousness of the disease, the degree of discomfort, the availability of specialized help, and the probable cost of obtaining assistance. If the disease is a "natural" one that is fairly serious or uncomfortable, a physician may be called in to assist rather early in its course, provided a doctor is available and the problem of payment is not insuperable. Physicians, it is felt, understand "natural" diseases and are able to do something about them. But if the disease is thought to be of magical or psychological origin, assistance is more likely to be sought from a *curandera*, a *bruja*, or some other type of folk specialist, since they are assumed to be more familiar with and, hence, better able to treat such diseases. A complaint of *susto* or *mal ojo* will be listened to understandingly by a folk specialist, and the patient will be assured that his ailment is being treated. But to make such a complaint to a practitioner of scientific medicine would be to expose oneself to the possibility of skeptical disbelief, condemnation, or even ridicule, a circumstance that most patients and their families prefer to avoid.

The folk medical beliefs and practices of Mexicans do not stop at the Rio Grande. Many of them find their way across the border and can be found, even far inland, in areas where Mexicans and Mexican-Americans are living. A welfare worker in California is told by a Mexican-American family that they cannot eat grapefruit because it thins the blood and increases the possibility of their contracting tuberculosis. A visiting nurse in Colorado is accused by a mother of inadvertently causing illness in a small child by having smiled and spoken pleasantly to him. A sociological investigator in south Texas finds *susto* and *mal ojo* to be two of the major causes of illness among Mexican-Americans there.[10] A tuberculosis patient receives a portable one-room dwelling from the county health department in order that he may live in it and not infect his family. Not considering himself ill, he invites his mother to come to live in the portable dwelling, while he moves back with the family.[11] A Mexican-American woman seeks a blood test from a public health agency because she believes she has "bad blood" and that the test is a cure for it. Old Mexican-American women wrap their faces tightly in *rebozos*, lest they be endangered by contact with the air. And Virginia Gurule gave birth to her baby on a hospital floor because she was afraid of the delivery room.[12]

Many of these and other people who still believe in and practice Mexican folk medicine also accept many of the ideas and procedures of scientific medicine. They permit their children to be immunized against specific disease conditions. They seek the services of professionals practicing scientific medicine. They attend clinics and enter hospitals. So long as there is no basic conflict with any of the more deeply held beliefs of the old culture and scientific medical practices can be shown to give observable results, there is no reason why Mexican-Americans should not more and more avail themselves of the techniques of scientific medicine. The extent to which they do so will be determined by such factors as the extent and nature of their exposure to new medical ways, the degree to which they may be motivated by the failure of old ways to meet their medical needs, the availability to them of scientific medical services, and the degree to which their experiences with scientific medical and health personnel are pleasant or unpleasant. Scientific medicine will not soon be entirely substituted for folk medicine among the Mexican-Americans, but if properly presented it can come to play a larger and larger part in their responses to illness and the threat of illness, with resulting benefits to the Anglo as well as the Spanish-speaking population.

Spanish-American Folk Medicine

The Spanish-Americans, like the Mexicans, have been exposed to a number of streams of medical influence, and their behavior with respect to illness and its treatment also includes a mixture of elements from several sources. In the villages during centuries of isolation, the folk medical notions of sixteenth-century Spain were blended with those of the several Indian tribal groups with whom the villagers came into contact and with ideas and practices brought from Mexico by the occasional traders, government officials, or others who had occasion to pass back and forth between the two areas. With the coming of Anglos into the Southwest, a new source of influence developed and Anglo folk medical ways began to be used in the villages. More recently, opportunities for drawing upon the resources and methods of scientific medicine have been made available and have been accepted, so that, both in parent villages and Anglo cities to which many Spanish-Americans have migrated, the medical beliefs and practices of the Spanish-American population now represent a mixture, if not always a blend, of widely diverse elements.

"Faith and fatalism," says Mrs. L. S. M. Curtin in the introduction to her *Healing Herbs of the Upper Rio Grande*, "are the first ingredients in folk medicine."[13] And faith and fatalism are qualities that the Spanish-American villagers had, and to an extent still have, in abundance. They are qualities that have served the people well in enabling them to adjust to the uncertainties and hardships of village life, qualities that have been of particular value in dealing with illness. However extensive folk medical knowledge may be and however effective the content of a given cultural group's medical bag of tricks, folk medicine is limited in many ways, and those who must rely on it alone for diagnosis and treatment have many opportunities for the exercise of both faith and fatalism.

Considering their long isolation and the resources they had to work with, the medical knowledge of Spanish-American villagers and the range of treatment materials and procedures were quite extensive.

"The Spanish people of New Mexico," as Mrs. Curtin has pointed out, "live on the soil; they live simply and they have long memories. They can remember the language of Spain three hundred years ago and they have not yet forgotten the ways and customs of those times. . . . They are a people accustomed to the harvest of their yearly nourishment from the earth, from the fields about their homes, and it is without strangeness that they also draw medicines from the same source. The ever-present earth supplies the needs of its children here, as elsewhere; it is the grocer and the druggist for those who belong to the earth."[14]

That the earth was bountiful and the Spanish-Americans ingenious in making use of its offerings can be seen in the list of remedies Mrs. Curtin has compiled and the illnesses for which they were, or are, used. The latter include many of the ills of the flesh known to scientific medicine and a few others, such as pains due to witchcraft or tarantula bite, which are peculiar to the region. Among the more common illnesses for which the village folk had numerous remedies were arthritis, asthma, bone fractures, bronchitis, cancer, colds, colic, diarrhea, earache, goiter, gonorrhea, headache, heart trouble, measles, mumps, nosebleed, paralysis, pneumonia, rheumatism, skin diseases, sore throat, stomach trouble, tonsillitis, tuberculosis, and whooping cough. As in the case of Mexican folk medicine, the range of techniques for utilizing remedies was somewhat limited, so that most treatments called for the drinking of an infusion, a medication in the form of a salve or powder, bathing in or applying medicated fluids, or mixing remedies with foods. Alternative treatment procedures were available for many diseases—Mrs. Curtin lists 46 remedies for rheumatism!—so that if one failed to give the expected relief others might be tried.

Probably one of the most widely used, and certainly one of the most efficacious, remedies of the Spanish-American villages was *oshá*, a plant of the parsley family, to which reference has already been made, whose properties were probably learned from the Indians. The healing qualities of *oshá* are largely concentrated in the root, which may be used in many ways to treat a wide variety of illnesses. Chewed raw or ground into a powder and made into a tea, it prevents flatulency and soothes the stomach.* Drunk in hot water with sugar and whiskey, it will break up a cold and help to cure such respiratory illnesses as influenza, pneumonia, and

* These statements about the healing properties of various folk remedies are not to be regarded as verified facts. They are, rather, the virtues these particular remedies are thought to have by the people who use them.

pulmonary tuberculosis. Taken internally it will also reduce fevers. Applied directly to a wound in powdered form, or worn over a wound, *oshá* promotes healing. An ointment for the relief and cure of cuts and sores can be made from mutton fat, candle wax, and turpentine into which is mixed some powdered *oshá* root, *manzanilla* (camomile), and *contrayerba* (caltrop). Mixed with olive oil, *oshá* can be used as a liniment in the treatment of rheumatic pains, and it is also useful, in the form of a paste, to draw out the poison from snakebites. In addition, this highly versatile plant is used as the basis of an enema, as a remedy for colic in children, and as a means of protection against snakes, which are believed to be repelled by its pungent odor. *Oshá* has recently entered into Anglo folk medicine as an ingredient in a cough remedy prepared and sold by a Denver druggist. It is also useful as a seasoning for soups and stews.

The familiar onion of Anglo home remedies is also put to many uses by the Spanish-Americans. Roasted and applied hot, *cebollas* are thought to be effective in treating chilblains. Teething babies are allowed to chew the leaves and stems to relieve the pain of swollen gums. A cough syrup made of the juice of fried or roasted onions sweetened with honey or sugar is thought to be an excellent treatment for colds, particularly in the case of babies. *Inmortal* (spider milkweed) likewise has many uses. Powdered and mixed with water, it can be drunk to reduce headache or chest pains or to bring down a fever. Made into a paste and used as a poultice, it will relieve pains of various kinds. It is also useful in childbirth. Rubbed on the abdomen or taken with cold water it will reduce labor pains, and drunk with hot water after delivery it helps to expel the placenta. Asthma, shortness of breath, and similar afflictions may be helped by drinking a tea made of *inmortal*.

Not even a representative sample of the many plants used in the folk medicine of Spanish-Americans can be given here. But some indication of the extent of the list and of the familiarity to Anglos of many items on it may be obtained from a brief mention of the popular Anglo names of a few of the plants used: cattails, garlic, cottonwood, basil, apricot, camphor, alfalfa, lavender, aster, licorice, sunflower, anise, sagebrush, cocklebur, pumpkin, thistle, elderberry, lupine, algae, oleander, milkweed, corn, mustard, goldenrod, tansy, and mint. And not only plants but animals, animal products, and nonorganic substances find their place in the list of remedies, as can be seen in a mention of rattlesnake oil, cowhide, lime, rennet, milk, red ants, bones, alum, earth, and rock of various kinds, each of which, along with many other substances, is used in the treatment of some type of illness.

Folk Medical Practices at Ranchos de Taos

One of the few reports focused on the medical practices of Spanish-Americans is that of Sister Mary Lucia van der Eerden,[15] who in 1944 completed the field work for a study of patterns of maternity care as they exist in the village of Ranchos de Taos in northern New Mexico. Since Sister Mary Lucia's observations are accurate, extensive, and representative of rural Spanish-American medical care today, after some years of exposure to Anglo medical ways, both folk and scientific, it may be useful to review briefly her findings.

Ranchos de Taos is a sprawling village of about 1,400 inhabitants, mostly Spanish-speaking, located a few miles southwest of Taos on the Santa Fe highway. The center of the village is the much-photographed Church of St. Francis, which stands on a site occupied by a Catholic church since 1733. Spanish is the everyday language of the village, and English is known mainly by school-age children, adults under thirty years, and a small proportion of those between the ages of thirty and fifty. Young people marry early, children are welcomed, and families tend to be large.

Pregnancy and childbirth are looked upon as part of the natural and normal life experience of women. Consequently, there is no generally held notion that the period of pregnancy preceding delivery requires the intervention of any persons with specialized medical knowledge or skill. Advice and information may be sought from one's mother or grandmother, and, in any case, such counsel will undoubtedly be offered once the fact of pregnancy becomes apparent. In general, however, the pregnant woman continues to follow her regular routine, taking care only to observe a few precautions to prevent harm to herself and the baby. She avoids moonlight while in bed, and, should there be an eclipse during her pregnancy, takes the prophylactic precaution of hanging some keys on a string around her waist, lest the baby be deformed by the effect of the moon's shadow falling on the mother.[16] Some months before her confinement regular bowel evacuations are advised. For attaining regularity, a cathartic in the form of castor oil or the powdered root of *inmortal* or *yerba del lobo* may be taken. About the time that the first movements of the baby are felt, the mother begins wearing a *muñeco*, a cord or cloth band which is wrapped tightly around the waist to keep the foetus in place and prevent its damaging the upper organs of the mother. A series of prayers designed to assure safe delivery through the intercession of Saint Ramon Nonnato are begun nine days before the expected date of confinement. These activities constitute the common prenatal observances. Few of the married women of Ranchos, at the time of Sister Mary Lucia's study, consulted a physician during pregnancy, although several were available in nearby Taos.

The period of labor and the subsequent time of enforced inactivity following delivery require some outside assistance for the mother. In Ranchos at least two choices are open: to use a *partera*, or midwife, or to go to the hospital at Taos or Embudo, where the delivery can be handled by a physician and the follow-up care given by trained nurses. In 1944, as perhaps today, many of the women of Ranchos preferred the *partera*.[17]

Village lore required that a woman in labor not be permitted to go to bed until after the birth of her baby. It was felt necessary that she keep in motion during the progress of labor, supporting herself by clinging to a chair or some other solid object during pains, but walking about in the intervals between them. To hasten delivery one or another of a number of medicinal plants might be used, depending on the knowledge of the *partera* and her judgment as to the condition of the patient. *Canela en raja*, powdered sticks of cinnamon, were usually given first, and if delivery did not follow soon, other herbs might be given. *Alvacar* (sweet basil), *yerba buena* (spearmint), *yerba del sapo* (an herb of the aster family), *pimienta* (black pepper) were all thought to be useful, as were garlic water or a raw onion. Fried onions sprinkled with dried *manzanilla* (camomile) and rubbed over the woman's body were also considered effective in speeding delivery. It was felt important that the delivery room be kept cheerful and happy, and that anything disturbing, exciting, or unpleasant be prevented from reaching the mother, lest she be placed in serious jeopardy.

The expectant mother usually was fully clothed, including stockings and shoes. The baby was born on a sheepskin or quilt spread on the floor, with the mother in a kneeling position, supporting herself by holding onto a chair or being held under the arms by her husband, the *partera*, or a female relative.[18] After delivery, the umbilical cord was cut with a pair of scissors, and the mother was permitted to go to bed, where the placenta was delivered. The baby was given an oil bath, and the stump of the cord treated with olive oil or a mixture of baking powder and olive oil or lard. The placenta was usually burned. Postpartum hemorrhage was treated with alhucema (lavender) either by spreading dried petals over burning coals and having the woman stand in the smoke, or by applying powdered lavender to the bleeding area. *Yerba buena* was a supplementary remedy.

FOLK MEDICINE AND SCIENTIFIC MEDICINE

Anglo practice and village practice with regard to childbirth differ in several important respects. Anglo physicians, who are in a position to advise practicing midwives, recommend that the patient be delivered in bed to lessen the possibility of postpartum hemorrhage.[19] They advise that the mother should remove her clothing, that the *partera* should scrub her hands and arms with strong soap before approaching the mother, that the scissors used for severing the cord be washed in soapy water, that the mother be given a sponge bath soon after delivery. There has been a strong tendency, however, for many of the *parteras* to look upon Anglo medical ways as different from but not appreciably better than their traditional medicine and to continue to use their own more familiar methods. Or, if the Anglo methods are adopted, their efficacy may be reduced by the failure of the *partera* to grasp the reasons behind their use. The scissors, after being washed with soap, may be dried with an unsterile cloth or placed on a table that has not been cleaned. Water that has been boiled may be poured when cool into an unsterile container. The acceptance of Anglo ways may represent merely the adoption of new elements into an old pattern in which the new procedures are not understood in terms of the Anglo reasons for their use, but instead are fitted into the already existing pattern of understanding with respect to causation and healing of illness and disease. Just as Anglo medical personnel tend to see many of the Spanish-American folk practices as either worthless or dangerous, so Spanish-Americans are inclined to be skeptical about the efficacy, necessity, and safety of some of the Anglo healing practices, and may be at times reluctant to accept them. Surgical procedures, in particular, are frequently regarded as harmful, dangerous, and unnecessary, and many villagers can tell of someone who was done irreparable damage by an operation or who, being advised by an Anglo physician that an operation was absolutely necessary, was thereafter cured by some folk procedure.

The transition from Spanish-American folkways to the acceptance and use of Anglo scientific medicine is complicated by the fact that folk medical knowledge is widely disseminated, so that anyone giving medical care is subject to the critical attention of relatives and friends of the patient, who are always ready to step in and insist on changes in treatment or to add to what is being done if they feel that proper care is not being given. Thus, the *partera* who has learned some new techniques from a physician or from the training program of the State Department of Public Health may find herself constrained by the pressure of family opinion to forgo her new knowledge and to continue with old ways. Knowing as well as she what herbs may be used to hasten delivery or check postpartum bleeding, the family have provided them, and they are likely to interpret the failure of the *partera* to use them as resulting from ignorance or indifference to the welfare of the patient. They *know* these traditional remedies assure comfort and safety for the patient, and they are likely to feel that no treatment process can be good which withholds them.

Among many Spanish-American villagers, Anglo medicine is regarded as something to be used chiefly as a last resort when all other known procedures have failed. Consequently, for a long time, the Anglo record of successful treatment was less good than it need have been because too frequently Anglo practitioners were not consulted until the case was practically hopeless. Most of the successes in treatment were thus credited to folk practices; many of the failures were charged to Anglo medicine. As a result, another barrier to the acceptance of Anglo medicine was raised through the development of the belief, which could be supported by reference to known cases, that Anglo medical institutions were places where people went to die.

The continued use of their own medical practices by Spanish-Americans sometimes leads the Anglo, who knows his ways are better, to characterize Spanish-Americans as ignorant or superstitious, to accuse them of being indifferent to the well-being of their families and friends, and to become impatient and annoyed at their failure to see the obvious benefits of Anglo procedures. What such Anglos fail to appreciate is that Spanish-Americans also *know* that their ways are superior and that their use, far from constituting neglect of or indifference to the needs of sick relatives and friends, actually constitutes the provision of first-rate medical care. The Anglo may argue that by the pragmatic test of results his *is* the best medicine and that the Spanish-American ought to have enough sense to see it. But the evidence of the superiority of Anglo medicine is not always available to the Spanish-American in a form that has meaning to him and, in any case, what is or is not "good sense" is relative to culture. In utilizing his own knowledge and that of his friends, relatives, and neighbors, and when that fails, in calling in a *médica* or *curandera* or even a *bruja*, the Spanish-American villager is acting in a way that is eminently sensible in the light of his convictions about the nature of disease and the proper ways to deal with it. To behave otherwise, to disregard what he knows and subject himself or a member of his family to a course of treatment that may bear no particular relationship to his understanding of disease, simply because some Anglos say that it is what he should do, would constitute a very strange kind of behavior indeed.

Sickness, particularly if it be serious, is likely to be viewed as a crisis, and in situations of crisis people in all cultures tend to resort to those patterns of thinking and acting that have been most deeply ingrained in them as a result of their cultural experiences. To meet a crisis with the resources of one's culture, whatever they may be, is to behave in a manner that is both sensible and sound; it is, in fact, to behave in the only way that most human beings can under such circumstances. The Spanish-American, in utilizing the medical ways of his culture is neither ignorant nor indifferent. If he knew no way of dealing with illness, he might be called ignorant. But he does know something to do, frequently many things. If he did nothing, he might be called indifferent. But he does something, and continues to do something while his resources remain undepleted or until he achieves results. The sequence in which he does things is determined by the differential value he places on the various procedures as they apply to the particular situation. If the seeking of Anglo medical care is, for a given illness, well down on the list, it is because this is the way he sees the particular procedure in relation to the others that are available to him. That an Anglo, in a similar situation, might have a different set of resources and a different order of importance for them, cannot be expected to have any considerable influence on his behavior.

Folk Practitioners

Although folk medicine is in general known by all members of a cultural group, some persons, because of age, experience, or special interest, may have a more extensive knowledge than their neighbors and friends and thus acquire a somewhat specialized status. The *partera*, or midwife, is an example of such a person. In the field of general medicine, *médicas* and *curanderas*, whose knowledge of herbs and household remedies is somewhat greater than that of the general population, perform a similar function, being called upon for assistance when a medical problem gets beyond the competence of the patient or his relatives. None of them, of course, is a specialist in the Anglo sense of having a specialized kind of training and being given distinctive formal recognition (licensure) for their skill. But they are specialists in the sense that they are considered to have a greater knowledge of medical matters than other people in the population and perform a specialized function. Like *parteras*, *médicas* and *curanderas* expect to be paid for their services, either in goods or in cash, and, like Anglo practitioners, they are called upon to do a certain amount of "charity" work for which they are not paid. In most instances, the commercial part of the transaction is definitely subordinated, although in urban areas where close village relationships are no longer possible, *médicas* and *curanderas* are likely to regard themselves and to be regarded as impersonal purveyors of medicines and services, and the commercial element in the relationship is quite prominent.

One type of "specialist" with no exact counterpart in Anglo folk or scientific medicine is the *bruja* or witch, whose extensive command of both the malevolent and benevolent techniques of witchcraft makes her a person both sought after and feared. Although a belief in magical powers is becoming less and less respectable, there are few Spanish-speaking communities in the Southwest that do not include among their inhabitants one or more persons known to be witches. Their continued activity has made possible the rise of another "specialty," that of the *albolaria* whose particular skill is the ability to thwart or render harmless the evil powers of *brujas*. Not many Spanish-speaking will admit a belief in witches any more, but nearly everyone can tell about someone else who believes in them, and it can be noted that the services of *albolarias* continue to be in demand.

The general patterns of behavior of both rural and urban Spanish-Americans with respect to illness and therapy are almost always a mixture of elements from their own and Anglo culture. A number of Spanish-Americans interviewed in the San Luis Valley of Colorado in 1952 indicated that in general they utilized the services of both folk and Anglo scientific medical practitioners, and that their knowledge of remedies for various conditions included items drawn from both cultures. One *médica*, who also performs as a *partera*, serves patients from many surrounding communities and works closely with an Anglo physician in caring for her maternity cases. When pregnant women come to her, they are sent to the doctor for a blood test and a "check-up" after which, if everything seems normal, they return to her for the actual delivery. Most of the deliveries take place in her home. Difficult cases are delivered by the doctor and in a hospital. For the treatment of other than maternity cases the *médica* uses remedies that she obtains by mail from supply houses in San Antonio and Trinidad.[20]

Nearly everyone interviewed knew of *médicas* and *curanderas* practicing in the vicinity, and many made no particular distinction between the services they offered and those available from Anglo physicians. The *médica* mentioned above thinks that many people do not like doctors and hospitals because they are afraid of both. Many women who come to see her, she said, refuse to go to the physician for a check-up and can be persuaded to do so only when she threatens to withhold her assistance. A man who was interviewed said that he does not consult a doctor until he is "about dead." He and his wife have four children, two of whom were delivered by *parteras* and two by physicians. He knows a good deal about folk remedies and uses them for himself and his family when indicated. A large proportion of his acquaintances use folk remedies, and a few have told him that they would not go to a doctor under any circumstances. One woman reported that a physician who came into the area just before the turn of the century used to take her mother, a *médica*, with him on his calls. By allowing her to make diagnoses and prescribe treatments, the mother said, he was able to learn the value of her *remedios* and later to use them in his own practice.

In cities, as well as in rural areas, the medical practices of Spanish-Americans continue to be a mixture of elements of both cultures, although because of greater availability of Anglo medicine, the somewhat better financial status of many Spanish-speaking persons, and a higher level of acculturation, Anglo medicine is used proportionately more in cities than in the country. *Remedios*, including both Anglo patent preparations and medicinal herbs, are sold in the "Mexican" sections of cities and large towns, and one who has need of the services of a *médica* or *curandera* does not have far to look for them. In addition to giving service, they will also prescribe and sell medicine.

No precise studies have been made of the extent to which Spanish-speaking people of the Southwest use one or another of the several types of medical aid available to them for particular kinds of illness. One small survey of a group of families living in Fort Collins, Colorado, showed a greater acceptance of Anglo practices by young people than by the older folk, but a rather large use of Anglo procedures by persons of all ages.[21] Another study of Colorado migrant families living in four agricultural areas of Colorado gives some evidence on the observed and re-ported use of Anglo medical personnel, facilities, and practices, but no comparative information on the use of folk medicine.[22] In this report a physician is quoted as saying, "We know that com-municable diseases are present among the migrants. The fatalistic acceptance of the situation, plus their poverty, makes the problem of medical care a critical one. Tuberculosis, enteritis, smallpox, typhoid fever, dysentery, and venereal diseases have been more often detected by accident or search by public health officials than by patients voluntarily seeking medical assistance."[23] A conspicuous finding of this study was that health and medical care services were not widely used by the migrants observed. Of 1,098 persons from whom information was obtained, 947 had not seen a doctor during the preceding year, and 955 of 1,101 per-sons giving information had not visited a dentist during that period. Of those who had consulted a dentist, the majority wanted extractions or went to get relief for a toothache. Of the few who had gone for prophylactic reasons, all were persons who had served in the armed forces or were members of households where there were ex-army personnel. Just over 42 per cent of the 631 children reported on had been vaccinated for smallpox; only a fifth had been immunized against whooping cough, and about the same proportion against diphtheria. Nine out of ten migrants above seven years of age had not been hospitalized at any time during the previous five years, and only 15 per cent had undergone physical examinations during that period, the majority of these having occurred during an illness or as a requirement for a job.

REASONS FOR ANGLO MEDICINE NOT BEING MORE EXTENSIVELY USED

A number of explanations can be found for the failure of Spanish-speaking people in close contact with Anglo culture to adopt completely its medical ways. One such factor is certainly the extent to which Anglo medical services and facilities are available. Although the Spanish-speaking are rapidly becoming urbanized, many of them still live in rural areas where medical personnel and facilities are not readily available. Large numbers of Spanish-speaking people live in sparsely settled areas where one has to drive many miles to see a physician or enter a hospital. A map of health facilities in New Mexico, prepared in 1946 for the New Mexico Health Council, showed four counties to be completely without medical facilities and a large part of the state to lie outside a 30-mile radius from any type of health facility.[24] In parts of Colorado, Arizona, and Texas, similar conditions exist. The present widespread distribution of automobiles and recent improvements in rural roads have done much to make Anglo medicine more readily available to rural Spanish-speaking people and have undoubtedly contributed to its somewhat greater use. But there still remain many areas where, either because of sparseness of population or a high concentration of Spanish-speaking people among the residents of the areas, it would be quite difficult to get to an Anglo doctor or hospital even if one were highly motivated to do so.

Another factor related to availability is that of cost. Anglo medical care is expensive and the Spanish-speaking, as a group, are poor. In many instances they cannot afford, or do not feel that they can afford, the services of a physician or a sojourn in a hospital. Anglo medicine involves bills for home or office calls, some likelihood of being given an expensive prescription, and the possibility of surgery, or hospitalization for some other reason, which may be very costly. A *médica* usually does not charge much and under certain circumstances can be paid with products instead of cash, a definite advantage to those living in rural areas. Her medicines are not likely to cost much, and there is little likelihood that she will recommend hospitalization or an operation. Diagnosis and treatment by oneself and one's family cost little or nothing, and for many minor illnesses can be quite satisfactory. These differences in costs certainly constitute an influence in the readiness or reluctance with which an individual or family makes the decision to seek any given type of medical care.

Lack of knowledge of Anglo medical ways is probably another factor in the extent to which Spanish-speaking people do or do not use Anglo practitioners and facilities. The simple matter of getting in touch with a doctor and putting oneself under his care can seem complicated to a person who is not at ease in either the English language or Anglo medical culture. How does one find a doctor? How can one be sure that the chosen doctor will be either competent or *simpatico?* How is a doctor approached? How can one know in advance how much the treatment will cost or what will be the expected manner of payment? What illnesses may properly be taken to a physician? These and other questions, the answers to which most of us take for granted, can be puzzling to persons not wholly familiar with Anglo culture, and can be effective barriers to the initiation of a doctor-patient relationship, particularly when the potential patient may not be highly motivated in the direction of wanting Anglo medicine.

Closely related to a lack of knowledge of Anglo medical ways as a deterrent to seeking Anglo medical care is the factor of fear. That which is strange or unknown is often feared, and there is much in Anglo medicine that is strange and fear inducing even to Anglo laymen. The instruments used, the pain that sometimes accompanies their use, and the unfamiliar surroundings of the office, clinic, or hospital in which they are used, all can arouse fear. So can the unfamiliar elements in the medical routine— the examination procedure, the invasion of one's physical and mental privacy, the uncertainty of the diagnostic procedure, the incomprehensible language that may be used. For a Spanish-speaking person, for example, a physical examination can be a very unpleasant experience, particularly if it involves the participation of persons of the opposite sex. The fear of being examined by a man is sometimes enough to keep Spanish-speaking women away from Anglo medical practitioners and to make traumatic for others the contact they have with Anglo medicine. Foster reports the failure of a considerable proportion of women coming to a prenatal clinic in Mexico City to return for a follow-up visit after their initial experience, which included an unexpected physical examination.[25] It is not without significance for the medical relations of Spanish-speaking and Anglos in the Southwest that most of the healing personnel in the culture of the Spanish-speaking are women, whereas proportionately more of those in the Anglo culture are men. Spanish-speaking men, too, are likely to have some reluctance to subjecting themselves to examination by Anglo physicians and to being placed in potentially embarrassing situations with Anglo nurses.

Another possible factor that may operate is resistance to being separated from one's family and being isolated for an indefinite time in an Anglo institution, where all relationships are likely to be impersonal. Good medical care, from the Anglo point of view, requires hospitalization for many conditions. Good medical care, as defined in the culture of the Spanish-Americans, requires that the patient be treated for almost any condition at home by relatives and friends, who are constantly in attendance and who provide emotional support as well as the technical skills required in treatment. In time of sickness one expects his family to surround and support him, and to supervise closely and critically, if not actually carry on, the treatment process. Members of the family, in turn, feel obligated to remain close to the patient, to take charge of his treatment, and to reassure him as to his place in and importance to the family group. The Anglo practice of hospitalization, with the treatment being taken over by professional strangers and the family relegated to the meager role permitted by the visiting regulations, runs counter to the expectation patterns of the Spanish-speaking and, thus, may be a factor in the reluctance of some members of the group to seek or accept Anglo medical care.

There are some illnesses for which Anglo medical care is not sought because, as has already been noted, the type of sickness is not ordinarily known to Anglo practitioners. A patient suffering from *mal ojo*, *susto*, and similar conditions seeks relief, if at all, from someone who is familiar with these diseases and who, therefore, may be expected to know something about the proper method of treatment. This difference between the two cultures in the conceptualization of disease serves to restrict the range of conditions for which Anglo medical assistance might be sought to those recognized by both cultural groups and gives to the folk practitioner almost exclusive influence in dealing with those conditions that are recognized only by the Spanish-speaking group.

A final factor that may be mentioned as possibly contributing to the hesitancy of Spanish-speaking people to use Anglo medicine is that such attempts as are made often do not provide the satisfactions that the Spanish-speaking expect. With the *curandera* and *médica* the whole process of diagnosis and treatment moves along in an atmosphere of informal cooperation and collaboration between patient, family, and the healer. Alternative procedures are discussed and courses of treatment agreed upon, with the opinions of patient and family frequently being given much weight in the final decisions. The folk practitioner works less as an independent specialist than as a consultant and technician who implements the therapeutic plans of the patient or his family, all of whom remain very much in the picture throughout the treatment period. All know what is going on and why. All are free to offer suggestions and criticisms. The diagnosis and treatment of illness thus involve active participation by the patient and members of his family in a situation in which the relationships are mainly personal and informal. Diagnosis is usually easy and swift, and treatment follows immediately.

By contrast, Anglo medicine is likely to be somewhat impersonal and formal. It is expected that the patient will be turned over to the physician, who will then direct the diagnostic and treatment procedures, largely without the benefit of advice or suggestion from either the patient or his family. Information may be sought from both, but usually only for the purpose of getting at the present complaints or learning the patient's medical history. Diagnosis may be slow and may involve techniques that are not understood by the patient or his family. Treatment may be delayed pending the establishment of a definite diagnosis and, when instituted, may involve hospitalization of the patient. The patient and his family are expected to be relatively passive participants in a situation in which most of the new relationships established are impersonal, businesslike, and, frequently, very unsatisfactory. In treatment by either folk practitioner or physician the possible range of outcomes is about the same. The patient may get better, may remain as he is, may get worse, may die. There being no conclusive evidence of the relatively greater frequency of desirable results when using Anglo medicine than when relying on folk healers, the amount of satisfaction that patient and family get in the medical relationship becomes an important factor in determining which of the two types of medicine they will select.

The most important differences between Spanish-American folk medicine and Anglo scientific medicine that influence the choice of one or the other are these: Anglo scientific medicine involves largely impersonal relations, procedures unfamiliar to laymen, a passive role for family members, hospital care, considerable control of the situation by professional healers, and high costs; by contrast the folk medicine of Spanish-American villagers is largely a matter of personal relations, familiar procedures, active family participation, home care, a large degree of control of the situation by the patient or his family, and relatively low costs. Given these differences, it is easy to understand why a considerable motivation would be necessary for a Spanish-American to have any strong preference for Anglo medicine over that which is not only more familiar and possibly psychologically more rewarding—or at least less punishing—but also less expensive.

Despite the many factors that operate to hinder the seeking and acceptance of Anglo medical care by Spanish-speaking people of the Southwest, however, Anglo medicine is rapidly coming to play an increasingly larger part in the total complex of attitudes and activities of the Spanish-speaking people with respect to illness and health. In cities where Anglo medical facilities and personnel are accessible, the use made of them by the Spanish-speaking probably is not greatly different in either amount or kind from that of Anglos of comparable social class status. In some rural areas, activities of private practitioners, medical groups, health cooperatives, local and state health departments, and, particularly, public health nurses have brought a considerable amount of Anglo medicine within the reach of Spanish-speaking people and have done much to develop the attitudes necessary to the acceptance and use of Anglo medical ways. If we think of the Spanish-speaking population as distributed along a continuum ranging from complete reliance on their own folk medicine at one pole to the complete acceptance of Anglo scientific medicine at the other, the greatest numbers would be concentrated near the center, with the highest proportion probably being found on the Anglo half of the continuum.

The families who live at 1407 Felicity Street in Arcadia illustrate a few of the many positions that might be found on such a continuum. Although Pedro Treviño has lived all his life in the United States and nearly twenty years in cities, he has little or no understanding of Anglo medicine and feels no particular need for it. His approach to illness and health is based on knowledge acquired in the New Mexican village of his childhood. Discomfort and pain are to be relieved when possible, endured when they cannot be alleviated. Health is so taken for granted that it is hardly conceptualized at all. Illness and pain are simply unpleasant interruptions of a normal condition. If not too insistent or too prolonged, they can be ignored; only if they interfere to any extent with his accustomed routines or become too unpleasant does he feel that he should try to do anything about them. And then he does whatever is easy and familiar from long usage. Pedro's hernia goes untreated because effective treatment is not possible within the range of his own knowledge of what to do, and because the discomfort it causes does not constitute sufficient motivation to overcome his lack of understanding of

Anglo medicine, his latent fear of surgery and hospitalization, and his generalized reluctance to enter into more than a bare minimum of relationships with Anglos. His seeming indifference to the medical needs of his daughter Linda derives in part from the fact that to him Linda is not sick. She is not in pain; she has no outstanding symptoms that are observable to him; she is able to behave in a more or less normal fashion. Since she does not show signs of illness, she is not defined as ill, and not being ill she is not entitled to the special consideration and treatment which are the privilege of the sick.

Alessandro Flores, the boarder in the Treviños' apartment, thought his hospitalization for symptoms of silicosis was quite unnecessary and, in spite of the efforts on the part of the hospital personnel to make his stay there comfortable and pleasant, he was uneasy and afraid and lonely and was very glad to get out. From his point of view, living with the Treviños is far better than being in a sanitarium or a nursing home, even though he might get more adequate care in either than is now available to him.

Virginia Gurule's health worries are not about her chronic fatigue, her swollen ankles, or her shortness of breath after exertion. She is rather concerned and hesitant and a little frightened about something that her Anglo doctor considers to be for her benefit. Hospital delivery is familiar and commonplace to him. It is strange and terrifying to her. Physically, Virginia would probably be better off in a hospital at the time of her confinement; emotionally, the experience could again be a very traumatic one. Rafael Gurule's excursions into Anglo medicine have not made a deep impression on him. The chiropractor whom he saw for his "rheumatism" was not able to give him any relief, and his experiences with the outpatient clinic of the Arcadia public hospital were not such as to develop in him any great conviction of the superiority of Anglo medicine. In his one real sickness he and his wife turned first to a *médica* and were satisfied with the treatment he received. So far folk medicine has met his needs in a manner that he considers to be satisfactory, and he is not motivated to go far beyond it.

Of all the residents of 1407 Felicity Street, Simoneta Roybal has perhaps had the most extensive contacts with Anglo medicine. Her years in a sanitarium and her experiences during the delivery and later hospitalization of her daughter have provided opportunities to observe and participate in Anglo medical ways. But because of her personal limitations, her lack of any formal education, and her slight understanding of any but the most superficial aspects of Anglo culture, she has not been able to profit much from her experiences. Her own health and that of her daughter have been neglected and will continue to be because Simoneta's personality and her lack of adjustment to Anglo ways represent almost insuperable barriers to the acquisition of knowledge and attitudes necessary to proper health protection and maintenance. From the Anglo point of view Simoneta *ought* to be concerned about her own health and about that of her daughter. She *ought* to develop some interest in and plans for the future for both of them. That she appears indifferent both to her present condition and future prospects is in large part due to factors that are not directly related to her cultural background—her intellectual limitations, her meager experience, her lack of family ties, and her migratory history—which prevented her from forming any close and lasting relationships with anyone. Simoneta would be a problem case regardless of her cultural background. But the fact that she is Spanish-American and thus, to some extent, unfamiliar with Anglo ways, complicates the problem of dealing with her.

In matters of health, the Atencios more nearly follow the Anglo patterns than do any of the other families in the apartment building. Through their reading of magazines and newspapers and their attention to Anglo radio programs, they have access to much popular information about health and medicine. As do many Anglos, they accept what they read and hear and spend a substantial amount of money each month on the preparations and appliances they learn about. Vitamins, antihistamines, laxatives, reducing aids, aspirin tablets, and other popular Anglo medications are frequently used both for minor ailments and for the prevention of illness. Their use of a *médica* for the treatment of

Rachel's kidney infection is outside the regular pattern of Anglo medicine, although the use of lay practitioners and marginal professionals is not uncommon among Anglos on the socio-economic level of the Atencios. It is perhaps of some significance that Rachel Atencio, like Alessandro Flores, Virginia Gurule, and Linda Treviño, was not satisfied with her hospital experience and sought other and less competent medical assistance. In all four cases a major reason was a lack of understanding about their condition and what was being done for it. A part of that lack of understanding was certainly due to cultural differences between those giving the hospital and medical care and those receiving it. But in the case of Rachel Atencio, and to a lesser extent in that of the others, a good part of the difficulty lay in the failure of the Anglo hospital personnel to provide information to the patients about their own illness and treatment.

María Vigil does not understand the nature of her illness and is not consciously aware of the fact that she may be infecting her children. She feels well and, to her, that is an indication of good health. She made a long step in the direction of accepting Anglo medicine when she took three of the children to a clinic for im-munization about a year ago, but the reactions to the "shots" were mildly unpleasant to the children and quite unexpected by her, so that she has not returned. She sees no reason why well children should be given treatments that make them sick. The dental caries of the children, as long as they do not produce tooth-aches, do not trouble her; nor do the bowed legs of Ruby, which she regards as somewhat unfortunate but of no particular con-sequence. Bowed legs are not very troubling to a baby nine months of age, and since the future remains largely unimagined by Maria, the possible future consequences of present conditions do not motivate her to any action. As a family, the Vigils have no great resistance to Anglo medicine—except when it involves the hospitalization and consequent separation of María from the family group—but neither do they have any strong motivation toward it and, in the absence of any condition that they define as serious or that causes considerable pain or discomfort to some member of the family, they are unlikely to initiate any contact with it.

The Rubios are perhaps the most actively resistant to Anglo medicine of any of the family groups living at 1407. The grandmother, Josefina, not only has a wide store of folk knowledge about illness and health, but also some positive views about the relative merits of the medicine she knows and that practiced by Anglo physicians and other medical personnel. Her service as a *partera* and the frequent consultations she gives her neighbors and friends on medical matters have won her the reputation of being a competent lay practitioner. Because of her attitude and prestige and the lack of any firm conviction by Concepción, the daughter-in-law, about illness and its treatment, the old lady sets the medical pattern for the whole Rubio family. While she remains alive and active, there is little likelihood of much receptivity to Anglo medical ideas or methods.

Like many other Spanish-speaking families, the inhabitants of 1407 Felicity Street represent a blend of acceptance of, indifference to, and resistance toward Anglo medicine with the particular attitude and behavior of a given family depending on varying experiences of the individual members and the total family group. Like people everywhere, the Spanish-speaking are motivated to do something about conditions which cause them discomfort or pain or which they define as illness. Like people everywhere, they do whatever seems appropriate to them, within the limits set by their material and intellectual resources. And they are more likely to do, among the range of things felt to be appropriate, whatever is easy and familiar rather than follow a course that may be difficult and strange. To the extent that "Spanish" folk medical techniques are known, are thought appropriate, and are available, they are used; similarly, Anglo "scientific" medical ways may be utilized if they are known, are available, and are thought appropriate.

The problem for Anglo medical professional personnel who work with Spanish-speaking people is to estimate the degree to which differences in attitudes, beliefs, and practices may affect their professional relationships and, in given cases, to modify their approaches and procedures to allow for such differences. How such estimates may be made and what directions such modifications might take will be considered in the chapter that follows.

Chapter V

BRIDGING THE GAP

IN PRECEDING CHAPTERS INFORMATION has been given about the number, distribution, and other characteristics of the Spanish-speaking people of the Southwest. Cultural differences between them and the Anglo population have been discussed and indication given that there may also be important subcultural differences between Anglo medical and health personnel and the Spanish-speaking individuals and families with whom they work. Some of the characteristics of the folk medicine used by Spanish-speaking people have been described, and mention has been made of factors in the culturally derived attitudes and practices of both groups and in the broad situations in which various subgroups among the Spanish-speaking population live that have operated to limit the quality and quantity of health and medical services they receive.

While it is hoped that the preceding discussions may have some intrinsic interest and value of their own, a primary reason for including them has been to provide a background of information against which to consider the problem with which this chapter is concerned: How can the influence of cultural and subcultural differences be reduced so that more and better health services and medical care can be provided for the Spanish-speaking population of the Southwest? A somewhat more general, but still related, question to which attention will be given here is: How can more and better health services and medical care be provided to any population whose members differ culturally or subculturally from those who have a professional responsibility to provide them? Some implications for the still more general question of how to give better health services and medical care to all should be expected from the discussion of our two more limited questions, but this problem is outside the scope of this book. The context within which these questions will be approached is not that of how to advance the frontiers of knowledge in the physical and biological sciences in order to develop improved techniques for the control of health and disease. It is, rather, that of how we can re-structure our social relationships and arrangements in order to make better use of the knowledge and techniques we already have, as well as those that may be devised.

Because of differences in the people themselves and in the circumstances under which they live, it seems best to give separate consideration to the rural and urban Spanish-speaking populations and then to take up the more general topic of what can be done to institute more effective practices and relationships across cultural and subcultural lines.

THE RURAL SITUATION

Generalizations can be better grasped when related to specific situations. For that reason and because the rural Spanish-speaking people are such a heterogeneous population that any attempt to consider them all would be so general as to be meaningless or so filled with tedious detail as to be incomprehensible, this discussion will largely be limited to two areas, Taos County, in New Mexico, and Costilla County, just across the state boundary in Colorado.[1] Each is predominantly rural; each has a high proportion of Spanish-Americans in the population; and both in recent years have been the scenes of rather ambitious attempts to set up programs to provide improved health services and medical care.

Taos County Cooperative Health Association

On October 1, 1942, the Taos County Cooperative Health Association began giving service to 907 paid-up member families in Taos County, New Mexico. At the time of its inauguration the Association had the formal approval and active support of the Taos County Medical Society, the benefit of financial aid and several types of nonmedical professional service from the Farm

Security Administration, and a background of interest and planning effort by the Taos County Project, an experiment in adult education undertaken in 1940 by the University of New Mexico and the Harwood Foundation with funds made available by the Carnegie Corporation of New York. The purpose of the Association was to provide medical care at the lowest possible cost to low-income families of Taos County, most of whom were Spanish-American and lived in fairly isolated communities far from a physician, clinic, or hospital.

Health conditions in Taos County at that time were not good. In the period 1937–1939, 64 per cent of the deaths reported had been listed as from "cause unknown," indicating that no physician was handling the case at the time of death, and in 1941 no death certificates had been issued for 62 per cent of those who died. Of the 1,629 births occurring in the 1937–1939 period, 1,122 babies were delivered by midwives, few of whom had had any formal training, and 193 by other persons with probably even less training.[2] The infant mortality rate was among the highest in the nation. For many families in the County, consulting a doctor meant a long and time-consuming trip into Taos or a very expensive mileage charge for a physician who might be persuaded to make a home call.

The Association set out to provide medical and dental care, clinic service, and hospitalization in a manner that would be convenient for the people and at a price they could afford to pay. Health centers were set up at three strategic points—Taos, Questa, and Peñasco—with each being staffed by a full-time registered nurse and visited on a regular schedule by physicians and dentists. Drugs were supplied on prescription by private drugstores or by the Association's dispensary; hospitalization was made available at Taos and Embudo; ambulance service was provided; and consultation or treatment by specialists was furnished when necessary. The cost of these services during the first year of operation amounted to $38.03 for each of the 1,145 families enrolled, of which more than 80 per cent was paid by a subsidy from the Farm Security Administration. No family paid more than $32; none paid less than $1.00. The average amount paid per family for complete medical and dental care was $3.75 per year.[3]

Here, it would seem, was an enterprise that could not fail. Here was a serious medical need that an organization had been set up to meet. Here was good medical care made available at a cost (including the Farm Security Administration's subsidy) of less than $8.00 per year per person. And yet, in spite of tremendous efforts, membership in the Association steadily declined until, in 1948, it ceased to function.

The causes for the failure of the Taos County Cooperative Health Association are many and complex and no satisfactory study of them has as yet been made. But one major cause was that the Association attempted to provide Anglo medical care to a people who were not yet culturally ready to receive or support it.[4]

Although the people of Taos County were among the first Spanish-Americans to come in contact with Anglos from the East as a result of the infiltration of their area by trappers and "mountain-men" in the early 1800's, and although the village of Taos is a tourist center of national repute, a large proportion of the population has remained relatively isolated. Having had but little contact with Anglo medicine and few opportunities to benefit from it, the people had long before worked out ways of handling, in a manner reasonably satisfactory to them, their problems of illness and disease. There is little in the record of the Taos Cooperative to indicate that the people of the County were averse to Anglo medical care. On the contrary, the records of the first year of operation shows that considerable use was made of the Association's services by member families. But the degree of acceptance was not such as to indicate marked preference for Anglo medicine over more traditional ways of dealing with sickness and its consequences, and it certainly was not great enough to enable the Association to become self-supporting when the financial subsidy of the Farm Security Administration was withdrawn. The evidence seems to be that the Taoseños were willing to accept Anglo medical care when it was brought to them and when the costs were largely paid by somebody else, but that they were not willing or able to keep the organization going or to pay

for medical care—at least through the Cooperative—when outside financial and administrative support was no longer given.

It is probable that many of the members of the Association never understood much about the organization or their relationship to it. Some indication that this was so is given in a study made at the end of the first year of operation of the Association.[5] This study, based on a random sample of about a tenth of the membership, showed that nearly 80 per cent of the family members interviewed had little or no knowledge of the purpose for which the organization was set up; that 40 per cent did not know the manager; 22 per cent did not know that the Association had a Board of Directors; that only 40 per cent could name one or more of its members; and that while over half knew how much their first year's fees were, less than half had any clear notion of how the amount of the fee had been determined. Five, about 15 per cent of the sample families interviewed, had paid for a midwife's services during the preceding year, even though hospitalization and delivery by a physician were included in the Association membership, and two families utilized the professional services of local healers. This lack of knowledge about the Association undoubtedly was an important factor in its subsequent failure, particularly among a people with no tradition of formal organization and with a custom of much personal relationship in all affairs.

Without attempting to assess the relative weight of all the factors responsible for the failure of the Taos County Cooperative Health Association, it can be fairly said that those responsible for planning and carrying out the program did not sufficiently take into account the factor of culture. This conclusion is supported by the experience of the Costilla County Health Association which, established a few years after the Taos project, limped along with diminishing membership for about six years and then also ceased to exist.

Costilla County Health Association

Costilla County, Colorado, is located in the San Luis Valley just across the state line from Taos County. The populations of the two counties are alike in that each consists of a rural, largely

Spanish-American group, somewhat isolated from the main centers of economic, political, health, and educational activity of its state. As a result of the promotional efforts of a member of the faculty of Adams State College, who had observed the activities of the Taos County health project and who was aware of the Farm Security Administration policy to help rural areas acquire more adequate medical facilities, a general meeting of the people of Costilla County was called in 1945 to discuss the health situation. At this meeting an organization was set up and officers were elected and charged with the responsibility of exploring the possibility of obtaining financial aid from the government.[6] Dissension within the group broke up this organization before anything could be accomplished, but early in 1946 a second general meeting was called, under the sponsorship of the San Luis Service Club, at which the Costilla County Health Association was formed and a Board of Directors elected.

With technical assistance from the Farm Security Administration, the Association worked out plans for a voluntary health cooperative which, it was hoped, would help to meet the medical needs of the County. A tentative budget of approximately $20,000 a year was decided on, with which it was thought provision could be made for one physician, two nurses, a manager, a clerk, a janitor, and a cook. The doctor was to be guaranteed a minimum salary of $6,000 from the Association, plus 36 per cent of the fees he received from practice among nonmembers. The Association was to assume the full cost of all overhead and in return was to receive 64 per cent of all returns from nonmember practice. It was estimated that a membership of 540 families, each of whom would pay $38 a year for medical service, would be needed to maintain the organization. For their family fee, members would be entitled to a physical examination, diagnostic services, treatment by a physician, such ordinary drugs as might customarily be dispensed from a doctor's bag, emergency home calls and emergency treatment at the Association's health center, obstetrical care either at home or at the center, pre- and postnatal examinations and advice, ambulance service from home to the center and from the center to the hospital at Alamosa, minor operations including tonsillectomies, immunizations, venereal disease treatment, and prescriptions. In order to avoid some of the difficulties of the Taos County Cooperative, it was decided that services of the Costilla Association should be self-supporting from the very beginning, with the Farm Security Administration providing funds only for the initial outlays for a center building, water supply, clinic equipment, and an ambulance.

On the basis of these decisions the Board of Directors of the Association and the San Luis Service Club began a membership drive. Meetings were held in every community in the County to acquaint the people with the Association's plans and to enroll them as members.

Near the end of May, 1946, when it appeared that the membership drive would be successful, the Board of Directors rented a building, equipped an office, employed a manager-solicitor, and began to look for a physician. The Farm Security Administration drew up blueprints for a health center building and the Association, not without some political jockeying, acquired a building site.

In spite of rather strenuous efforts made by the organizers and the cooperation they received from the newspapers, a radio station, churches, and business groups, memberships came in slowly and by June the number was still far short of the goal of 540 families. A former president of the Association has suggested several factors that might have contributed to the reluctance of people to become members. The type of program proposed by the Association was new in the area and at the time of the membership drive it existed only on paper. There was as yet no physician associated with it, and those who joined and paid for a membership would have to go to Alamosa for medical treatment until the program had actually begun. Furthermore, there was no assurance that the doctor employed would be "good," or that members would like him. Not all of those who participated in the membership drive were able to answer accurately the questions asked, and some misinformation was given to prospective members. Rumors, usually based on erroneous information, circulated in the County. The timing of the drive was bad for a rural agricultural people, who could not be expected to have much ready cash in the spring. The interest of some businessmen was lukewarm, and there was mild opposition from a small group of physicians in an adjoining county.

Late in the summer, however, the goal of 540 memberships was reached (135 of these families had paid only $10 and agreed to pay the remaining $28 when the doctor arrived), and the Farm Security Administration made a grant to the Association of $41,950 for a building and equipment. A physician was hired in November and the Association began giving service on December 1. In addition to the doctor, the staff consisted of two nurses, a receptionist-clerk, a bookkeeper, a janitor, and a part-time manager, who divided his time between the Taos and Costilla County associations. Clinic equipment was obtained and a station wagon, which could double as an ambulance, was purchased.

The doctor was well received by many of the people of the County and soon had more work than he could comfortably handle. Within a radius of 20 miles of San Luis, where the center was located, are 10 towns and villages which he was expected to serve; in addition, he frequently had patients in the hospital at Alamosa 40 miles away. As one board member phrased it, with almost classic understatement: "By the time the doctor made at least one trip to Alamosa, kept his office hours, made his regular house calls in the County, and went on a few emergency night calls, he had worked a full day."

Although the Association seemed to run smoothly enough, there were present from the first knotty problems which, in time, were to wreck it. One of these was the apathy of the members, who participated only to the extent of using the medical facilities and contributed little or nothing to the promotional and organizational work needed to keep the Association functioning. The first annual meeting, scheduled for February, 1947, drew fewer than 30 members. A second meeting called two months later also failed to attract the necessary attendance to constitute a quorum. It was not until July that enough members could be brought together to hold a business session, and then the meeting was possible only because the Association was on the verge of collapse.

A second persistent problem was that of memberships. At no time did the number of paid-up members exceed 405, which was considerably short of the 540 needed to keep the organization solvent. Many of the 135 who had paid $10 and pledged the rest dropped out after receiving service for three months. The doctor's salary was based on the number of members ($1.00 a month per member), so that as the membership went down his salary decreased proportionately. By June, after only six months of operation, the situation was so serious that he was considering resigning when his contract expired. Fearing the loss of the Farm Security Administration grant, which had not been spent, businessmen in the County took the lead in reviving the membership campaign. As a result, by late July of 1947 the number had climbed to 544, but only 287 of these represented paid-up members and the remaining 257 consisted of $10 pledges, few of which were ever converted to paid-up memberships. From this point the membership went steadily downward until, in 1952, the Association ceased to function.[7]

Closely related to the problem of membership was that of the collection of fees. Under his contract the physician was permitted to perform many services not provided by the Association, for which he was expected to make additional charges. He also served nonmember patients, with the Association receiving 64 per cent of the amount derived from this source. It was one thing to assess fees, however, and another to collect them. In one month, for example, statements totaling some $2,000 were sent out and payments totaling only $190 received.

In spite of the difficulties the first physician stayed on for a second year. During that year plans for the health center were finished and bids solicited. However, building costs had increased rapidly between the time the Farm Security grant was made and the letting of the bids, so that when bids were received it was found that there were not enough funds to construct the building as planned.

By 1948 membership was down to 90. The doctor left the Association that year and was succeeded by another within a month. In 1949 the membership was 60. The directors had been working zealously to readjust their building plans in accordance with the money available, but by the time modifications were approved in Washington, building costs had again risen and there was still not enough money for the center.

The Board of Directors elected in July, 1947, continued to serve through subsequent years because it was never possible to attract enough members to a business meeting to elect another board. Meetings were called each year, in accordance with the by-laws, but at no time was there a quorum.

In 1953 a physician was still in the County, doing private practice, and using some of the Association's equipment, under an arrangement worked out with the directors. Most of the Farm Security Administration grant remained unspent, although the Costilla Association's board had agreed to transfer approximately $20,000 of the money to a community in another county whenever this community could show that an additional $20,000 would enable it to begin construction of a projected hospital.[8]

The experiences of Taos and Costilla counties, in trying to organize health programs for a rural, Spanish-speaking group, have been described in some detail to illustrate how difficult it is to provide Anglo medical care to people of a somewhat different cultural orientation, without adapting the program to the customs, the values, and the needs of the people for whom the program is intended—as they see them.[9] The Costilla County program, like that of Taos County, had the benefit of sound professional advice and guidance in the planning and organizational stages. But the plans and the organizational work were predicated largely on Anglo motivations, goals, and practices rather than on those of the Spanish-speaking population. In both instances natively Spanish-speaking persons participated actively, and in Taos County the formation of a health association was preceded by a period of fairly intensive efforts, in which Spanish-Americans shared, to stimulate people to become aware of their problems and of the resources available. However, even without knowing the specific individuals involved in planning and organizing, it can be said that they probably came from the most, rather than the least, acculturated elements in the Spanish-speaking population, and thus approached their task more with the perspective of the Anglo than with that of the somewhat less acculturated Spanish-American population to be served by the new organizations.

The histories of the Taos and Costilla health associations suggest that there is nothing in Anglo medicine *per se* that makes it unacceptable to Spanish-speaking people. In both instances considerable use was made of the facilities and services by those who were entitled or needed to use them.

The Spanish-speaking people of the Southwest, like those of the Latin American countries studied by Foster and his colleagues,[10] are pragmatic enough to accept Anglo medicine when it can be demonstrated to be technically superior to and thus more effective than their own traditional medicine. But technical considerations are not the only factors in determining what kind of medical assistance, if any, an individual or family group will seek.

All things being equal, many of the Spanish-speaking people of Taos and Costilla counties would as readily accept, or maybe would even prefer, Anglo medicine to their own traditional healing practices. But all things are not equal. Anglo medicine costs more, and this is an important consideration to a people who have little money and no strong tradition of paying cash for medical assistance. Anglo medicine, in many aspects, is strange and unfamiliar, both in its procedures and its rationale. The language of its practitioners is often incomprehensible and their therapeutic activities do not always seem relevant to the illness conditions being treated. People who consider themselves to be perfectly well—those, for example, in the early stages of active tuberculosis—are expected to remain in bed for long periods; people who are obviously sick, such as those who have recently undergone surgery, are hustled out of bed and made to bestir themselves. Anglo medicine is administered by strangers whom the patient and his family frequently know only in their professional roles and who, at best, are likely to be impersonal in their ministrations and, at worst, impatient or brusque. It frequently requires that an individual be separated from the family group and isolated in a hospital where his very life may be in the hands of persons whom he does not know. And, for those who joined the Taos and Costilla associations, Anglo medicine meant devoting time and effort to an organization, largely composed of strangers, which did not seem to have any very direct connection with the medical care received. Furthermore, participation in these associations required making decisions about medical care and paying out money for it in anticipation of possible future illness. And why should one pay out money now for benefits which can be enjoyed only in the future? Obviously one should not; and equally obviously, in the experience of these associations, one did not, except when under the influence of crowd contagion at a meeting or when urged by a person whom one was reluctant to disappoint.

Reasons for Failure of the Costilla County Health Association

The failure of the Costilla County Health Association, like that of the Taos Cooperative, cannot be ascribed to any single cause. A number of factors contributed to the lack of success of the program. Some of these have been noted by Julian Samora, who served as first president of the Association.[11]

One of the difficulties was that the insurance principle played no very meaningful role in the culture of the Costilla County residents. In large part, and particularly among rural people, problems tend to be met and solved on a day-to-day basis, rather than being anticipated and prepared for in advance.[12] The preventive and insurance aspects of the program were thus not well understood, and many persons who had no illness during the first year felt that the money they had paid for a membership had been wasted. As one man said when asked his reason for not renewing his membership: "Why should I renew it? Last year I paid $38 and no one in my family was sick."

A second important factor in the lack of success in the Costilla program may have been that most of the leadership in planning, organizing, and managing the Association was provided by individuals with whom the people of the County could not easily identify. The original impetus came from a man who, although an oldtimer in the County and a person well accepted by the residents, was an Anglo. The representative of the Farm Security Administration was both an Anglo and a newcomer. The first set of officers was largely made up of persons who were either Anglos or newcomers, or both. The second group were chiefly Spanish-Americans, but all, except a priest, were businessmen and thus personally oriented toward Anglo culture. It is doubtful if many of the officers or those who were active in promoting the Association were persons with whom a majority of the Spanish-speaking people of the County could feel a close, spontaneous, identifying "we-group" relationship.

The whole process of planning and setting up such an association required a point of view, a type of activity, and a leader-follower relation that were much more characteristic of the Anglo culture than of the traditional ways of the Spanish-Americans.[13] And this is an area in which the two cultures are quite different. In the Anglo pattern the leadership role is largely achieved in the sense that it is related to the personal characteristics—personality, energy, knowledge, special interest, special skills—of the individual who takes it on; it is particularistic, limited to a single area of interest or activity; it is formal in that it is expressed through a deliberately created organizational structure; and it is impersonal in the sense that the leader-follower relationship is not necessarily affected by the substitution of one person for another in either of the roles. By contrast, in the Spanish-American pattern the leadership role is ascribed in that it is acquired irrespective of one's personal characteristics; it tends to be universalistic in that it carries over into many areas of interest or activity; it is largely informal, since it requires no special organization for its expression; and it is personal in that the substitution of one person for another in the role does affect the relationship.[14] Even though many of the leadership positions in the organization and management of the Costilla Association were filled by persons who were natively Spanish-speaking and thus at least peripheral ingroup members of the Spanish-American community, the activities were more characteristic of the Anglo than of the Spanish-American pattern and, as such, could not be

expected to be wholly acceptable to the less acculturated "follower" group.

Closely related to the leader-follower hiatus as a factor in the
downfall of the Costilla Association is the cultural difference in
the way in which Anglo and Spanish-American groups characteristically handle "problems." Anglos much more readily characterize a given set of conditions as a "problem" and more
quickly come to feel that some sort of concerted action is required. Where an Anglo community might, for example, come
to regard a given health condition as a social problem and set up
a special program to deal with it on a community basis, a
Spanish-American community might see the same condition only
in terms of its effect on individuals and leave the matter of coping
with it to those individuals or their families. Moreover, the Anglo
approach is, in a sense, indirect. If there exists an undesirable
health condition of such magnitude as to be defined as a community "problem"—say, for example, a high prevalence of
tuberculosis among members of the community—those who become concerned with it do not immediately begin to work with
the sick and others who may have been affected. Instead, much
effort is first put into setting up an organization that will serve as
the focal point for the interests and activities of a variety of persons, some of whom will be directly concerned with changing the
undesirable condition. Anglos generally understand the reasons
for such indirection. They are used to forming and participating
in organizations, and it seems entirely reasonable to them that if
there is a need for better medical care in Costilla County the
way to get it is first to do something else. In this case the way was
to talk about the problem, call and attend meetings, assess dues,
rent a building, buy equipment, and engage in the numerous
activities that are necessary for the planning and creation of a
health organization.

A person looking at the "problem" from the standpoint of
Spanish-American culture might not understand the need for all
this activity; it might seem to him to have little immediate
relevance to getting assistance when someone is ill. For dealing
with the matter of illness, the Spanish-American culture, as we

have seen, provides two resources: the general knowledge possessed by the patient, his family, or his friends; and a somewhat more extensive and slightly specialized knowledge that is the possession of a few categories of part-time practitioners, *médicas*, *albolarias*, *curanderas*, *parteras*, and *brujas*. By contrast, the Anglo culture has a wide range of resources, which include not only many kinds of specialized occupational roles but also a variety of institutions such as hospitals, sanitariums, laboratories, clinics, and convalescent homes, and a considerable number of both private and governmental agencies with both broad and specialized interests and programs. In Spanish-American culture sickness is dealt with simply and directly by applying the knowledge of the patient, a relative, a friend, or a lay specialist to the relief or cure of the sick person. In Anglo culture the process is usually much more complicated and indirect and frequently involves the establishment of interactive relationships with and between specialized medical personnel, members of institutional staffs, and professional persons in organizations and agencies. To one not thoroughly familiar with Anglo cultural ways the whole process could easily seem so complicated that he might be unwilling to enter into it.

Another, and perhaps simpler, way of making the same point is to recall that setting up and joining a voluntary organization is a familiar pattern of behavior to Anglos. It is not so familiar to Spanish-Americans. For the purpose of maintaining and regaining health, as for many other reasons, Anglos are "joiners." They join voluntary associations, such as those in the fields of tuberculosis, cancer, heart disease, poliomyelitis; they become members of insurance plans like the Blue Cross, the Blue Shield, and the White Cross; they create and join cooperative health associations, such as those of Taos and Costilla counties. In the Spanish-American culture there has been little or nothing to join.[15] One is a member of a community, a family, a church, and perhaps of one or two church-related voluntary organizations with semi-religious functions. Beyond these there is nothing to join. Thus, there is little cultural reinforcement for the kinds of activity and the type of relationships needed to maintain such an organization

as the Costilla County Health Association. And this is perhaps
one of the reasons it was not successful.

Requisites of a Health and Medical Care Program for the Rural Spanish-Speaking

The experiences of the two health associations described illustrate the point that medical programs directed toward a people
who are culturally or subculturally different from those administering the programs must be adapted to the points of view, the
accustomed patterns of behavior, the existing types of relationships, the beliefs and preferences of those for whom they are
intended. It is not enough to provide services or facilities in the
Anglo pattern and hope that non-Anglos will take advantage of
them. The true test of a medical program is not whether it conforms in all details to the Anglo ideal of what it should be, but
rather whether it works and, if so, how well. If the people for
whom it was initiated, use it, support it, and derive benefit from
it, it is effective; if they do not, it is a worthless program, however
good it may look on paper or however much it may be in accord
with the "best" Anglo practice. A medical program that would
be supported by rural Spanish-speaking people in Taos and
Costilla counties or similar areas in the Southwest might require
practices and relationships, both medical and administrative,
that would seem unsatisfactory to Anglo physicians and administrators. If so, that is the kind of program that should be set up.
However, in view of the fact that Anglo medicine, in some of its
aspects, has been used by many rural Spanish-speaking people,
it is not likely that a program which would meet their needs, *as
they see them*, would have to be radically different from one designed for rural Anglos. It would, however, require some imagination and ingenuity, some willingness and ability to see the
"problem" from the point of view of the Spanish-speaking people
themselves, and some readiness to shape the program to the
wishes, expectations, and motivations of the group it is intended
to serve.

There is no formula for a health program that would meet all
the needs of rural Spanish-speaking people throughout the South-

west. Local conditions are too varied, the group too heterogeneous. But it is possible to mention some factors that should be
taken into account in designing a program for any given area.

Any health program directed at rural Spanish-speaking people
in the Southwest would have to deal with the kinds of problems
that plague promoters and administrators of rural health programs everywhere—problems arising out of low incomes, dis-
persal of population, and difficulties in transportation and communication. Many Spanish-speaking people, particularly in
northern New Mexico, southern Colorado, southwest Texas, and
parts of Arizona live on isolated farms and ranches or in small,
widely scattered communities spaced along second- or third-rate
roads. They are frequently without telephone service. Obviously,
in such areas the variety, amount, and quality of health services
and medical attention available to urban populations cannot be
provided, and such services as can be given are necessarily more
costly than comparable ones in an urban area. Illness in a
Spanish-speaking community frequently means—if Anglo medical services are to be used—a long and somewhat difficult trip to
a population center where a physician is available, or an equally
difficult, time-consuming, and expensive home visit by the physician, provided there is some means of getting word to him that
his services are required. In either case the service is costly, not
only in money but also in terms of time and possible discomfort
or danger for the patient. Under such conditions the threshold of
motivation to seek the kind of medical assistance rendered by the
independent, private physician is likely to be high, and it is probable that needed medical services frequently are not sought because they are felt to be too costly, or too inconvenient, or both.

If Anglo medicine is to compete with other types of health
measures and medical care available to rural Spanish-speaking
people, ways must be found to bring it within the price range that
such people can and will pay and to make access to it convenient.
Where folk medicine is cheap, readily available, and familiar,
Anglo medical practices, regardless of how superior they may be
technically, are at a disadvantage and may not be readily accepted—except in the case of illness thought to be outside the

competence of native practitioners or in which they have failed to bring about relief or cure—unless they, too, can be made inexpensive, easy to obtain, and familiar. Familiarity, of course, is a by-product of contact and association, and can only follow them. Reduction in cost can be achieved by an outside subsidy, as in the case of the Taos County Cooperative, by economies made possible through most efficient use of equipment and personnel, by restricting services to a desirable minimum, and by using to the fullest extent minimally trained volunteer or paid personnel. Convenience can be promoted by making services available at times when people can most easily seek them and by holding frequent, regular clinics in local communities. This approach also contributes to familiarity, since it permits local people to seek and receive medical services in surroundings where they feel at ease. The exact arrangements for keeping costs down, for making services easy to obtain, for promoting a familiarity with Anglo medicine, and for motivating Spanish-speaking people to seek Anglo preventive and therapeutic services would necessarily be different from one area to another, but each of these goals certainly should be pursued if any program for providing health services to rural Spanish-speaking persons is to be successful.

To overcome the difficulties posed by the spatial distribution, low-income level, and cultural orientation of rural Spanish-speaking populations of such areas as Taos and Costilla counties, a health and medical care program would have to meet at least three requisites: (1) It should be designed, at least in its early stages, to provide only minimum services. (2) It should utilize a well-organized team approach, involving possibly some new relationships between categories of health and medical personnel, new functions for some of them, and the drawing in of persons not now usually included in organized health programs. (3) It should have financial assistance from public or private sources over a reasonably long period of time.

A minimum program does not necessarily mean an inadequate program. It means simply the scaling down of expectations to those possible within the limitations of the situation and the exercise of imagination, ingenuity, and cooperative effort to make the best use of resources. Specifically, it means that a variety of specialized skills will not be available, so that generalized skills must be developed and used by personnel working in the program and provision made for taking patients to specialists in cities when medically indicated. It means limiting hospitalization to the minimum required by patient welfare, conserving the time of physicians, and making the greatest possible use of the home and unpaid family members and friends in the therapeutic process. It means the provision of small clinics staffed for the most part by nurses who, under the supervision of physicians, can screen patients and treat minor ailments. It means the maximum use of preventive services in order to reduce the incidence and prevalence of disease. It means a heavy reliance on visiting nurses to make such home calls as are necessary for the purpose of assessing the need for a physician's services or providing the follow-up treatment or care a physician has prescribed. It means home deliveries for uncomplicated obstetrical cases and the use of trained and licensed midwives. It means, in short, some compromise with the Anglo ideal of the hospital as treatment center, the specialist as a ready consultant, and the physician as the only person qualified to give any kind of medical care, and the development of programs which, however much they may have to deviate from this ideal, will have the merit of providing better and more extensive services than were formerly available.

A team approach will be necessary if for no other reason than to save the time of physicians for the tasks that nobody else can perform. Doctors are scarce in rural Spanish-speaking areas and will continue to be. It is essential that the best possible use be made of their time and skills. This means restricting their activities to those that only a physician can perform and making maximum use of the abilities and knowledge of a variety of auxiliary personnel. Midwives, for example, can safely handle normal, uncomplicated deliveries; let them do so, with advice, instruction, and supervision from the physician. Nurses can do innumerable things, such as treating small cuts and minor upper-respiratory infections, making preliminary diagnoses for screening purposes, making follow-up home visits, staffing clinics, and relieving minor emergency conditions such as earaches. They can serve as extra pairs of eyes and ears and hands for physicians. Why not let them do these things and others that they could be taught to do, up to a maximum consistent with the safety and well-being of the people being served?

A group of people can accomplish more working together as a team than they can separately. But, it must be remembered, a team is more than an aggregation of individuals working on a common task. It is a cooperative endeavor based on shared interests, complementary abilities and skills, mutual respect for each other's roles, and common goals. It functions well only if its members have high morale, only if each has a sense of the importance of his contribution and its place in the whole endeavor. But these do not come about by chance. Somebody has to develop and nourish them. Somebody has to be concerned about them. On a health team that somebody is the physician.[16] Because of his technical competence and legal responsibility, he must direct the team. If it is to function as a coordinated group and not as a collection of persons with separate skills and goals, he must be prepared to play a role somewhat different from that of the physician as ordinarily conceived. A good part of his time and attention will need to be devoted to other members of the team. He will have to instruct and advise and encourage and support them. He will have to teach them to undertake tasks that he would ordinarily perform. He will have to make them dependable extensions of himself. He will have to have confidence in them and develop their confidence in him.

Another reason for using the team approach is that it is the most effective means of drawing into the health program members of nonmedical professional groups and laymen with special skills. Even in small rural communities there are persons with professional and other abilities whose occupation or interests make them potentially useful in health programs. Priests and ministers have extensive knowledge of their parishioners and a professional interest in improving their health and welfare, and could be very helpful in enlisting the cooperation of their congregations and interpreting to them certain aspects of the health program. School teachers are professionally concerned with health, and, through their contacts with children as well as by virtue of their prestige in small communities, are in a position to influence the health practices and attitudes of both children and adults. Agricultural extension workers sometimes have very close relationships with the people they serve and would be valuable allies in a concerted attack on health problems. Home demonstration agents are already partly concerned with health matters through their interest in food preparation, nutrition, and accident prevention. They have easy access to homes and frequently have developed such a high degree of rapport with families that they could perform important liaison and teaching functions. Social workers from state and local departments of welfare and other agencies are often active in rural Spanish-speaking communities, and their training and interest is such as to make them alert to health problems and capable of giving valuable aid. Health educators, particularly those with knowledge of the communities in which programs might operate, have much to contribute toward raising the general level of understanding about health and sickness and reducing the barriers to an acceptance of new programs. And, finally, in the knowledge of the community and relationships already established by *parteras*, *médicas*, *curanderas*, and other lay healers there is a valuable resource for winning the confidence of community members and facilitating the transition from a heavy reliance on traditional folk practices to the adoption of Anglo medical ways.

To make the fullest use of these and other aides who might be found, a health program should probably be integrated with other ongoing programs designed to deal with community problems in areas having some relation to health. By working with and through such agencies as the public and parochial schools, the church, the Extension Service, departments of public welfare and private social service agencies, a health program could multiply its strength and effectiveness and minimize its difficulties.

Use of the team approach in the field of health would in many areas require an outside source of funds for a fairly long period of time, if not indefinitely. Such funds should probably come from public sources. And there is no compelling reason why they should not be provided. The principle of community responsibility for public health services is well established in urban areas. Public health units, including salaried personnel such as public health nurses, already operate in many rural counties. No great increase in funds would be required in such counties. All that would be needed is an extension of the range of interest and activity of present departments to include the function of planning, organizing, and managing the kind of program necessary to meet the health needs of rural Spanish-speaking people. Costs could be kept low by making the best possible use of school teachers, social workers, and extension service people who are already on public payrolls; by using clergymen and other volunteer personnel; by using, wherever feasible, minimally trained people; and by charging a small amount for services. A full-time salaried physician and a public health nurse, with a small budget to cover administrative expenses and the cost of auxiliary services, could, if they were persons with energy, enthusiasm, ingenuity, and sensitivity, develop in a rural Spanish-speaking county a program that would go far toward providing the essentials for good health. No elaborate organization would be required; no great change in philosophy would be called for.

In pointing out the necessity for public funds for health programs for rural Spanish-speaking people, no implication is intended that such programs should supplant private medical care. Rather, they should supplement it, utilizing the services of private practitioners and privately managed clinics and hospitals to the fullest possible extent. The operation of such programs, both immediately and in the long run, would result in more rather than less work for private physicians and institutions as persons needing attention were found and encouraged to seek treatment, and as long-range educational and attitude-changing activities began to have effect. There are some things that private practitioners, however altruistic they may be individually, cannot be expected to do. For the most part, they are fully occupied with the medical problems that come to their attention. They do not have the time to organize health programs, to enlist the assistance of and give guidance and support to auxiliary personnel, to plan and institute measures designed to overcome the culturally derived obstacles to the acceptance and use of Anglo medicine, to set up and direct activities aimed at raising the educational level of Spanish-speaking communities with respect to health maintenance and disease prevention. Theirs is an exceedingly important role. But they cannot be expected to do the whole job in rural areas any more than they do in cities, where health is the concern of both private practitioners and publicly employed professional people.

The points made here about better health programs for rural Spanish-speaking people are very general. They are deliberately so. The purpose of the discussion has not been to draw up a blueprint for an ideal program, but rather to call attention to the fact that the success of any program will depend less upon the quality of its paper plan or the perfection of its organizational scheme than upon the interest, imagination, social perceptiveness, and human warmth of the people who staff it. Given people with these qualities, along with time to work, a few resources, and freedom to experiment with new arrangements, good health services and medical care for rural Spanish-speaking people could become a reality.

A special problem in setting up a health program for rural Spanish-speaking people is posed by the extensive mobility of a good proportion of this group. Large numbers of Mexicans—many of them wetbacks—move in and through the Southwest with such fluidity that it has been exceedingly difficult to plan and administer an adequate program for them. They, together with the thousands of Mexican-Americans whose seasonal migrations are keyed to the various agricultural harvest periods, appear in many communities in such numbers that local public health agencies as presently staffed and financed cannot conceivably meet their need for public health services, and private and public medical personnel and institutions have rarely been able to do more than offer the most limited types of emergency care. In the case of Spanish-speaking migrants, there are added to the already great difficulties of planning and providing adequate medical and health care to a people who are poor, rural, dispersed into relatively small population units, and culturally deviant in some respects, the enormous additional problem of meeting the needs of a group that is highly mobile and for whom no one has needed to assume any particular responsibility for more than the briefest periods of time. An excellent discussion of this problem and some concrete suggestions for handling it will be found in the report of the President's Commission on Migratory Labor.[17]

In addition to the general factors of poverty, low population density, poor transportation and communication facilities, and excessive mobility there are other factors, deriving from the cultural orientation of the Spanish-speaking people, which have some relevance for any program that might be proposed for giving medical and health services to members of that group. As the experiences of the Taos and Costilla associations indicate, it is probably important to discover, identify with, and work through the indigenous leaders. A common tendency is to seek the aid and influence of those persons who have the requisites for leadership in an Anglo community—business or professional status, fairly good income, skill at verbalization, a reputation for being "civic minded"—and to pass over as unimportant persons who may have none of the Anglo leadership attributes but whose actions and opinions are followed and esteemed by local Spanish-speaking people. The latter are hard to find; few if any of the criteria of leadership among Anglos are useful in identifying them. They may not have formal education, or financial standing or aggressive personalities or any of the other qualities thought necessary to leadership in the Anglo culture. They may not even be recognized as leaders either by themselves or by other people in the community. But they exist in nearly every community, and their interest and support can mean the difference between success and failure for a given project.

These indigenous "central" leaders are not easy to work with. The considerations that make sense to them are likely to be somewhat different from those that would appeal to Anglos or to highly acculturated "peripheral" leaders. For the most part, they will be persons who embody most fully the norms, values, attitudes, and viewpoints of the group they represent. To win their cooperation programs must be designed and presented in terms that are meaningful for the interests, goals, and preferences of Spanish-speaking people. Ingenuity, flexibility, and knowledge of both cultures are necessary if Anglos are to develop a plan which, without sacrificing "rightness" from the Anglo point of view, will serve to draw in and give satisfactions to those on the other side of the cultural fence. This may mean, as has been suggested, giving up or modifying some of the relationships and forms of organization that seem proper to Anglos. It may mean, temporarily at least, forgoing what seem the more important goals to Anglos in order to pursue goals that appear to be of more immediate importance to the Spanish-speaking. It may mean restricting the use of some techniques and skills—for example, hospitalization or the use of medical specialists—which are valued by Anglos. It will certainly require a willingness to compromise on means in order to attain long-range ends, and to recognize and respect the possibly different goals and values of other people.

Desirable Features for a Rural Health Program for the Spanish-Speaking

Some of the features that such a program might conceivably require can be mentioned here. As has already been indicated, participant physicians, nurses, and other professional health personnel connected with the program should have a good knowledge of the value systems and the cultural orientations of the people with whom they are working, along with some self-conscious awareness of their own values and goals, insofar as these are culturally derived. It would be desirable in many communities for them to know Spanish, in order that they might more readily communicate with patients or family members who either do not know English well or are not easy in their use of it. In a given situation consideration might need to be given to the question of whether or not many or all of the workers should be members of the Catholic faith and to the possible benefits of using professional people who are themselves natively Spanish-speaking.

A fee-for-service principle of payment would probably be preferable to a prepayment plan, at least in the early years of a program, since it more closely conforms with the existing and traditional patterns of Spanish-speaking people in paying for medical assistance.

The required participation of Spanish-speaking laymen in the administrative or organizational aspects of the program should probably be held to a minimum. Attending meetings, voting, electing officers, formulating policy, participating in making administrative decisions, and similar activities not immediately and directly relevant to the giving or receiving of medical care should not become requisites to obtaining such care. These activities can undoubtedly have an educational function which, in the long run, might permit a given program more nearly to approach the Anglo ideal, but to require them as a condition of getting medical care is to add greatly to the difficulties of acceptance by rural Spanish-speaking people.

This is not to suggest that Spanish-speaking persons be excluded from such activities. On the contrary, the more they can be drawn in the better for the success of the program. Some like organizational activity and perform it exceedingly well. They should certainly be encouraged to participate. However, no one should be excluded from participation in the program because of lack of interest in organizational activities.

Relations between those giving medical care and those receiving it should be as direct, personal, and convenient as possible. The physician or nurse should be easily accessible, and there should be a minimum of waiting by patients and a minimum of preliminary contacts with clerical personnel. If it is necessary for a clerk to obtain information from patient or family member, this is perhaps better done after the doctor or nurse is seen than before. Relationships and procedures should be made as informal as possible, and there may be times when efficiency needs to be sacrificed for informality. The personalities of the physician and nurse are important factors and, wherever possible, should be taken into consideration along with more technical qualifications when health personnel are being recruited. If a choice must be made, it may be better—at least in the early stages of any program—to give greater weight to personality factors than to

professional qualifications. Personality should also be considered in selecting nonmedical personnel, especially those who are likely to have any direct contact with patients or their families. A system of precisely timed appointments should probably not be used, and if possible all matters pertaining to a given illness should be taken care of at a single visit. In the instances where this cannot be done, every effort should be made to see that the patient or a near relative has a clear understanding of the illness and the probable course of diagnostic or treatment procedures. And enough should be known about the individual patient and his environment to ensure that the medical orders given are realistic for his situation. This may be particularly important for orders that concern foods. Physicians and others in professional roles will probably have to accept a somewhat more personal relationship than would be necessary with an urban Anglo clientele. Once a good relationship has been established, they can expect to be consulted about many nonmedical matters.

More initiative may also be required, particularly in the case of those services concerned with preventing rather than remedying illness. A prospective mother, left to her own devices, might never seek prenatal examination and advice. The same woman might readily accompany a visiting nurse or someone else who explained the desirability of such a procedure and offered to go with her the first time. Similarly, a person with a nondisabling chronic disease might benefit from services which, on his own initiative, he would never seek but would accept if someone put him in touch with them. Illnesses involving considerable pain or discomfort probably supply their own motivations, but those with ailments to which one can adjust with reasonable comfort or which require activity now to achieve or prevent some future condition are likely to require assistance from another person. With a rural Spanish-speaking group it is not enough to announce that medical services of various kinds are available and that anyone needing them should present himself and be treated. For many ills, particularly when an initial contact with any part of the medical program is involved, additional and frequently personal stimulation is needed, in some instances even to the extent of bringing the service to the person or the person to the service. Treatment of the sick in their homes and by their families, which until recently was the rule rather than the exception in the Anglo culture, and again is being endorsed in certain types of illness, notably tuberculosis, is still a strong tradition among rural Spanish-speaking people. And any program which, too rapidly, seeks to bring about changes in this area is likely to encounter considerable resistance. Hospitalization of the patient and the use of specialized nursing and auxiliary personnel probably result in better care from a technical point of view, more physical comfort and greater safety for the patient, convenience for the physician, and the opportunity to use a wider range of specialized devices, services, and procedures than would otherwise be possible. These values are very well known to Anglo medical people and to many Anglo laymen. They are perhaps less well appreciated by rural Spanish-speaking laymen, many of whom would, in given situations, tend to regard them as more harmful than helpful and their use as an indefensible abrogation of the family's responsibility for the sick member.

Along with drawing the family into the treatment process more than is customary among Anglos, an attempt might well be made to utilize the skills and relationships of lay practitioners in the Spanish-speaking culture. The midwife training program, carried on by the New Mexico State Department of Health, represents such an effort. Through it women already accepted and used as *parteras* in Spanish-speaking communities are given at least a minimum of instruction designed to improve their techniques, alert them to possibly dangerous conditions beyond their range of competence, and provide the basis for cross-cultural and cross-professional understanding that will enable them to consult with and transfer patients to Anglo physicians when such consultation or transfer is indicated. Just as *parteras* continue to be used in areas where Anglo medicine is not always easily available or entirely acceptable, so might some plan be devised to utilize the skills of *médicas* and *curanderas*, whose familiarity with the preparation and giving of medicine and treatments of many kinds and acceptability to rural Spanish-speaking patients in general could constitute a valuable resource in providing better medical care. Such lay practitioners "know" their own culture; they know the attitudes and responses of their friends and neighbors to various types of illness. Given minimal training in Anglo medical ways and supervised by Anglo physicians and nurses they might become a valuable liaison between scientific medicine and the rural Spanish-speaking patient. Similarly, *albolarias*, many of whom have a good working knowledge of processes whereby psychological and social maladjustment may be corrected or minimized, could be used as valuable aides in certain areas.

Certainly it would be unwise, in attempting to institute a medical program for rural Spanish-speaking people, to fail to consider lay practitioners. For, in the absence of acceptable Anglo medical facilities and personnel, they are the ultimate medical resource of the people who use their services, and it is not likely that their influence will abruptly cease when scientific medical care is introduced. They should be drawn into any new program if for no other reason than that their good will or ill will may be a powerful influence in determining the degree of acceptance or rejection of the undertaking. But their usefulness need not stop at lending passive approval. They could give some types of treatment and perform some nursing functions. They could supervise the carrying out of doctors' or nurses' orders by the patient. They could provide an easier and more certain entrée to patients than an Anglo physician or nurse might be able to achieve working alone. In many cases of language difficulty, they could interpret to patients the physician's instructions. To suggest that they be drawn into a program is not to imply that all of their present folk medical knowledge need be recognized as sound or all of their present practices approved. But if that part of their knowledge which is sound could be retained and broadened, and the part that is potentially harmful could be reduced or eliminated, not by forbidding or ridiculing or ignoring, but through friendly, relaxed, informal teaching, lay practitioners could become valuable allies in the development of adequate medical programs for rural Spanish-speaking people.

The foregoing suggestions indicate that health programs need to be flexible enough to permit modification to fit varying situations. But flexibility is not easily attained. There is bound to be some rigidity owing to the fact that any program requires an organizational framework. Formal organizations are necessarily somewhat inflexible, and the larger they get the less adaptable they are likely to become. Organization requires that relationships be structured, which is to say that the privileges and responsibilities of each position be specified and delimited; that time and energy be devoted to activities and ends not directly related to the purpose for which the organization was formed; and, not infrequently, that its major goal be subordinated to other considerations. Organizations also are modeled after preexisting patterns and this, too, introduces a degree of rigidity.

Not only is the organization itself likely to be somewhat inflexible, but it operates in an environment that imposes limits on its range of activity. Some of these restrictions are formal, such as the laws that specify what various types of organizations can and cannot do. Others are informal, but no less restrictive. Consider, for example, the kinds of control a state or county medical society can exercise over the operations of a health program.

There is likely to be inflexibility, too, on the part of the persons who operate the program. Health personnel, as those in other areas of professional activity, come to have what is, to use Veblen's phrase, virtually a trained incapacity for practicing their professions under any but a rather narrowly limited range of circumstances. Their deep immersion in scientific medicine, their reliance on the urban hospital, in which most of them were trained, their shared conceptions of their own professional roles and functions, their somewhat specialized value judgments with respect to health and disease, all make difficult for many the concessions necessary if their professional skills are to be acceptable to rural laymen. In the treatment of disease there can be no compromise with the highest professional standards; in the treatment of people there may have to be some compromise if the treatment relationship is to be accepted. Part of the inflexibility is due to failure to recognize that the social circumstances in which medical care is given do not necessarily influence the content of that care. Innumerable varieties of physician-patient relationships are consistent with the use of an antibiotic to combat infection. Modification in the approach to and handling of a person need not be accompanied by a change in the treatment of his disease. But because it is so difficult on the practical level to separate medical procedure from the accompanying circumstances in which it is used, any suggestion for change in the circumstances is easily interpreted as requiring change in these procedures. And so medical programs designed for rural Spanish-speaking people are less flexible than they might ideally be because of the tendency of Anglo professional persons to resist experimentation in social arrangements for giving care, in the belief that they are protecting the quality of that care.

For some time to come, the greater part of the impetus required for improving medical care for rural Spanish-speaking people will probably have to be supplied by Anglos and those in the Spanish-speaking population who are the most Anglicized. And there is much to indicate that the effort will be made. Increasing numbers of natively Spanish-speaking men and women are receiving training that will fit them for professional careers in medicine and related fields. Many of these, because of their bicultural conditioning, will be able to gain an acceptance of their professional services more easily than an Anglo could and will thus become strong acculturating influences. Anglo physicians are learning that they can earn a living and make satisfactory use of their professional skills in rural communities that are largely or wholly Spanish-speaking. Organizations such as the New Mexico Health Foundation have provided stimulation and some financial help in the building and staffing of small rural clinics. Public health services are slowly being extended into new geographic areas and the range and scope of services offered are being expanded. The type of federal aid provided under the Hill-Burton bill has stimulated interest in rural hospitals and made possible some that otherwise might not have been built. International organizations such as the World Health Organization are exploring new arrangements for improving rural health services among people of diverse cultures, and some of their findings may well be applicable in the Southwest. The developing concept of the medical team is improving communication and understanding between various levels of health personnel and between them and laymen, widening the area of possible cooperative action. Medical, nursing, and social work educators are becoming increasingly concerned with the need to introduce their students to some of the concepts and methods of the social sciences, particularly in reference to cultural differences and the ways in which attitudes may be understood and modified and behavior patterns changed. Renewed emphasis is being placed on preventive medicine and health promotion. There is a growing awareness of the gains to be made by adjusting health activities and programs to the levels of acceptance and understanding of the populations to be served. And from these and other trends, rural Spanish-speaking people are certain to benefit.

THE URBAN SITUATION

Providing health services and medical care for Spanish-speaking populations of urban areas is for obvious reasons somewhat easier than for those who live in the country. The very fact that these populations live close together in large numbers makes feasible the use of medical institutions, specialized services, environmental sanitation programs, health education activities, and programs for the prevention and control of disease. Urban Spanish-speaking have much greater opportunity for intensive contact with Anglos and their culture than do those in rural sections and are likely to be more acculturated and, hence, more accepting of Anglo medicine. Public health and visiting nurses go into their homes. They receive service in hospitals and clinics largely staffed by Anglos. They consult Anglo practitioners. They patronize Anglo drugstores. They are influenced by the remarks and actions of Anglo friends and neighbors.

It cannot be assumed, however, that Anglo medicine is fully available or acceptable to Spanish-speaking people who live in cities. Many of them are below the average of their community in education and income and could not afford adequate medical care even if they understood it and were motivated to seek it. As has been noted, in most of the large cities of the Southwest, the Spanish-speaking population generally lives apart from the English-speaking group in separate sections where the opportunities for interaction with Anglos are few. In these areas the Mexican or Spanish-American cultural traditions remain strong. Adjustments have been made to fit village ways to the needs of urban life, but the resulting patterns of belief and behavior are often still recognizably different from many of those of Anglos living in the same cities.

In working with a Spanish-speaking individual or family, in either a rural or urban setting, more perhaps needs to be known about the person or family than would be necessary in working with Anglos in comparable situations. Because a given Spanish-speaking person lives in Los Angeles or Houston or Phoenix, it cannot be assumed he is thoroughly familiar with Anglo culture and can be expected to understand, accept, and respond to Anglo medicine exactly as an Anglo would. Nor can it be taken for granted that because a Spanish-speaking individual lives in an isolated rural village, he is entirely ignorant of or unreceptive to Anglo medical practices. There is no Spanish-speaking person in the Southwest who has not had some contact with Anglo culture and, therefore, some opportunity to acquire part of it. There are few, if any, who never had or have entirely lost characteristics derived from the Mexican or Spanish-American cultural heritages. Any given individual will bear the stamp of both cultures in varying degree, depending on what his particular life experiences have been. The point can be illustrated if we imagine a continuum ranging from complete identification with Anglo culture at one pole to complete identification with Spanish-American or Mexican culture at the other. If it were possible to ascertain with some precision the exact degree of participation in one or another of the cultures of each Spanish-speaking person in the Southwest, and if we should then plot separately on our continuum the place of every urban and rural Spanish-speaking individual, the result would probably be that presented in the chart on page 207.

No Spanish-speaking people would be found at either pole, but some would be very close to one or the other. Many urban dwellers would be closer to the "Mexican" cultural pole than many of the rural people; many living in rural areas would be closer to the Anglo cultural pole than some who live in cities. A higher proportion of urbanites than of rural people would be found on the Anglo half of the continuum; a majority of the rural Spanish-speaking probably would be located somewhat to the right of the center line. In general, then, it can be anticipated that urban Spanish-speaking people will be more familiar with and accepting of Anglo ways than will rural Spanish-speaking people. But since a given individual from either group may belong any-

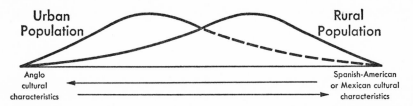

HYPOTHETICAL DISTRIBUTIONS OF URBAN AND RURAL POPULATIONS BY RELATIVE IMPORTANCE OF ANGLO AND SPANISH-AMERICAN OR MEXICAN CULTURAL TRAITS

where on the continuum, it is necessary to know something about his background before anything can be assumed about his particular characteristics.

Speaking generally, questions such as the following need to be answered before any conclusions could be reached about the particular cultural characteristics of a given Spanish-speaking individual and, therefore, about the kinds of modification which might be necessary to make Anglo medicine acceptable to him: To what extent has he had opportunities to be influenced by the Anglo or "Mexican" cultural heritages? Where was he born? Where has he lived? With whom did he live, particularly during the early years of his childhood? To what extent have his experiences been in urban or rural settings? What is the subcultural status of his family? To what degree have the extended family relationships been continued? What have been his unique indi-

vidual experiences? What acceptance or rejection has he received from Anglos? It can probably be safely assumed that any given Spanish-speaking individual will have had a degree of participation in some aspect of "Mexican" culture, some exposure to folk culture, urban industrial culture, or both; extensive participation in the activities and relationships of one or more family groups; and some experiences which in their totality are unique to him. The way he behaves in a given situation is in part a function of his background in each of these areas of experience and, if his behavior is to be satisfactorily predicted, understood, adjusted to, or controlled, a knowledge of his life history is necessary.

This is not to suggest that a detailed life history analysis need be made of every Spanish-speaking person who presents himself for medical care or becomes a client or patient of an Anglo medical program. In most cases no information beyond that routinely gathered in registering people for services or taking a medical history is needed. In such easily observable or elicited information as place of birth, places of residence, present address, years of schooling, occupation, ability to use English, religious preference, and family relationships can be found clues that will give the discerning person a good deal of insight into the probable degree of acculturation. It is not more information that is needed, but a greater sensitivity to the implications of information now routinely gathered, if medical and health services and facilities are to be made available to Spanish-speaking people in such a form that they can be readily understood and accepted. Two men may have been born on the same day, may have the same name and the same disease or disability. Physiologically they may respond in the same way to a given kind of therapy. But if one was born in Mexico, lived in a small village until he was sixteen years of age, speaks almost no English, had two years of formal education, has been a migrant agricultural worker all his life, and usually treats himself or relies on a *médica* when he is ill, and the other was born in a hospital in Austin, has lived all his life in a middle-class neighborhood in the city of his birth, is a graduate of the University of Texas and a practicing lawyer, the circumstances under which medical care is offered to each may be important.

If Anglo medicine is to serve effectively urban Spanish-speaking populations, those giving the service need to have some awareness of the range, extent, and implications for behavior of possible cultural differences, and of the desirability of making modifications in their programs to allow for such differences. This point can be illustrated with the experience of a visiting nurse who had in her district a Spanish-American woman having but little formal education and a low income. The woman together with her four children, all under school age, lived in the basement of a building located just across the street from a housing project in which a well-baby clinic was held. None of the children had been immunized, and the nurse was eager to have all of them receive routine immunizations and the baby seen regularly at the clinic. She had talked to the mother a number of times about the necessity for immunizations and for regular examinations of the baby and had found her at least verbally receptive to the idea. One morning she notified the mother that the weekly clinic would be held the following day at ten and that the children should be taken there. The woman said she and the children would be on hand.

Around noon on the clinic day the nurse stopped by to see the children. They were fine, playing in the street and alley as usual, and had obviously not been to the clinic. Disappointed, the nurse hurried in to ask the mother why. The excuse was not very good. She had intended to go, but by the time she had completed her morning housework it was too late to get the children ready. The nurse again went over the reasons for immunization, assured the mother that she would be well received at the clinic, and extracted a promise that she would take the children the following week. Again the nurse called at the home late on clinic day and found that no one had gone. This time the excuse was even more feeble. The mother had forgotten. Twice more the experience was repeated, and still the children remained unimmunized. Each time the excuse was weak; each time the nurse upbraided the mother for her failure; each time the once friendly relations between nurse and mother became a little more strained.

At the end of a month the nurse was ready to give up. She had spent a great deal of time on the family without getting any results, except a gradual deterioration of her relationship with the mother. She was convinced that the mother was ignorant, stupid, and irresponsible. And she was almost ready to generalize her feelings about the mother to include all Spanish-American mothers, since she had had similar experiences with others. In discussing the matter at a staff conference she was asked why one day she had not gone an hour early, helped the mother get the children ready, and escorted them all to the clinic. Her reply was that she could not do that; that if she went to such lengths with one Spanish-American mother all would expect the same service and she would become nothing but a glorified taxi driver. It was obviously considered better to stick to a certain established approach, even though it got no results, than to modify the procedure to an extent that was thought to be professionally undesirable, even though the change might have yielded easy and economical results. Half a dozen families might have been immunized in the time spent on this one if the desired end had been kept clearly in sight and the procedure for reaching it had been flexible.

Importance of Family Relationships

One cultural trait of the Spanish-speaking people that is constantly underevaluated by Anglo medical professionals in both rural and urban areas is the strong family relationship and the extent to which family affairs take precedence over matters that Anglos consider more important.[18] One Spanish-American woman, for example, has a record of having left a tuberculosis ward seven times against medical advice. Each time a minor family crisis was involved. Once she left because her brother was coming up for trial in juvenile court; once because her parents were in court charged with a traffic offense; once because her parents had been evicted from their home; once because she wanted to see one of her children on his birthday. In the village cultural pattern such a sense of responsibility toward other family members is not unusual; even among Anglos events of this nature normally call for some rallying of the family group. But this woman is regarded as a problem by the staff of the hospital where she is being treated, and her chart records her as a "submissive, immature, dependent person who cannot separate from her family because she has such a need of acceptance by them." Thus, behavior which would be regarded as normal, if not socially obligatory, among the Spanish-speaking is defined from the Anglo point of view as pathological; and the woman who is behaving as she thinks a dutiful daughter, sister, and mother properly should is a source of exasperation to the staff that are treating her.

Another instance is that of a Spanish-American woman who was injured in an automobile accident and was confined to a hospital with two broken bones. After a few days she and her husband decided that she should go home. Physicians argued that the woman needed to be in traction if the bones were to heal properly and that she also required specialized care that could not be given in the home. The argument made no impression on either husband or wife. The husband was slightly perturbed when he learned that the traction equipment could not be borrowed, but still stood his ground. The physicians angrily gave in and sent the woman out—without a cast—saying that she and her husband were stupid and there was no sense in trying to help her. A social worker asked for a visiting nurse referral, which the doctors refused to make because they felt it would do no good. A better understanding of what the family relationship meant in this case might have led the physicians in charge to compromise with their feeling that the woman required hospital care, while at the same time assuring that some kind of professional supervision, however inadequate from their point of view, could be available in her home.

That recognition of the importance of family relationship can sometimes lead to better physician-patient relationships was illustrated in the handling of an elderly Spanish-American woman who was being treated for cancer of the uterus. The woman, a member of a religious group that accepts faith healing, was reluctant to submit to hospital treatment and was persuaded to do so only by the insistence of her family. Early in the course of therapy, her grandson died suddenly, and she asked permission to attend the funeral. Her son, the father of the dead child, also indicated that he felt it important that she attend. In spite of their feeling that the funeral was not so important as the treatment, the physicians took out their radium implants and released the patient for a day. She went to the funeral and returned afterward for a continuation of her therapy. It is not possible to say definitely how she might have behaved had permission to go to the funeral been withheld. But it can be safely presumed that she might have gone without permission and that she might not have returned. Although the woman remains somewhat skeptical of the efficacy of medical treatment, both she and her son think the doctors are persons of fairness and understanding and are probably more willing to cooperate in her future care than they otherwise might be.

Importance of a Dependent Relationship

Another trait of the Spanish-speaking group that is not always understood by Anglos working in medicine is the tendency toward dependency. The Anglo ideal, as has been previously noted, is that of independence, and any tendency for an able-bodied adult to be dependent, either materially or psychologically, is likely to be regarded as potentially pathological. In the cultures of the Spanish-speaking people, however, there is a tradition of dependence and a correlative lack of any emphasis on the necessity for independence, which, to some extent, are carried over into the Anglo urban situation. A preference for independence of thought and action, like any other value, has to be learned. The Spanish-speaking villager who comes into the Anglo urban environment cannot be expected immediately to shed his cultural ways and take on those of the city. There must be time to learn the new ways, but time alone will not assure that they are learned. There must also be interaction with Anglos to bring the new ways to attention and demonstrate that they are useful in adjusting to life in an Anglo urban setting. If these interactive situations are to result in the Spanish-speaking persons' learning and accepting

Anglo ways and values, the Anglos who participate in them must be patient, understanding, and helpful. It is not enough to point out a pattern of behavior and say, in effect, "This is the way to do this; do it this way and you will be rewarded." There must also be some efforts designed to teach how to do it and to develop a desire that it be done. Specifically, if Spanish-speaking people are to learn Anglo ways of promoting health and relieving or curing illness, some degree of dependency may have to be permitted and possibly even encouraged. In the case described above, the fear of the visiting nurse that she might encourage too much dependence resulted in her wasting time and in the mother's learning nothing about Anglo medicine except that the nurse thought immunizations a good thing. Had she taken the woman and her children to the clinic, the nurse might have made the mother somewhat dependent on her—which might not have been a bad thing for the course of their future relationship—but she would also have obtained the positive goal of getting the children immunized, and would have "broken the ice" for the woman at the clinic and allayed any fears the mother might have had concerning the clinic process or her reception by the Anglo strangers in charge.

Importance of Help in Decision-Making

In dealing with Spanish-speaking people who are in the early stages of acculturation, Anglo physicians, nurses, and social workers should be prepared to make more decisions and take more initiative than they would with a similar group of Anglos. It is not enough to present the Spanish-speaking person with a set of alternatives and point out a course of action, because his choice between the alternatives and judgment about the action may be determined by considerations that are either largely outside the Anglo cultural pattern or not highly valued in it. To illustrate: a southwestern hospital has trouble in getting donations of blood from relatives to replace that given to Spanish-speaking patients. Two types of appeal are made. One is a mimeographed form, printed in English, briefly stating in somewhat abstract terms the need for blood, the fact that it can be obtained only from human beings, and the moral obligation of family members to replace that used for their relatives. The other is a verbal request made by the physician in charge of the patient. In both, the relative is asked to present himself at another building between certain hours on an unspecified future date. With the exception of three evenings when the blood bank is open until eight o'clock, the hours are those in which people with jobs cannot conveniently come. No explanation is routinely made about the process of drawing blood. It may be said in a verbal appeal that it is not painful, but no particular attempt is made to point out that the procedure is not harmful to the donor. Not many Spanish-speaking people respond. More might, however, if the requests were better adapted to their cultural and subcultural patterns of belief and behavior. The printed appeal could be made available in Spanish as well as English. The content could be simplified and made as concrete and specific as possible. Little reliance, however, should be placed on the written appeal, since reading, as a way of acquiring information, is of relatively less importance in the culture of the Spanish-speaking than in that of the Anglo.

The verbal request, insofar as possible, should be made personal, stressing not merely that relatives ought to give blood but that the particular relative is expected to give blood and that, in so doing, he will be rendering a favor to the physician as well as helping a family member. The fact that the blood-letting procedure is simple and painless should be stressed. The exact procedure should be described, and it should be carefully emphasized that no harmful effects will follow. Blood is regarded as a powerful, mysterious, and frightening substance by many laymen. The sight or even mention of it can often produce such undesirable reactions as fear, weakness, faintness, or withdrawal. In the cultures of the Spanish-speaking people it sometimes has special meanings. The taking of blood for any purpose may be regarded as a potentially dangerous procedure. Among males loss of blood is thought to be related to a reduction in sexual potency; withdrawal of any quantity, no matter how small, is considered certain to lead to loss or diminution of one's *machismo*. A clear, simple explanation of the fact that blood-giving is not harmful is therefore essential. Appointments should not be made for a future date, nor the prospective donor left with the notion that he should come in whenever convenient. If possible, agreement to give blood should be obtained during the original visit, and the donor should immediately be accompanied to the blood bank and assisted in making the necessary arrangements. If technically feasible, the blood should be taken then. If not, an appointment should be made at a time convenient for the donor, and soon, preferably on his next visit to his sick relative. It may again be desirable for someone to escort him to the blood bank, although if the first experience has been pleasant, this may not be necessary. Even though such a procedure would require special initiative and effort, it might result in blood donations—which is the primary aim of the program—and at the same time strengthen the relationship and understanding between Spanish-speaking donors and Anglo health personnel.

SUGGESTIONS FOR WORKING WITH SPANISH-SPEAKING PEOPLE

Although there is no formula that will serve as an infallible guide to Anglos in their professional medical relations with Spanish-speaking people, a few suggestions can be made as a summary and slight extension of the point of view which has been presented. Most of these apply equally well to relationships with Anglos, which suggests that perhaps what constitutes good medical service to one group might also prove to be good for another.

1. Health personnel should resist the temptation to equate cultural or subcultural differences in behavior with ignorance or lack of intelligence. People may be relatively ignorant in the sense that they do not know the same things we do, but it is unlikely that many are either completely or largely lacking in "knowledge" of disease and its treatment. Certainly, not many Spanish-speaking people are so lacking. Depending on their background, they may have different ideas of what should be done to diagnose and treat a given illness, but that is not the same as having no ideas. Intelligence defined operationally is the use of judgment in the selection and application of knowledge in adjusting to situations. Before anything can be said about the quality of judgment, however,

account must be taken of what knowledge was available and how the situation was defined.

The term "intelligent" is one that is frequently used by persons in the field of medicine. Nearly everyone who has associated with physicians, nurses, public health workers, and members of other professional groups is aware of the extent to which judgments of intelligence or its lack are made. "She is not very intelligent," "he is moderately intelligent," "she seems quite intelligent," and similar statements are frequently heard. What is often meant by these evaluations is that he or she did or did not behave in the particular situation as the speaker would have done. It is undoubtedly comforting to place the blame for failure to achieve rapport on the mental shortcomings of the other person, but to do so is to block rather than open the way to improvement in the relationship. If what seems to be unintelligent action can be examined with an eye to learning what knowledge was available to the actor and how he viewed the situation in which he was behaving, the action may come to seem intelligent and ways may be found to change it so that it begins to appear intelligent even from a professional point of view.

2. Since Spanish-speaking people, to a somewhat greater extent than Anglos in comparable situations, may be expected to feel uneasiness, anxiety, or fear in the medical situation, professional personnel need to be alert to signs of tension and prepared to take positive steps to relieve it. Additional patience, gentleness, and consideration may be indicated in some instances, as may be the need for clear and complete explanations of procedures, equipment, and other aspects of the medical routine that may be unfamiliar to laymen. Additional time for establishing a relationship and for interpreting his condition to the patient may be required. Access to various categories of personnel should be simple and easy; care must be taken that directions are clear and well understood; when it is necessary to route a patient from one person to another, it may be desirable to accompany him until the new contact is made. Those unfamiliar with institutional routines and with the limits of interest and competence imposed by a high degree of professional specialization do not always under-

stand why all aspects of their problem cannot be handled by a single person. They may come to feel, because they are asked to go from one person to another, frequently with some delay or the necessity for repeating information already given, that no one is interested in them or taking care of their needs. In some institutional programs in which no one person is responsible for all aspects of the patient's problem, sometimes no one, including the patient, is aware of all that is being done by the institution to handle his difficulty. When this occurs, there is always the possibility that aspects of the problem may be missed, that the patient may be baffled by his inability to see the relationship between the various services that are being given him, and that faulty or incomplete communication between specialists may lead to something less than the optimum care being given. As indicated above, Spanish-speaking people are more likely than Anglos to prefer and need a personal element in their relationships with clinic and hospital staffs. In the segmented, institutional situation this need is not routinely met. It is necessary, then, if the Spanish-speaking patient is to be made as comfortable as possible, that those working with him be aware of this need and so structure their relationships that it can to some extent be satisfied.

3. Gaps in communication are more likely to occur when working with Spanish-speaking patients than with Anglos under comparable conditions. These may result from a lack of ability to speak or understand English well, from differences in educational levels, from differing cultural orientations, from the use of technical language, or from differences in familiarity with the particular kind of medical situation. The personality pattern of many Spanish-speaking people is such that often they will not voluntarily call attention to areas of misunderstanding. Rather, they are likely to agree to what is asked of them, to respond to leading questions in the way they think the physician or other worker would like them answered, and to reply in the affirmative when asked if they understand, even though they do not. Particularly when working with older people, rural people, persons with relatively little formal education, recent migrants from Mexico, and others who may not be expected to have a strong under-

standing of Anglo ways, too many precautions cannot be taken to assure that both patient and staff member fully understand each other. In eliciting information leading questions should be avoided as much as possible and the questioner should be alert to the possibility that the patient may at times, in an effort to please, improvise the details which he cannot remember but about which the questioner seems eager to be informed. In giving information to patients, care should be taken to make the language simple and to avoid concepts that might be unfamiliar. Speaking slowly and enunciating clearly will be helpful. Contrary to the belief of some, content that is difficult to grasp because of unfamiliarity with the language or the concepts used does not become more comprehensible with an increase of volume. Hence, except in those cases where there is a definite hearing difficulty, raising the voice beyond the volume required for normal conversation does not result in any effective increase of communication.

4. Since Spanish-speaking persons, particularly older persons and those with relatively little familiarity with Anglo culture, are likely to be more sensitive to violations of modesty than Anglos, special precautions should be taken in making physical examinations or in discussing bodily organs and functions. As Hawley and Senter have pointed out,[19] the concept of modesty is learned early. Except for very small children, individuals rarely see others undressed, even those of the same sex, and even where families live under very crowded circumstances, care is taken to assure the individual some measure of privacy when donning, removing, or changing his clothes. Discussions of bodily functions are embarrassing, particularly if a third person is present. Such observations would seem to indicate the desirability of carefully explaining to Spanish-speaking patients the procedure to be followed in a physical examination and the need for undertaking it; of having examinations of females made by women whenever possible; of exposing the patient as little as possible during the examination; of avoiding long waiting periods in even a partially unclothed state; and of having the minimum number of persons present during an examination. Observations and discussion of the human body is a commonplace and routine task to Anglo physi-

cians and nurses, but to the Spanish-speaking patient who is being examined, the experience may be uncomfortable, if not actually traumatic, unless precautions are taken to minimize any violations of his or her notions of modesty. Information about bodily functions or instructions involving them should be obtained or given in conversations involving only the patient and a single professional worker, preferably of the same sex. Care may also be needed to assure that technical terms for organs or functions are understood, particularly if the patient is likely to have heard only the more common words.

5. A knowledge of the folk medical notions of Spanish-speaking patients could be an invaluable resource for an Anglo physician, nurse, or social worker. Such a knowledge should make him aware of the areas where the conceptualizations of the patient about a given disease or its cure might differ significantly from his and should provide him with some guides as to how his ideas might be made meaningful to the patient. Also there is much in the folk medical knowledge that can be utilized to obtain the cooperation of patients in some procedures which, when presented in Anglo terms, are not accepted. A simple illustration is that given by Foster.[20] A physician who wanted a baby he was treating for diarrhea to have boiled water prescribed a weak tea made with an herb that was already familiar to the mother. A request to boil the water the baby drank would not have tapped any store of knowledge the mother had concerning the proper procedure to use in treating illness; a request that the baby be given tea made sense and her cooperation was easy to obtain. The physician got what he wanted, sterile water for the baby; in addition, he strengthened the relationship between himself and the mother because he prescribed a remedy that she already knew was good.

The problem of the physician is to enlist the cooperation of the patient and his family in the course of prescribed treatment. It can be more easily obtained if the physician knows the remedies and practices which the layman already uses. This is not to imply that the physician should make a specialized study of folk medicine or that he should accept the validity of any folk remedy or practice. All that is required is that he be aware of the fact that patients both know and evaluate the relative merits of a variety of procedures and remedies for treating sick people, that for a given patient or category of patients he be careful to avoid violating their notions of what constitutes proper treatment and, insofar as he can do so without compromising his own professional knowledge, that he utilize their knowledge and preferences.[21] This demands a flexibility of approach that is not always easy for one who has undergone rigid scientific training and who is likely to be somewhat disposed, therefore, to see things in clear-cut terms and to be averse to allowing any but the strictest of scientific considerations to influence his clinical judgments. But since it does not always make a difference to the physician whether the patient drinks boiled water or weak tea, or whether a medicine is taken three times a day or four, or whether the patient wears a copper loop above his aching joint, or whether vitamin C is obtained from chile or oranges, it can perhaps be argued that such flexibility may sometimes gain more in increased understanding and cooperation by the patient than is lost in departing from strictly orthodox procedure.

6. In dealing with Spanish-speaking patients it may prove wise not to expect rigid adherence to time schedules. Clinical and public health personnel should not be surprised if an appointment that has been scheduled for several weeks is not kept, or if what seems to them the weakest of excuses or none at all is offered when the patient finally appears. Long-in-the-future appointments should be avoided or, if necessary, should include provision for jogging the memory of the patient at the latest convenient time. Family affairs and other "trivial" considerations may sometimes be expected to take precedence over medical appointments. When this occurs, it may be helpful to remember that routine medical appointments are likely to be considered less important by the Spanish-speaking patient than by the Anglo practitioner or staff and family affairs more important than Anglos usually consider them. In prescribing medicines, it may be advisable to specify that they be taken at mealtime or before going to bed rather than at an arbitrary hour like two o'clock or at indefinite intervals like four times a day. The clock is a much less noticed

piece of equipment in Spanish-speaking patients' homes than in professional offices, and one can easily "forget" to watch for the proper time to take his pill.

In speaking of time, mention perhaps should be made of the need of professional people to be a little more considerate of that of their patients. Physicians are busy people and if their services are to be made available to the largest possible number of patients, they cannot be expected to adjust their procedures to suit the convenience of each patient. Neither can they be expected to work on a stop-watch schedule. But, in protecting their time, many physicians, particularly those working in institutional programs, have set up routines that make it inconvenient, if not impossible for some patients to obtain their services. Clinic hours are only infrequently so scheduled that people holding regular daytime jobs can attend without loss of time from their work. Frequently large numbers of patients are asked to appear at the same hour, with the result that many of them have to wait excessively for service. Mothers of large families are given appointments at hours when their husbands are not available to look after the children, so that considerable labor and expense is sometimes required to get the children ready and transport them to the office or clinic with her. Much inconvenience to patients might easily be avoided if there were wider recognition of the fact that time is important to patients as well as to professional people.

7. In ordering treatment procedures special care should be taken to ascertain whether the patient can be expected to carry them out. Here, as in the case of other low-income people, factors of income and housing are important. There is not much point in prescribing plenty of fresh air for a patient who lives in two rooms with eleven other people, several of whom have a fear of night air. Nor is it realistic to expect a mother with, say, six children, four of whom are under school age, to keep a seven-year-old rheumatic fever patient on quiet bed rest for extended periods in a four-room upstairs apartment. It does not help much to work out a diet for a young diabetic boarding with an elderly Spanish-speaking couple, who recently moved in from a country village

and who follow their customary dietary pattern, unless some additional provision is made for getting him into an environment where the items of his diet can be obtained. In cases such as these, it is important to know not only the economic circumstances of the patient or his family but something of their cultural background as well, in order to be certain that the course of treatment is acceptable to them and within their means. Babies of Spanish-speaking parents are not infrequently brought into southwestern hospitals with symptoms of severe malnutrition. They are put on a diet and given the care necessary to restore them to normal condition and then returned to the parents. Several months later they are brought back in the same condition. Such incidents, which happen over and over again, illustrate the need to take into account the limitations of understanding and means of patients when giving them medical orders or advice. In the case of malnourished babies, a good part of the difficulty undoubtedly lies in the fact that, while it is the responsibility of the clinic or hospital to restore the infants to health when they are brought to attention, usually neither public health nurses nor social workers, nor anyone else has the responsibility of working closely with the parents to show them how, within the limitations of their resources, their living conditions, and their food habits and preferences, they can provide an adequate diet for their children.

Although it can be argued, as it has been here, that the provision of good medical care for Spanish-speaking people in the Southwest requires some modification of the approaches and procedures that have worked well in making medical care available to and accepted by a great many Anglos, it can also be said that in a sense the elements of good medicine are the same in all situations. Foremost among those elements is technical competence, and for that there can be no substitute. The medical professional person—whether he is a general physician, nurse, social worker, radiologist, or other specialist—must know his field. But no amount of technical or professional training will enable him to be fully effective unless he also has a second skill, that of competence in interpersonal relations. Here his compe-

tence may be intuitive or informed; it may have been unconsciously or deliberately acquired; it may have been formally or
spontaneously developed. What matters is that he have it and
use it in his professional relationships.

As has been said, the practice of medicine is a social activity
involving interaction between two or more persons, all of whom
have been conditioned by their entire previous experience to respond to various kinds of situations in a great number of patterned ways. The professional person, no less than the layman, is
in part a creation of his culture and his subculture and his behavior, like that of his patients, is to a considerable degree culturally determined. He who recognizes this fact and understands
some of its implications acquires thereby a flexibility that can be
of considerable value in his relationships with both colleagues
and patients. Understanding the degree to which his own beliefs
and behavior are derived from his cultural experiences, he is
better able to understand the beliefs and behavior of others and
to see, underlying the apparent whimsicalities of individual difference, the vast areas of uniformity in human behavior that make
organized group life possible. Understanding culture and the way
in which it molds individuals, he gains an appreciation of the
paradoxical fact that culture—or better, the group of people who
are the bearers and transmitters of culture—is strongly resistant
to change and is at the same time constantly changing. Thus, he
is able to accept, without frustration or impatience, the slowness
of change, and without dismay or fear, the inevitability of change.
Understanding culture and knowing something of the variety of
ways which cultural and subcultural groups have devised to cope
with essentially similar events and conditions, he is able to develop a perspective from which to view both his own behavior
and that of other people and to achieve some measure of objec-
tivity about his own responses and those of others, insofar as these
are seen to be culturally determined. Any member of the health
team who is aware of the social component of his professional
practices and relationships and who can adjust his approach and
procedures to the social and psychological as well as the physiological requirements of his patients is certainly a more versatile

and probably a more effective practitioner than one who lacks such understanding and expects all the adjusting to be done by the patient.

The people living in the 1400 block on Felicity Street in Arcadia, like those of a thousand comparable blocks in cities everywhere in the Southwest, and like the rural inhabitants of Taos, Costilla, and similar counties, need more and better medical care than they are now receiving. They do not always know what they need or how to go about getting it, but they would be a healthier, and possibly a happier, people if their needs were more adequately met. There are many correctable disabilities on Felicity Street, many acute and chronic conditions that require attention and treatment, many unexploited opportunities for the prevention of disease and for rehabilitating those who are disabled. Pedro Treviño's hernia, the bowed legs of Ruby Vigil, the dental caries of the other Vigil children, Simoneta Roybal's goiter might all be remedied if medical care were available in a form that these people understood, would accept, and could afford. Eye examinations and possibly glasses for Arturo Rubio and Larry Treviño, immunizations for the Vigil and Gurule children, better nourishment for Josie Roybal, and intelligent and sympathetic guidance for Louis Gurule might arrest or prevent conditions which could prove detrimental not only to these individuals but to the entire community as well. Effective medical care would perhaps add a few years to Linda Treviño's brief life expectancy. It might prevent the spread of María Vigil's tuberculosis, relieve Rafael Gurule's "rheumatism" and the arthritic pains of Enrique Rubio, and help Frank Gurule to understand and live with his epilepsy. The unmet medical needs of the residents of Felicity Street are not beyond the potential resources of Arcadia for meeting them. Personnel, facilities, and technical skills exist. The major stumbling blocks are two interrelated factors: the low economic level of most of the people on Felicity Street, which makes it impossible for them individually to pay the costs of medical service; and differences in cultural background between the Anglo population of Arcadia and the people of

Felicity Street, which prevent their making full use of the services and facilities available to them.

On Felicity Street, as elsewhere in the Southwest, a two-way adjustment is necessary to bridge the gap between the medical problems of Spanish-speaking people and the medical resources of the areas and communities in which they live. Many Spanish-speaking people need more rapidly to acquire Anglo ways of thinking and acting with respect to illness and health. For such acquisition the encouragement and assistance of both Anglos and the more highly acculturated members of the Spanish-speaking group are essential. Anglo medical professional people need to devise ways to make their services, skills, and knowledge available and acceptable to Spanish-speaking people of all levels of acculturation. Both kinds of adjustment have been and are being made in some areas. Neither kind has made much headway in others. In all areas, the greatest initiative will, for a time at least, have to be taken by Anglos. In the interest and effort of Anglos of many professions and particularly in the skills, knowledge, perceptiveness, and flexibility of medical personnel lie much of the opportunity and promise for improving health and minimizing the extent and effects of disease among *la gente de la raza*.

Chapter VI

A WIDENING VIEW

ALTHOUGH ATTENTION IN THIS BOOK has been largely centered on a single population group, the Spanish-speaking people of the American Southwest, the point of view presented has implications that go far beyond the needs and problems and relationships of any particular group. Scientific medicine in the form in which it is known and practiced in the United States and other centers of western civilization is, together with other elements of that civilization, being rapidly disseminated throughout the world, both through the unintended processes of cultural diffusion and through deliberate attempts to improve health conditions for the people of many countries.

HEALTH SERVICES FOR MEDICALLY UNDERDEVELOPED AREAS

In many parts of the world, technical and professional experts, trained in North American and European centers, are offering their services to people for whom they represent a considerable departure from traditional knowledge and practice. The World Health Organization has concerned itself with the health status and problems of people in many areas and has established in a number of countries centers for the provision of medical and health services and the training of local people.[1] Technical aid missions have been sent out from the United States to such places as India and Burma and the *altiplano* of Ecuador and Peru to inaugurate programs of sanitation, public health, and medical care. Philanthropic foundations have brought people from remote areas to receive training in western ways and have encouraged them to return to their own countries at the end of the training period to put into practice what they have learned. Medical missionaries journey to "backward" areas to succor the bodies as well as the souls of the inhabitants. Hospitals similar in design to those of New York or London or Paris have been set up deep in the jungle areas of the Congo. Rural health programs, patterned after those operating in parts of the United States, have been instituted in Egypt and Iran. Many international organizations, national governments, philanthropic institutions, religious organizations, professional societies, and private individuals are vigorously promoting activities designed to bring to bear the technical knowledge and resources of western civilization on the health problems and needs of a variety of people.

In some areas these new, intrusive programs contain much that is already familiar, and only slight modifications in traditional beliefs and practices are necessary to fit them into the existing cultural pattern. For others the new undertakings are based upon concepts and include practices that would require for acceptance radical adjustments in their ways of thinking and acting and radical changes in long-established patterns of relationships. It is perhaps unfortunate that only occasionally in such programs has recognition been given to the fact that in the practice of medicine or the development of public health programs social relationships and cultural patterns are of crucial importance.[2]

In general, health programs for medically "underdeveloped" areas are planned, organized, and carried out by persons trained almost exclusively in the biological and physical sciences. Such persons may and frequently do have profound knowledge of the human organism, of the physical environment that surrounds that organism, and of the reciprocal influences of the one upon the other. They are, in addition, highly competent technicians, having at their command the latest and best technological knowledge and other resources for improving health and preventing, minimizing, curing, or alleviating disease. If the problems they face were such that they could be confined to biological and physical science levels, a high proportion of successful outcomes would be assured. But the problems cannot be so confined. In all programs for "improving" health conditions and practices of people who are culturally different from those doing the improving, one inescapable and highly important variable is the human population itself. These populations are more than simply aggregations of biological organisms that respond passively to manipulation as does a population of *Drosophila* in a laboratory. They are in every instance an organized social group with long-established relationships and patterns of behavior. They have strongly held tastes and preferences and prejudices. They have techniques of their own and ideas about their worth or appropriateness relative to any others that may be introduced. They have customs that shape their behavior, and systems of values and beliefs that give meaning to that behavior. And they frequently have a way of stubbornly resisting change that can be very frustrating to persons who attempt to introduce new ways.

Medical and public health practices involve much more than the application of knowledge and procedures derived from the biological and physical sciences to the problems of the adjustments of the human organism to its internal and external environments. Such practices are inevitably intertwined and interlocking parts of larger systems of practice that have implications for and relations with all aspects of organized group life. In other cultures, as in ours, medicine is a major institutional complex made up of an intricately interrelated composite of practices, beliefs, values, rituals, symbols, ideologies, norms, and nonrational elements. The medical practitioner who moves from one culture to work among the people of another takes with him not only his technical knowledge and skills but also enormous cultural baggage consisting of ideas, beliefs, preferences, attitudes, opinions, and judgments, all of which bear upon and influence his work. For the people to whom he goes, medicine is also an institution, comparable in complexity to that of his culture but composed of somewhat different elements. They, too, have technical knowledge and skills, supported by systems of belief and preference. They, too, have ideas, attitudes, and opinions about health and disease that may, but frequently do not, coincide with his. Thus, the extent of acceptance of the practitioner's knowledge and skills is a function not only of the degree to which his ways can be demonstrated to be technically superior, but also of the degree to which they fit or can be made to fit into the existing institutional patterns of belief and behavior of the intruded social group.[3]

Not only is medicine itself an institutional complex, but it also has ramifications that penetrate all the other institutions of a given society, while it, in turn, is influenced by them. In the United States, for example, governmental agencies specify who may or may not practice medicine and prohibit or regulate certain types of practice that physicians are technically qualified to carry on, such as abortion and the administration of narcotics. Organized religion has much to say about and much influence over some areas of medical practice, and certain religious groups go so far as to claim that religious faith is the only therapeutic technique their members need to use. Medical knowledge is transmitted through the processes and structures of formal education and it is by means of educational techniques and in educational situations that student physicians, nurses, social workers, and other personnel in the health field acquire the subcultural characteristics of their profession. The organization of hospitals is influenced by our cultural notions concerning relations between the sexes as in the provision of separate wards for men and women patients, and the physical structure and internal arrangements of our medical buildings change from time to time in conformity with changing styles in architecture and new construction techniques. The practice of medicine requires time and effort, equipment and supplies, and so it is necessarily interrelated with many aspects of our economy. Medicine so interpenetrates and is penetrated by all other areas of organized group life, that it is difficult to separate even conceptually. No medical act has meaning out of its cultural context, and a given act may have quite different meanings in different cultures. It is this close identification of medicine with the whole of culture that makes difficult the transplanting of medical techniques from one culture to another.[4]

Cross-cultural medical and public health programs, to be even minimally effective and to have any assurance of continuance after the original impetus is withdrawn, must be integrated into the culture of the people they are intended to benefit. This integration may come about, at least partially, through the chance

coincidence of elements in the medicine of the intrusive and in-
vaded cultures. Such coincidence is not unusual where the two
cultures are related through a common stream of influence such,
for example, as that represented by western civilization. But this
type of coincidence cannot be depended upon, particularly when
the medicine of one culture is being introduced into another that
derives from a quite dissimilar cultural source. In such instances,
the necessary amalgamation can come about only through the
slow, random, costly, and sometimes disruptive process of trial
and error, or through the deliberate shaping of the intrusive program to adapt it to the culture into which it must fit.

CONTRIBUTIONS OF THE SOCIAL SCIENCES TO
MEDICAL PROGRAMS

The processes of planning, organizing, and operating a medical
program that attempts to bring the knowledge and skills of one
culture to the service of the people of another call for considerable
knowledge of the general concepts of culture and social organization and of the particular culture for which the program is
designed. They require also, if the program is to have anything
more than a chance expectation of success, that those responsible
for its planning, organization, and operation have some systematic knowledge of their own culture and of the ways in which
their thinking and their behavior may be influenced by it. As
Scudder Mekeel has said, "One must know oneself and the culture of which one is a part before one can even begin to understand anyone else."

The disciplines from which such knowledge may be expected
to come are the social sciences, particularly social psychology,
sociology, and cultural anthropology. Each has taken as its
province of special interest an area of human behavior, and all
have extensive theoretical formulations, accumulations of factual
information about many cultures including our own, and one or
more specialized frames of reference in terms of which workers in
these disciplines perceive the objects of their study and order
their findings. There is much in the theories, the knowledge, and
the points of view of behavioral scientists that could be highly

useful in the practical task of planning and carrying out medical programs for people of another culture. Until recently, however, very little use of social science has been made by those responsible for medical and health services, and even now such use is more exceptional than common.

There are, broadly speaking, two ways in which social science knowledge and points of view can be made available to medical and related personnel. One is through the introduction of social science concepts, methods, and content into the curricula of schools of medicine, nursing, public health, and social work, or into the preprofessional preparation of students in such schools, so that training in this area could become a part of the regular professional educational program. The other is through the use of social scientists from the several disciplines as participants in the planning and operation of health and medical programs. An encouraging trend in the direction of both can be noted.

Anthropologists and sociologists have had faculty rank in the Harvard and Pittsburgh Schools of Public Health and in the medical schools of Yale, Cornell, Washington University in St. Louis, State University of New York, University of North Carolina, and University of Colorado, to name only a few. In addition to the part-time employment of social scientists to teach sociology and psychology in many schools of nursing, at least three university schools have recently made provision for full-time social science consultants. Social scientists have worked or are working successfully with professional people in medicine or related disciplines in such diversified settings as the World Health Organization, the New York School of Social Work, Veterans Administration hospitals, the Family Health Maintenance Demonstration of Montefiore Hospital in New York, the Langley Porter Clinic in San Francisco, the Boston Psychopathic Hospital, Chestnut Lodge Sanitarium, outside Washington, D. C., the Jewish Board of Guardians, the Menninger Foundation, the American Nurses' Association, and the Pan American Sanitary Bureau, again to mention only examples that quickly come to mind. Consultants from social psychology, anthropology, and sociology were invited to the 1952 Conference of Professors of Preventive Medicine at which the roles of the social sciences and humanities in professional and preprofessional education were extensively discussed.[5] Anthropology is scheduled to take its place along with anatomy, histology, and embryology as a subject-matter area in one of a series of Teaching Institutes planned by the Association of American Medical Colleges.[6]

Medical colleges are beginning to reexamine their entrance requirements and to pay at least lip service to the point of view that students should study social sciences and the humanities during their preprofessional training. The extensive and growing literature in the field of "comprehensive medicine" or "social medicine" gives indication of the vigor of the current trend and the directions in which events are moving.[7] Already such cooperative efforts have demonstrated that close working relations between medicine and social science can be as beneficial and stimulating to both as was the development of similar relations between medicine and the biological sciences fifty to seventy-five years ago. Enough effort has been expended also to demonstrate that it takes more than good will and noble intentions on both sides of the disciplinary fence to assure a functioning relationship. The professional in medicine and related fields, if he is to work with social scientists, needs to know something of social science—its preoccupations, its assumptions, its peculiar points of view, its aims and methods, its limitations, and its technical language. The social scientist, if he is to work with specialists in the field of medicine, needs to have comparable knowledge of medicine and of the underlying biological and physical sciences. Only when each is equipped with some understanding of the other's area of professional competence can effective working relations be developed. Such a knowledge can, of course, be acquired in the working relationship, but it is probably gained more easily, more certainly, and at less cost during the period of professional training.[8]

While there is beginning to be considerable agreement that students in medicine and related fields *ought* to know something of the social sciences, there is less consensus about where, when, and under what circumstances such knowledge should be acquired. One point of view is that ideally students planning to go into medicine should concentrate on the social sciences and humanities during their preprofessional training period. Unfortunately, the present admission requirements for most medical schools and the assumptions made about the knowledge and skills students will bring to their first year of medical training are such as to impose a serious handicap on the student who does not devote himself to learning the rudiments of biological and physical sciences during his first few college years. There is no reason, however, why preprofessional students, if properly stimulated by their undergraduate advisers or motivated by additional prerequisites for admission to medical schools, should not acquire during their first years in college a broad background in the social sciences and humanities as well as the general knowledge of physics, chemistry, and biology necessary to cope with the medical curriculum.[9] Some believe there should be a core curriculum strongly emphasizing the social sciences, which would be required for all students planning to enter any field of endeavor in which human beings are the focus of professional concern. Others argue for the inclusion of social science materials in the various professional curricula, but differ as to whether ideally they should be presented separately or integrated into the departmental offerings of other disciplines.[10] Hopeful, from the point of view of those who see a need for the understanding of social science content and methods by people working in health and medicine, is the trend, mentioned above, for an increasing number of social scientists to join the full-time faculties of medical, nursing, and public health schools. Hopeful, too, are the considerable study of and experimentation with ways and means of fitting social science into the professional education of medicine and related fields that is now going on.[11]

BIASES OF THE "COMMON SENSE" APPROACH TO HUMAN BEHAVIOR

Professional people who operate medical service programs for persons living in other countries or who, in their own country, work with members of ethnic minorities or social class groups on a level different from their own have frequent opportunities to observe behaviors that differ, slightly or grossly, from those they would consider appropriate. In these circumstances, responses are sometimes oriented in terms of certain types of bias that result from reliance on a "common sense" approach to understanding human behavior which, if allowed to influence professional judgments or actions, can result in blocking or making more difficult the attainment of desirable professional goals. Specific mention and brief discussion of a few of the more prevalent of these biases may be useful here.[12]

One such bias is that of assuming a universal human nature which presumably leads all normal people to respond in certain uniform ways in given situations. The prevalence of this bias is revealed in the frequency with which references to human nature are heard during discussions of either actual or potential be-haviors of individuals or groups.[13] Certainly one of the most ubiquitous of phrases is the oft-repeated "You can't change hu-man nature." The persistence of crime, war, poverty, willfulness, disease, and virtually any condition that meets with disapproval is ascribed to the operation—usually in others—of a fixed, innate nature which predisposes people to respond in certain ways to social situations. The great utility of this bias is that it can be used both to "explain" behavior and to avoid explaining it, and that it can justify and validate almost any notion about behavior that one wishes to hold. If some people are reluctant to accept the advice or the services of surgeons, it can be said that "it is human nature to be afraid of surgery" and surgeons thus be absolved from any necessity for modifying their approach to patients. If "it is human nature to want to be well," there is no reason to adapt medical programs to fit the needs of different ethnic groups, since their nature will lead members of such groups to recognize superior medical technology and impel them to seek its services. If "it is human nature to want to get something for nothing," then those giving medical services must be careful to keep their fees high or make access to their services difficult by some other means lest they be overwhelmed by demands for service from people who are not "really" sick, but who are merely seeking a medical bargain. Statements such as these illustrate the ways in which assumptions about human nature can be used, either consciously or unconsciously, to defend the *status quo*, support invidious judgments about the behavior of groups and individuals, and provide moral support for engaging in courses of action or inaction which could not be approved if rationalized under a different set of assumptions.

What is wrong with the notion of an innate, fixed human nature common to all people is that it is fiction. Rather than reacting in the same way to the same influences, regardless of their individual or social experience, human groups have worked out innumerable patterns of response to the environmental stimuli which they receive. How any given individual will, in fact, behave in any given situation is determined in large part by his learned perceptions of the elements of that situation and their meanings, and his learned set of responses, from which he selects those that seem appropriate. His "nature" certainly endows him with the capacity for learning and both makes possible and limits his learning and subsequent performance. But the particular ways in which, within those limits, he responds to situations is largely a matter of cultural conditioning rather than genetic inheritance.

A second type of misconception, that can sometimes be avoided or minimized by training in the social sciences, is the rationalistic bias. Most of us in this culture—and perhaps the medical profession to a somewhat greater degree than laymen, because of their training in science and preoccupation with scientific concerns— commonly exaggerate the extent to which reason is a controlling and determining force in human behavior and minimize the influence of tastes, preferences, emotions, customs, cultural norms, and other nonrational behavior motivating and orienting forces. Man is assumed to be a thinking and reasoning animal, conscious of and able to select and control the goals he is seeking and the means to achieve them. But although many of man's tremendous accomplishments have come about because of his ability to use and apply reason, a relatively small amount of what any of us does in a given day is motivated or given direction by strictly rational considerations.[14] It is not very accurate even to attempt to distinguish between rational and nonrational behavior, since most of the ends or goals toward which "rational" activities are directed were not selected by any particular logical process and since there are always nonrational elements that enter into the selection of means for working toward these goals.

The rationalistic bias can lead medical men and women working in cross-cultural situations to see their own behavior as being highly determined by rational considerations and that of persons from another culture, to the extent that it may differ from theirs, as resulting from irrationality, ignorance, or stupidity. Such a bias can obscure awareness of the fact that no given example of behavior can properly be judged as to its rationality unless the person making such a judgment knows the assumptions from which the behavior proceeds, the knowledge available to the actor, and the goals toward which the behavior is directed. If, for example, health is assumed to be a positive state which can and should be maintained by positive measures, then immunization for the prevention of disease is a rational act and failure to be immunized when the opportunity offers may, in the absence of other considerations, be fairly deemed irrational. But if disease is considered to be the positive state and if it is thought to be caused by the magical intervention of other persons or the malevolence of supernatural spirits or forces, then immunization as we practice it is, in the light of the assumptions, knowledge, and goals of the one holding this view, an irrelevant act whose rejection is not unreasonable.

People in medicine and related fields who work in cross-cultural situations will have many opportunities to observe behavior that, from the point of view of their assumptions, knowledge, and goals, will seem irrational. In such instances, application of the rationalistic bias can result in wasted effort by minimizing or ignoring the importance of nonrational bases of behavior and limiting attempts at remedying the situation to those designed to dispel ignorance or appeal to reasoning ability. The rationalistic bias, too, can lead to the classifying of many folk medical practices as superstition or ignorance, with the implication that lack of knowledge is all that prevents the followers of these ways from behaving in a "rational" manner. The danger here is that of overlooking the intricate and complex interrelationships of folk medical practices and beliefs and other elements of the culture, and of wasting much time and effort in the attempt to change behavior patterns at a point where they may be particularly resistant to change.

Another type of bias that may influence judgment in cross-cultural situations is that of ethnocentrism. Ethnocentrism is simply the universal tendency of human beings to think that their ways of thinking, acting, and believing are the only right, proper, and natural ones and to regard the beliefs and practices of other people, particularly if they differ greatly, as strange, bizarre, or unenlightened.[15] The tribesman who relishes a diet of slugs picked out of the crumbling wood of a rotting log would be likely, if he thought of it at all, to consider perverse, if not downright nonhuman, the appetites of those of us who consume oatmeal. The Texan seated before his thick, red steak and the Hindu who looks upon the eating of beef as a sacrilege are each likely to view the other as a sort of barbarian. Monogamous wives ponder the sad state of the polygamous wife who must share her husband with five other women, while Mrs. Polygamy pities the plight of Mrs. Monogamy, who has to put up with a husband all by herself. A midwestern housewife shudders delicately and wonders how anyone can be so callous as she reads in her ladies' magazine about the parricidal practices of a tribal group and thinks how well off her own parents are rocking on the porch at the old folks' home. The medical intern, with his white coat, his stethoscope, his horn-rimmed glasses, his hypodermic needle, and his speculum chuckles over a cartoon depicting an African witch doctor with his various masks and fetishes. Ethnocentrism is a pervasive and insidious characteristic, and, because of the extent to which our cultural ways and values are internalized in each of us, a very difficult one to avoid.

In cross-cultural medical programs ethnocentrism is likely to operate from two directions. Unless they are careful, medical personnel may find themselves making invidious judgments about people who impress them as being dirty, lazy, unambitious, promiscuous, ignorant, superstitious, and backward, while those being served by the program may have occasion to talk among themselves about the crazy foreigners who make a fetish of time, wear outlandish clothes, are compulsive about bathing, do women's work, and know nothing of the real causes of illness and disease. In such situations only limited cooperation between the native and intrusive groups can be expected. As the intrusive group, those providing medical and health services to people of another culture will have to take the initiative in avoiding and overcoming the effects of ethnocentrism. They must be prepared to make some effort to understand the behavior and viewpoints of the people they are working among and to make some modification in professional practices in order to make them acceptable.[16] That this is difficult to accomplish is partly due to the operation of a fourth kind of bias, the tendency to equate scientific medicine with a particular kind of social organization.

In our own culture physicians, nurses, medical social workers, and auxiliary medical personnel are trained mainly in urban areas and in institutions which, although differing in some details, generally follow a similar pattern with respect to physical surroundings, social and economic relationships, and equipment and supplies used. Aside from relatively unimportant differences in physical arrangements, differences in size of staff and of budget, and some very real differences in intellectual and emotional tone and *esprit de corps*, one medical school is much like another and each hospital and clinic tends in general to resemble all the others. Wherever the student goes for his professional training, he finds medicine being taught and practiced in the same, familiar social and physical environment. Thus, the classroom, the laboratory, the hospital, the ward, the clinic, specialization, private practice, the chart, the daily bath, the segregated nursery, the nurse, the orderly, the technician, the outpatient department, and all of the other social groups, physical objects, and patterns of organization come to seem essential parts of the practice of scientific medicine rather than what they are—more or less fortuitous arrangements of cultural elements which in their totality make up one institutional complex in one particular culture. These objects, persons, and arrangements facilitate the practice of medicine, but they are not essential to it. They aid the scientific process, but they are not necessary parts of that process.

During his educational period and during the time in which the physician practices in the country of his training, the particular social organization (including reciprocal expectations between doctor and patient), technological aids, and patterns of physical arrangements of the culture in which he studies or works come to be taken for granted. They form a pervasive background, a familiar environment that comes to seem right and natural and necessary for the kinds of activities in which he engages.

But the physician who goes to work in a cross-cultural program may, at the beginning of his work, find himself in a bewildering situation. The familiar background is gone. People behave differently. The hospital does not exist. Dependable assistants are rare. New routines are required. New relationships must be established. Much of what was solid and natural and right is gone, and in its place are people who behave in unpredictable ways, physical arrangements in which things are in the wrong places or entirely lacking, and social arrangements that do violence to one's sense of propriety.

In such situations there are strong pressures for medical men and women to behave in one of two ways: to conclude that the new program is unworkable, that scientific medicine cannot be practiced under these conditions, and to give up the attempt; or to set about the task of reconstructing the situation in the image of the familiar environment of home. If the latter course is taken, equipment and supplies may be imported, routines set up, hospitals built and clinics organized and familiar types of personal and professional relations established. Regardless of the amount or type of such re-structuring of the medical situation, the rationalization usually is that these arrangements are necessary for the giving of medical care or service. Underlying such rationalizations is the general assumption that good or adequate health service or medical care can be given only under a certain type of social organization which, on examination, frequently turns out to be a close approximation to the patterns with which the persons undertaking the program are most familiar.

The tendency to want to work under familiar conditions is an understandable one which people in health and medicine share with practically everyone else. If not understood or controlled, however, it can result in importing techniques and arrangements unsuited to the area in which a cross-cultural program is working and thus negate or hamper its operation.

Still another type of bias that can sometimes influence the effectiveness of cross-cultural health or medical undertakings is that of assuming that the practice of medicine is a matter involving only practitioner and patient, thus leaving out of consideration other elements in the social or physical environment that may be highly relevant to the therapeutic process or able to influence the context in which it occurs. In any community it can be safely assumed that there are interests which will be threatened by any new programs and which can adversely affect them. Native practitioners frequently stand to lose status and economic advantages in direct proportion to the degree of acceptance of the new project and thus may be expected, unless drawn into and given a part in it, to oppose it, either openly or covertly. What goes on in the intrusive program, particularly if it operates in a fairly small community, will be known, talked about, and judged by the entire community. Families of patients, friends, neighbors, or other interested persons may exercise a controlling influence which will determine whether or not a community member submits himself for treatment and, if so, to what extent he will cooperate in the treatment process.[17] The medical worker in such a situation will need to look beyond the patient and his symptoms and to be aware of the extent to which the immediate medical or public health situation influences and is influenced either favorably or adversely by many other elements in the social environment.

A final bias that may be mentioned is the familiar one of concentrating on disease and forgetting people.[18] There has been much discussion and there is an extensive literature devoted to this point, but in spite of it students are still graduated from medical and related professional schools with a strong orientation toward disease or other "problems" and a relatively weak one toward people. Medical students, in particular, undergo a course of training in which disease and malfunctioning are the center of attention and in which there are relatively few opportunities for considering human behavior in a wider context. During the first year in traditionally organized schools their contacts are with dead people, who certainly represent the maximum in physiological malfunctioning and the minimum of social responsiveness. In the second year they concentrate heavily on disease in its various manifestations. Only in the clinical years do they begin to work with patients. But the people they see are diseased, and the circumstances under which they are seen are such as to focus attention on the disease and away from any other characteristics they may have. Most of the contacts of medical students with patients occur in hospital or clinic, each of which is admirably designed to block out and make difficult the consideration of anything beyond the immediate or related disease conditions. The faculty, after whom the students pattern their own behavior, are largely preoccupied with learning and teaching about certain bodily systems or disease entities.

The hospital patient is stripped of his clothing and other identifying symbols, is separated from his normal associations and relationships, and is placed in a single status category, that of patient, which thereafter defines and determines all his relationships to everyone in the hospital situation. Once in a hospital bed, the patient is so bereft of his group memberships and individual characteristics that there is little left to identify or distinguish him but his disease. He has a name still, but it might as well be a number, since its only function is to assure that he gets the intended medicines and treatments. There is some information about him on a chart, but only that which is thought to be immediately useful in understanding and managing the course of his disease. The only expressions of individuality permitted him are those that can be identified as having some relevance for his disease or its treatment and that can be talked about and recorded as matters of professional interest. "His bowels moved three times." "He put one of the pills under his tongue and spit it out after I left." "His fever came down very rapidly." "He asked to sit up today." Rarely, if ever, does anyone ever note or mention that the patient quoted Wordsworth just before breakfast, or that he once won a six-day bicycle race, or that when he was nineteen he wanted to visit Tahiti, or that during the last campaign he shook hands with a candidate for the Vice-Presidency of the United States. Such details as these, if known at all, are considered inconsequential, since they have or appear to have no relevance to the disease, which is the sole excuse for doing anything with or for the patient.

The ambulatory clinic patient fares a little better, in that he is permitted to pop in and out of the patient status and is thus somewhat less detached from his other statuses and his individuality. But even with him the focus of attention is on the complaint that brought him to the clinic and little is learned about him that does not directly or indirectly bear upon his illness. As in the case of the hospital patient, certain perfunctory and routine questions are asked about his residence, his family, his job, and his income, but these are only for the purpose of determining his eligibility for service or of providing possible clues to some aspects of his present illness. In both clinic and hospital the student learns by precept and example, if not through verbal expression, that the interesting and important thing is the disease, and it is that point of view that he is likely to use in his own professional practice and pass on to other students if subsequently he enters a teaching relationship.

There is no intent here to minimize the importance of a thorough knowledge of both the healthy and diseased organism. Training in the biological sciences has been and must continue to be the hard core of medical education. And physicians will and should continue to be largely preoccupied with problems of disease. But the practice of medicine requires knowledge and skills *in addition to* those acquired through a training in the biological and physical sciences. One reason is that the development of psychiatry in the past half-century or so has focused attention on the fact that physiological function influences and is influenced by both psychological states and social relationships. It is now recognized that many of the causal factors in disease are to be found outside the physiological organism and in the social rather than physical environment. The diagnosis, treatment, or prevention of disease thus requires a knowledge of that environment and of the many ways in which it contributes both to health and disease. One need recall only a few of the more obvious disease conditions such as peptic ulcer, asthma, chronic fatigue, or obesity to be aware of the tremendous influence the social environment exercises over the physiological organism and of the importance to the medical profession of being able to understand and at times use that environment.

A further reason why some formal knowledge of human behavior on the social level is needed is that the practice of medicine is a cooperative relationship requiring at least two persons, practitioner and patient. This relationship is a precondition for and an accompaniment to the exercise of the physician's diagnostic and therapeutic skills. Unless it is and remains satisfactory to the patient, the practitioner cannot perform his professional function. The practice of medicine thus includes much more than the application of medical skills. It means entering into a relationship with the patient, and usually with his family if he has one, and so handling that relationship that the patient will cooperate fully in the diagnostic and treatment procedures decided upon. The social relationship is not something apart from medical practice which, like the icing on a cake, can be included or left out at the discretion of the practitioner. It is rather an integral and necessary part of medical practice, without which there is no practice. The patient who withdraws from a medical relationship before the termination of the relationship is medically indicated has received poor care just as much as if a preventable error in diagnosis had been made or the wrong drug administered. The physician who, because of his manner or his lack of understanding of individual or group-related differences, is unable to establish a relationship which gives satisfaction to the patient cannot give good medical care, in the fullest sense of that phrase, however skilled he may be in the other techniques of his craft.

One of the skills needed by the physician—and equally by the nurse, social worker, and others who work with people—then, is a skill in establishing and maintaining mutually satisfying social relationships. Such skills are based upon a knowledge of the psychological and social factors underlying the behavior of people, including oneself. Some few people may acquire them intuitively through the give and take of their everyday experiences. For the majority of us, however, they can be most effectively and most certainly developed through formal training in the psychological and social sciences. Certainly for those going into any of the health professions, the development of these skills can no more reasonably be left to chance than can those more directly relating to the management of health and disease, for only if they are developed and exercised can the health services function at their highest level.

Formal training in the social sciences is not an automatic and certain guarantee of the elimination of the specific biases that have been mentioned or of others that might have been discussed. Certainly social scientists themselves, who as a group have had more formal training in the behavior sciences than anyone else, exhibit these and many other types of bias. Nor is social science training the magic ingredient by the addition of which medical education and medical practice will attain perfection. But such training can provide additional skills that will enable those professionally concerned with health to make more effective use of all their knowledge and abilities, and thus contribute to the attainment of their individual and collective professional goals.

As Dr. Edward J. Stieglitz has written: "Man is the core of medicine. Visualizing individual man in relation to the cosmos, we see that on the one hand he is composed of myriads of minute cells and microscopic structures operating in health as a highly integrated, harmonious, cooperative, semi-conscious, cellular biochemical organism. On the other hand, man, when multiplied many-fold, becomes society. But the whole is more than the sum of its parts. As man is composed of cells, so society is composed of men. Man, the individual, lives in two concomitant environments. Both are complex. The tissues and chemical reactions and equilibria of the organism constitute the realm of the biological sciences; the social and external environment is the realm of social medicine. Clinical medicine, between these two, is concerned with the indivisible individual. Psyche and soma, internal homeostasis, growth and atrophy, and adaptation to external environmental forces are all part of the domain of clinical medicine. Looking at man with the naked eye he is an individual. Studying man with microscopes, both visual and electronic, he is biological. Stepping back and viewing man through a telescope, he becomes a small unit of society. All three perspectives are requisite for full comprehension."[19]

NOTES

Chapter I. FELICITY STREET

1. The term "group" is used throughout this book in its broad meaning, to include all forms of associations and aggregations, without reference to size, structure, duration, or the existence of interaction between the members.

2. The concept of culture is a hard one to pin down to a precise definition. It is easy to say in general terms what culture is, but it is difficult to formulate a definition that will exactly reveal the heart of the concept. One useful definition is that by Paul A. Walter, Jr.: "Culture is the learned ways of acting and thinking which are transmitted by group members to other group members and which provide for each individual ready-made and tested solutions for vital life problems. Every human culture," Dr. Walter continues, "is a historical growth, and only as such can it be explained or understood. Since the very essence of culture is its transmission through generations, a culture may be thought of as the experience of the past entering as a determinant of thought and action in the present, and carrying, of course, important relation to the future of a group." *Race and Culture Relations,* McGraw-Hill Book Co., New York, 1952, pp. 17–18.

As defined by Robert Redfield, culture is "an abstraction: it is the type toward which the meanings that the same act or object has for the different members of the society tend to conform. The meanings are expressed in action and in the results of action, from which we infer them; so we may as well identify 'culture' with the extent to which the conventionalized behavior of members of the society is for all the same.

". . . the quality of organization among the conveniently separable elements of the whole of a culture is probably a universal feature of culture and may be added to the definition: culture is an organization of conventional understandings manifest in act and artifact." *The Folk Culture of Yucatan,* University of Chicago Press, 1941, pp. 132–133.

A third definition that may be given here is that by Margaret Mead and her associates. "Culture . . . is an abstraction from the body of learned behaviour which a group of people, who share the same tradition, transmit entire to their children, and, in part, to adult immigrants who become members of the society. It covers not only the arts and sciences, religions and philosophies to which the word culture has historically applied, but also the system of technology, the political practices, the small intimate habits of daily life, such as the way of preparing or eating food, or of hushing a child to sleep, as well as the method of electing a prime minister or changing the constitution." *Cultural Patterns and Technical Change*, United Nations Educational, Scientific, and Cultural Organization, Paris, 1953, pp. 9–10.

Additional definitions and extended discussions of the concept of culture will be found in the following works: Benedict, Ruth, *Patterns of Culture*, Penguin Books, Inc., New York, 1947 (originally published in 1934 by Houghton Mifflin Co., Boston); Boas, Franz, *Race, Language, and Culture*, Macmillan Co., New York, 1940; Eubank, Earl E., *The Concepts of Sociology*, D.C. Heath and Co., Boston, 1932, pp. 337–379; Faris, Ellsworth, *The Nature of Human Nature*, McGraw-Hill Book Co., New York, 1937; Kluckhohn, Clyde, *Mirror for Man*, McGraw-Hill Book Co., 1949; Kroeber, A. L., and Clyde Kluckhohn, *Culture: A Critical Review of Concepts and Definitions*, Peabody Museum, Cambridge, 1952; Linton, Ralph, *The Study of Man*, Appleton-Century-Crofts, Inc., New York, 1936; Sumner, William G., *Folkways*, Ginn and Co., Boston, 1906.

There are several attributes of culture that are particularly relevant to the point of view presented in this book.

1. Culture is a complex whole, the several parts of which are functionally interrelated.

2. Culture has historical continuity transcending the time span of any given generation. It is thus coercive for the individual, who, being born into it, has no choice but to accept it.

3. Culture exercises a strong determining influence in the way individuals come to perceive themselves and their relations to other people and to the nonhuman environment.

4. It provides ready-made guides to behavior, including ways of thinking and feeling as well as the more overt types of acting.

5. It changes, and it can be changed.

6. Since culture is very complex and the processes by which it is transmitted somewhat inefficient, no individual ever acquires the whole of a culture. It is thus possible to distinguish within cultural groups, subgroups made up of persons who share traits that are not common to other members of the larger group. In our culture, for example, physicians can be thought of as a subcultural group because of their possession of special knowledge and skills. Because no two individuals could have identical total experiences, there is a sense in which each individual has a subculture all to himself. However, the term will be used here to designate fairly large aggregations of people who, although members of a larger cultural group (or in process of transition from one cultural identification to another), have shared characteristics which are not common to all members of the culture and which enable them to be thought of as a distinguishable subgroup.

3. The Negro population, although much larger than the Spanish-speaking, is here thought of as differing *subculturally* rather than *culturally* from the larger population among whom both live. A considerable part of the distinctive culture of the Spanish-speaking people still survives; the influence of the various African cultures on the present-day Negro population of the United States is very slight. Some students of cultural relations in the United States, however, hold the point of view that there is a distinguishable Negro culture. For one discussion of the

antecedents and components of that culture, see Schermerhorn, R. A., "The American Negro: His Broken Culture" in *These Our People*, D.C. Heath and Co., Boston, 1949, chap. 5.

4. The Southwest, as used herein, is thought of as including all of Arizona and New Mexico and parts of California, Colorado, and Texas. It is an area which roughly coincides with that of Spanish colonization west of the Mississippi, an area which Carey McWilliams has referred to as "the fan of settlement." It is not identical with the Southwest as delineated by Howard W. Odum and Harry E. Moore in their *American Regionalism*, Henry Holt and Co., New York, 1938. Odum and Moore, following state boundaries, included Oklahoma as part of the Southwest, but left out Colorado and California.

There are many concentrations of Spanish-speaking population in the United States outside the Southwest—for example, those in Illinois, Minnesota, Michigan, Wisconsin, and New York—who share in varying degree the cultural characteristics of Spanish-speaking southwesterners. Although much that will be said about the behavior and cultural characteristics of the Spanish-speaking people of the Southwest is applicable to these other groups, we shall be concerned only with the Southwest, and no attempt will be made to extend any descriptions or analyses to include Spanish-speaking people in other parts of the country.

5. The term "Anglo" will be used throughout this book, as it is commonly used in the Southwest, to refer to the numerically dominant, natively English-speaking population whose culture is, with minor regional variations, that of the United States as a whole. So used, it designates a residual category that includes anyone who is not identifiable as Spanish-speaking or Indian. Negroes, Chinese- and Japanese-Americans, Jews, and persons of various European national backgrounds are thus grouped together as Anglos.

"In most portions of the Southwest the term 'Anglo' is used as a catchall expression to designate all persons who are neither Mexican nor Indian, while the term 'Hispano' is used to designate the Spanish-speaking. In essence, therefore, the terms 'Anglo' and 'Hispano' are the heads and the tails of a single coin, a single ethnic system; each term has meaning only as the other is implied. The terms do not define homogeneous entities; they define a relationship. For the term 'Anglo' is essentially as meaningless as the term 'Hispano'; it embraces all elements in the population that are not Spanish-speaking." McWilliams, Carey, *North from Mexico:* The Spanish-Speaking People of the United States, J.B. Lippincott Co., Philadelphia, 1949, p. 8.

6. *Oshá* is a medicinal herb of the parsley family, which is used for many purposes by Indians and Spanish-Americans throughout the Southwest. For a precise botanical identification and more information about the medical uses of this and other plants mentioned here and in later chapters, see Curtin, L.S.M., *Healing Herbs of the Upper Rio Grande*, Laboratory of Anthropology, Santa Fe, 1947.

7. It is not unusual that Rosalie was in the third grade after four years in school. Many studies of educational levels of Spanish-speaking children made in the 1930's and 1940's showed a very high proportion of retardation. See, for example, George Sánchez's *Forgotten People*, University of New Mexico Press,

Albuquerque, 1940, which shows that, in the area investigated, 55 per cent of Spanish-speaking children in grades above the first were more than two years over age for their grade. Similar findings were reported by Wilson Little in his study of *Spanish-Speaking Children in Texas*, University of Texas Press, Austin, 1944.

8. The *médica* is one of several types of folk healers used by the Spanish-speaking people in the Southwest. *Médicas* are believed to have extensive knowledge of herbs and other household remedies, and their help is sought in the diagnosis and treatment of a wide variety of ailments. Typically, they have had no formal training in medicine or related fields.

In giving the Spanish terms for *médicas* and other types of lay practitioner the female form of the noun will be used throughout this book. There are, however, male practitioners in all of these "specialties" except that of the *partera* or midwife.

9. *Cañutillo del campo*, a desert shrub, is a familiar remedy in the folk pharmacopoeia of the Southwest.

10. A plant of the mint family, *orégano* is used as a seasoning in foods and, in the form of tea, to relieve coughs and sore throat. It is a commonly used household remedy in the Southwest.

11. *Mal ojo*, or evil eye, is a folk disease recognized by Spanish-speaking people throughout the Americas. Children are thought to be particularly susceptible. The disease is caused, usually inadvertently, by the powerful glance of some person who admires or praises a child without taking the necessary ritualistic steps to counteract the harm this may do. For a description of the disease, its symptoms, etiology, and cure see: Foster, George M., editor, *A Cross-Cultural Anthropological Analysis of a Technical Aid Program*, Smithsonian Institution, Washington, July 25, 1951, mimeographed; Foster, George M., "Relationships Between Theoretical and Applied Anthropology: A Public Health Program Analysis," *Human Organization*, vol. 11, Fall, 1952, pp. 5–16.

In some parts of the Southwest, *mal ojo* is a very prevalent disease. For a brief discussion of symptoms and cures in South Texas, see Simmons, Ozzie, *Anglo Americans and Mexican Americans in South Texas:* A Study in Dominant-Subordinate Group Relations, Ph.D. dissertation, Harvard University, 1951, pp. 98–102.

12. In describing the inhabitants of 1407 Felicity Street no attempt has been made to limit the description to those characteristics that derive entirely from their participation in a culture somewhat different from that of Anglos. To have done so would have been to present a distorted picture, since Spanish-speaking people in the Southwest have had a long history of contact with Anglos and most of them have taken on a good many Anglo cultural characteristics. A complete description of any groups of real Spanish-speaking southwesterners would show them to possess a complex and intricate blend of characteristics, some of which could be traced to their Spanish-Indian culture heritage, some that would be due to the fact that they are a people in transition from one culture to another, and some that would be found to be identical with those of Anglos of similar class status.

Some of the characteristics of the people of 1407 Felicity Street, then, reflect a *cultural* difference, for example, their use of the Spanish language for everyday communication in the home, the frequent appearance of tortillas and pinto beans in their diet, the type of family relationship which permits the "borrowing" of children, as in the case of Simoneta Roybal. Characteristics such as the use of midwives, the fear of surgery, low educational attainments, intermittent and unskilled employment, which are also found among members of the Anglo cultural group, are manifestations of *subcultural* or social class differences. Both types of characteristics have important implications for the work of practitioners of any of the healing arts or related professional groups.

Chapter II. LA GENTE DE LA RAZA

1. *La raza* is an expression used by Spanish-speaking people in the Southwest to designate their own group. Literally translated, it means "the race." It should be remembered, however, that "*la raza*" has a somewhat different meaning from the English word "race," and that in using it the Spanish-speaking people intend no implication that they are biologically different from the majority of Anglos. Their own genetic background is a topic on which a great many Spanish-speaking people are highly sensitive, as the United States Bureau of the Census learned when, in 1930, it classified "Mexicans" as nonwhite.

In terms of the conventional anthropological categories of race, the Spanish-speaking people are probably a mixture of Mongoloid and Caucasoid stocks, since the group, viewed as a whole and without reference to any given individual or family, is the product of intermarriage between a relatively small number of European immigrants and a relatively large number of Central and North American Indians. The sense of identification with one or another racial group varies widely among the Spanish-speaking. Some, particularly among those recently arrived from rural Mexico, readily speak of "the whites and the Mexicans." Others bitterly resent any implication that they are nonwhite. Still others are not particularly concerned about racial identification except when, as happens in some parts of the Southwest, classification as nonwhite leads to various types of discrimination.

The confusion about racial identification is reflected in writings by and about Spanish-speaking people. In an article entitled "Who Are You?" (*Lulac News*, vol. 2, September, 1932) Spanish-speaking people were told: "Conditions have reached a point where your neighbors say, 'a white man and a Mexican!' Yet in your veins races the hot blood of adventurous Castilian noblemen, the whitest blood in the world, and the blood of the cultured Aztecs and fierce Apaches, the reddest blood in the world! So why this disrespectful slap in the face? You can hold your head up with the best, and you should do so, in order to keep your ancestors from turning in their graves." In another article, also in *Lulac News* (vol. 13, June, 1947), George Garza discussed "Our Classification —What Is It?" and said in part: "To our illiterate and semi-illiterate fellow Americans we are 'Mescins'; to those more literate we are 'Mexicans' with the deep and resonant emphasis on the 'xi'; to respectful but classification-minded Americans we are 'Spanish'; to those who classify themselves as our friends we are 'Latin-Americans'; to hate-impregnated nincompoops we are 'damn greasers'; to other similar minded persons we are 'peons or pilados'; and to still others we may be any number of unmentionable and unprintable names or titles. In short, we are called everything but Americans and considered anything but American nationals and members of the Caucasian or white race." Yet at a ceremony in San Antonio in September, 1947, honoring two Spanish-speaking men for distinguished civic service, the speaker, who had earlier spoken on the topic "Our Racial Problems," referred to the honored guests as "hombres mas magnificos de la raza de bronce."

With respect to any statements about or attitudes toward the racial classification of the Spanish-speaking population, three facts need to be kept clearly in mind: (1) Racial identification has social meaning and is frequently invested with emotional significance. (2) Membership in or identification with the "white" race in parts of the Southwest carries prestige and confers benefits and privileges not granted to those classified as nonwhite. (3) There is no scientific confirmation of popularly held notions about the inherent or genetic superiority of one racial group over another. For a brief summary of some of the evidence on this final point, see Klineberg, Otto, "Racial Psychology" in *The Science of Man*, edited by Ralph Linton, Columbia University Press, New York, 1945.

2. "The real test of affiliation with the Mexican ethnic group, however, is the feeling of belonging to a body which, on the whole, has cultural and 'racial' unity. In the case of the Mexican, ethnic consciousness is expressed by his identification with *La Raza*, 'The Race'—a genetic denomination by which he includes all Mexicans regardless of class differences or place of birth. This ethnic consciousness becomes intensified in those who live in a predominantly Anglo or non-Latin society that regards Mexicans as culturally different and, for the most part, socially inferior. Sociologically, therefore, recognizable physical or cultural characteristics do not *per se* indicate membership in an ethnic group. It is rather the identification of self with the group or the 'we-feeling' that is significant. One Mexican voiced this when he expressed himself in regard to his association with another, 'I joined him that time, thinking, "he's all right, he's a Mexican" '." Woods, Sister Frances Jerome, *Mexican Ethnic Leadership in San Antonio, Texas*, the Catholic University of America Press, Washington, 1949, chap. 1. In her study Sister Frances Jerome used the term "Mexican" to refer to the Spanish-speaking population of San Antonio, whatever their national background.

"No matter how sharply the Spanish-speaking may differ among themselves over the question of nomenclature, the sense of cleavage from or opposition to the Anglos has always been an important factor in their lives and it is this feeling which gives cohesion to the group. The sense of group identity also arises from the fact that the Spanish-speaking have had a similar history and experience and have been influenced by a similar relationship to a sharply differentiated environment." McWilliams, Carey, *North from Mexico:* The Spanish-Speaking People of the United States, J. B. Lippincott Co., Philadelphia, 1949, p. 8.

3. Some information about the physical characteristics and genetic background of a small sample of Spanish-speaking people, together with a selected bibliography of further references, will be found in Goldstein, Marcus S., *Demographic and Bodily Changes in Descendants of Mexican Immigrants*, University of Texas, Institute of Latin-American Studies, Austin, 1943.

4. At a conference of social workers held in Denver in 1953 a worker, who was of Spanish-American descent herself, spoke about the social distance separating Spanish-Americans and Mexicans in her community, notwithstanding the fact that many of the latter group were residents of long standing. Similar deep social cleavages between various subgroups within the larger Spanish-speaking population can be noted in many parts of the Southwest.

5. A considerable number of books and articles have been written about the Spanish-American group. Many of these will be found listed in Saunders, Lyle, *A Guide to Materials Bearing on Cultural Relations in New Mexico*, University of New Mexico Press, Albuquerque, 1944, and in "A Guide to the Literature of the Southwest," a regular bibliographical feature in the *New Mexico Quarterly Review* since 1942. Specific writings that may be of interest to the reader seeking more information about the group include: Burma, John H., "The Present Status of the Spanish-Americans of New Mexico," *Social Forces*, vol. 28, December, 1949, pp. 133–138; Calvin, Ross, *Sky Determines*, University of New Mexico Press, Albuquerque, 1948, chaps. 7 and 9; Davis, William W. H., *El Gringo*, Rydal Press, Santa Fe, 1938 (originally published in 1857); Fergusson, Erna, *New Mexico:* Pageant of Three Peoples, Alfred A. Knopf, New York, 1951; Johansen, Sigurd, *Rural Social Organization in a Spanish-American Culture Area*, Ph.D. dissertation, University of Wisconsin, 1941; Kluckhohn, Florence, *Los Atarqueños:* A Study of Patterns and Configurations in a New Mexico Village, Ph.D. dissertation, Radcliffe College, 1941; Leonard, Olen E., *The Role of the Land Grant in the Social Organization and Social Processes of a Spanish-American Village in New Mexico*, Ph.D. dissertation, Louisiana State University, 1943 (lithoprinted by Edwards Bros., Ann Arbor, Mich., 1948); Long, Haniel, *Piñon Country*, Little, Brown and Co., Boston, 1941; Loomis, Charles P., and Olen E. Leonard, *Culture of a Contemporary Rural Community*, El Cerrito, New Mexico, Bureau of Agricultural Economics, U.S. Dept. of Agriculture, Rural Life Studies, No. 1, Washington, November, 1941; McWilliams, Carey, *Op. cit.;* "The Spanish-Americans of New Mexico, U.S.A." in *Cultural Patterns and Technical Change*, edited by Margaret Mead, United Nations Educational, Scientific, and Cultural Organization, Paris, 1953, pp. 168–193; Sánchez, George I., *Forgotten People*, University of New Mexico Press, Albuquerque, 1940; Walter, Paul A., Jr., "Spanish-Speaking Americans," in *Race and Culture Relations*, McGraw-Hill Book Co., New York, 1952; Idem, *A Study of Isolation and Social Change in Three Spanish-Speaking Villages of New Mexico*, Ph.D. dissertation, Stanford University, 1938; and Zeleny, Carolyn, *Relations Between the Spanish-Americans and Anglo-Americans in New Mexico:* A Study of Conflict and Accommodation in a Dual Ethnic Relationship, Ph.D. dissertation, Yale University, 1944.

6. Much has been written about the early history of the Spanish-American villages by noted historians of the Southwest, including George Bancroft, Frank Wilson Blackmar, Herbert Bolton, George Hammond, France Scholes, and Ralph E. Twitchell. For an extensive list of references on this period, see Saunders, Lyle, *Op. cit.*

7. "The great majority of the Spanish-speaking people of the United States . . . are *mestizo*, or mixed Spanish and Indian stock. The mestizos have different proportions of Spanish and Indian blood, ranging from almost 'pure' European to 'pure' Indian, but in all probability they are chiefly Indian by race. The Indian blood probably represents a variety in stock, however, because Indians of both Mexico and the American Southwest are of differing physiological types.

"The racial background of the great majority of the Spanish-speaking people of the country gives them a social visibility which has been sufficient to set them apart in general thinking as a distinct racial group and to bring into play a racial factor in most intergroup contacts in which they have been involved." Walter, Paul A., Jr., *Race and Culture Relations*, McGraw-Hill Book Co., New York, 1952, pp. 326–327.

8. "Isolation is the key to the New Mexico cultural complex. 'The deepest penetration of civilized man in North America,' New Mexico was a lonely outpost of Spanish settlement for three hundred years—isolated from Mexico, California, Texas, and Arizona; isolated by deserts, mountain ranges, and hostile Indian tribes. It would be difficult, in fact, to imagine an isolation more nearly complete than that which encompassed New Mexico from 1598 to 1820. For its isolation was multiple and compound: geographic isolation bred social and cultural isolation; isolated in space, New Mexico was also in time. Primitive means of transportation and the lack of navigable streams extended distances a thousandfold. It took the New Mexicans five months to make the 1,200-mile round trip, along the Turquoise Trail, from Santa Fe to Chihuahua. On the west, the north, and the east, the settlements were hemmed in by warlike nomadic tribes whose presence in these areas isolated New Mexico more effectively than distance or the lack of natural communications. . . .

"No new currents of life moved in this remote colony of Spain for nearly three hundred years. Education had little meaning in a society in which there was literally nothing to learn. Competition and change, initiative and innovation were, for similar reasons, mostly non-existent. The life of any today was the same as the most remote yesterday that anyone could remember; and tasks were performed as they had always been performed." McWilliams, Carey, *Op. cit.*, pp. 63–64, 71.

"New Mexico is the anomaly of the Republic. It is a century older in European civilization than the rest, and several centuries older still in a happier semi-civilization of its own. It had its little walled cities of stone before Columbus had grandparents-to-be; and it has them yet. The most incredible pioneering the world has ever seen overran it with the zeal of a prairie-fire three hundred and fifty years ago; and the embers of that unparalleled blaze of exploration are not quite dead today. The most superhuman privations, the most devoted heroism, the most unsleeping vigilance wrested this bare, brown land to the world; and having wrested it, went to sleep." Lummis, Charles F., *The Land of Poco Tiempo*, University of New Mexico Press, Albuquerque, 1952, pp. 1–2. (Originally published in 1893 by Charles Scribner's Sons, New York.)

9. A good account of the characteristics of village life during Spanish rule will be found in Blackmar, Frank W., *Spanish Institutions of the Southwest*, Johns Hopkins Press, Baltimore, 1891. Excellent photographs of one present-day village and its people are included in Rusinow, Irving, *A Camera Report on El Cerrito:* A Typical Spanish-American Community in New Mexico, Bureau of Agricultural Economics, U.S. Dept. of Agriculture, Miscellaneous Publications, No. 479, Washington, January, 1942.

10. ". . . every article of European manufacture that reached the consumer still had to be shipped across the wider part of the Atlantic to the port of Vera Cruz, freighted by pack horse or in snail-slow ox-carts to Mexico City, and thence northward past Durango, Chihuahua, and El Paso del Norte for two thousand perilous, Indian-haunted miles to remote Santa Fe. Naturally commerce was out of the question and trade would be limited to barter among neighbors. . . . In this inaccessible valley beyond the desert, goods could neither come in nor go out, and thus there was not one gainful occupation to attract settlers." Calvin, Ross, *Sky Determines*, University of New Mexico Press, Albuquerque, 1948, p. 164.

11. For an extended discussion of the role of both family and church in the social organization of New Mexican villages see Walter, Paul A., Jr., *A Study of Isolation and Social Change in Three Spanish-Speaking Villages of New Mexico*, 1938. The importance of the family is also discussed in Johansen, Sigurd, "Family Organization in a Spanish-American Culture Area," *Sociology and Social Research*, vol. 28, November–December, 1942, pp. 123–131; and "The Spanish-Americans of New Mexico, U.S.A." in *Cultural Patterns and Technical Change*, edited by Margaret Mead, 1953, pp. 170–174.

12. Many communities, for example, Los Lunas, Los Chavez, were named for their principal family. One, Cundiyo—sometimes referred to as Los Vigiles —until a few years ago had a population entirely made up of people named Vigil.

13. Lay religious leadership in many communities took the form of membership in the *penitente* brotherhood, a deviant, Catholic flagellant sect that was introduced into New Mexico by the early colonists. Although officially disapproved by the Catholic Church until recently, the *penitente* organization has been very strong in many villages and has exercised considerable influence in both sacred and secular affairs. Long a secret society, the order is now semi-public in that no particular efforts are made to conceal either membership or religious ritual. There is some evidence that membership is increasing at the present time. Early reports on the order were made by Charles Lummis, particularly in his *The Land of Poco Tiempo*, already cited. Other good writings are: Austin, Mary, "The Trail of the Blood," *Century Magazine*, vol. 108, May, 1924, pp. 35–44; Henderson, Alice C., *Brothers of Light:* The Penitentes of the Southwest, Harcourt, Brace and Co., New York, 1937; and Woodward, Dorothy, *The Penitentes of New Mexico*, Ph.D. dissertation, Yale University, 1935.

14. The best account of the three major institutions of Spanish-American villages, Paul Walter's *Study of Isolation and Social Change in Three Spanish-Speaking Villages of New Mexico*, unfortunately remains unpublished. A brief discussion of the *patrón* system is included in *Cultural Patterns and Technical Change*, edited by Margaret Mead, 1953, pp. 174–176.

15. An understanding of the institution of the *patrón* can give many insights into the relationships Spanish-Americans have developed with welfare and other service agencies and organizations. It may not be too much of an exaggeration to point out that in the 1930's the WPA and other federal relief agencies assumed, in the eyes of many Spanish-Americans, the role of *patrón*, or that today, even in urban areas, many welfare workers may be regarded as partly filling the *patrón* role.

16. There has not been, until recently, a good formal study of leadership among Spanish-Americans. Probably the most nearly complete statement on the subject is that by Julian Samora, *Minority Leadership in a Bi-cultural Community*, Ph.D. dissertation, Washington University, 1953, which discusses both intraethnic and interethnic leadership patterns. Samora, who was good enough to read this chapter in manuscript, disagrees with the account of village leadership given here, on the ground that it too greatly restricts the concept of leadership and exaggerates the lack of individual initiative and the institutional aspect of leadership.

17. Redfield, Robert, "The Folk Society," *American Journal of Sociology*, vol. 52, January, 1947, pp. 292–308.

18. "In moving from the village background into Anglicized urbanization, the Manito [Spanish-American] is bridging a period of three centuries of development within one general culture (western European) and may be puzzled by necessary adaptations and miss their meaning. His native culture, language, and behavior patterns remain relics of old Spain, although modified by three centuries of isolated frontier development. . . .

"Manitos who, without adequate acculturation, have attempted participation in the broad American pattern of life, have found social and economic equality almost nonexistent. This condition stems from two basic facts: (1) the recognized tendency of a majority group to question the position of any people *different* from themselves; and, (2) the obviousness of the differences in basic idealisms of the group-designed personality pattern characteristic of the Manitos (lower and middle classes), differences so fundamental that the majority group cannot overlook them nor can the minority group quickly change them. The ethical concept behind this modal Manito behavior pattern can be generalized as distinctly relativistic rather than positivistic, relaxed rather than tense with inner urges, and concentrated on psychological rather than on material values and loyalties, especially in relation to the extended family." Hawley, Florence, and Donovan Senter, "Group-Designed Behavior Patterns in Two Acculturating Groups," *Southwestern Journal of Anthropology*, vol. 2, Summer, 1946, p. 149.

For a summarized account of the effect of the change from Mexican to United States rule in the Southwest, see Saunders, Lyle, "The Social History of Spanish-speaking People in Southwestern United States Since 1846," *Proceedings of the First Congress of Historians from Mexico and the United States . . .* Monterrey, September 4–9, 1949, Editorial Cultura, Mexico, 1950, pp. 152–165.

19. Soil Conservation Service, U.S. Dept. of Agriculture, *Federal Relief Expenditures for Labor in Three Sub-Areas of the Upper Rio Grande Watershed During 1935-36*, Conservation Economics Series 14, Regional Bulletin 41, Albuquerque, July, 1937. For a thorough discussion of the economic problems of the area in which many Spanish-Americans live, see Harper, Allan G., Andrew R. Cordova, and Kalervo Oberg, *Man and Resources in the Middle Rio Grande Valley*, University of New Mexico Press, Albuquerque, 1943.

20. Loomis, Charles P., "Wartime Migration from the Rural Spanish-Speaking Villages of New Mexico," *Rural Sociology*, vol. 7, December, 1942, pp. 384-395.

21. The extent to which the Spanish-Americans were neglected by both state and national governments has been abundantly documented by George I. Sánchez in his *Forgotten People*, 1940.

22. For an account of the difference the G.I. benefits made in the college enrollment of Spanish-name students in one state see Fogartie, Ruth A., *Texas-Born, Spanish-Name Students in Texas Colleges and Universities, 1945-1946*, University of Texas Press, Austin, March, 1948.

23. For information on the extent to which Spanish-speaking people in the Southwest live in urban areas, see Table 5, p. 293.

24. Among the few good works dealing wholly or in part with Mexican-Americans in the United States are: Gamio, Manuel, *The Mexican Immigrant*, University of Chicago Press, 1931; Idem, *Mexican Immigration to the United States*, University of Chicago Press, 1930; Kibbe, Pauline R., *Latin Americans in Texas*, University of New Mexico Press, Albuquerque, 1946; McWilliams, Carey, *Op. cit.*; Simmons, Ozzie, *Anglo Americans and Mexican Americans in South Texas:* A Study in Dominant-Subordinate Group Relations, Ph.D. dissertation, Harvard University, 1951; Taylor, Paul S., *An American-Mexican Frontier, Nueces County, Texas*, University of North Carolina Press, Chapel Hill, 1934; Tuck, Ruth, *Not with the Fist*, Harcourt, Brace and Co., New York, 1946.

There is a considerable amount of literature on Mexico from which to obtain further information about the cultural backgrounds of Mexican-Americans and Mexicans who have come to this country. Among the best-known writings are: Chase, Stuart, *Mexico:* A Study of Two Americas, Macmillan Co., New York, 1931; Lewis, Oscar, *Life in a Mexican Village:* Tepoztlán Restudied, University of Illinois Press, Urbana, 1951; Parsons, Elsie Clews, *Mitla, Town of Souls*, University of Chicago Press, 1936; Redfield, Robert, *The Folk Culture of Yucatan*, University of Chicago Press, 1941; Idem, *Tepoztlán, a Mexican Village*, University of Chicago Press, 1930; Sánchez, George I., *Mexico:* A Revolution by Education, Viking Press, New York, 1936; Simpson, Eyler, *The Ejido:* Mexico's Way Out, University of North Carolina Press, Chapel Hill, 1937; Whetten, Nathan L., *Rural Mexico*, University of Chicago Press, 1948.

A recent revealing account of some of the cultural beliefs and practices of the developing upper-middle class in Mexico will be found in de Treviño, Elizabeth Borton, *My Heart Lies South:* The Story of My Mexican Marriage, Thomas Y. Crowell Co., New York, 1953.

25. "It must be remembered that the bulk of Mexican Americans came to this country from a rural or semirural environment, often from a folk or even an Indian background. The immigration of Mexican-Americans has tended to be in waves, the earliest smaller wave being drawn from the border states about the turn of the century. The second wave came during World War I and was drawn almost entirely from the west central plateau states of Jalisco, Michoacán, Zacatecas, and Aguas Calientes. This area has apparently continued to supply the bulk of more recent migration so far as we can judge, although because of the large numbers of illegal immigrants it is difficult to establish precise data. However, in the California area, at least, it is the World War I immigrants who have founded most of the Mexican-American communities and who give the specific shape to Mexican-American culture.

"It is well to remember, then, that the dominant group consists of elderly people who came to this country before the social revolution which has been going on in Mexico for the last thirty years, individuals who came as small children and have little memory of Mexico, and second and third generation individuals who have never been in Mexico. Except for recent immigrants in the last decade, the second and third generation in Southern California probably comprise about sixty per cent of the Mexican-American population.

"The World War I immigrants came from a limited area of Mexico, were from an economy which was nonindustrialized and nonmechanized, and from a region where the feudal characteristics of society and church were and to some extent still are most persistent in all of Mexico. Although many were originally small agriculturists, artisans, and small tradespeople (rather than peons on haciendas), they mainly entered illegally in World War I, stimulated by illegal labor contractors or *coyoteros* (of Anglo-American origin) and began their life in this country as railway or migrant agricultural laborers. Few were of the upper class and at that time there was virtually no true Mexican middle class." Beals, Ralph L., "Culture Patterns of Mexican-American Life," *Proceedings of the Fifth Annual Conference, Southwestern Conference on the Education of Spanish-Speaking People*, Los Angeles, January 18–20, 1951, pp. 7–8.

26. The periods of greatest immigration from Mexico were the decades 1911–1920, when 219,004 Mexicans came, and 1921–1930, in which 459,287 immigrants from Mexico were recorded. The reversal of the stream during the period 1931–1940 can be seen from the fact that in those ten years only 22,319 immigrants were admitted from Mexico. These figures, which refer only to legal, recorded immigration from Mexico, have been taken from Table 4 of the U.S. Department of Justice *Annual Report of the Immigration and Naturalization Service, for the Fiscal Year Ended June 30, 1948*. There is no accurate source of information on the number of Mexicans who entered the United States illegally during these years.

For a good discussion of the various periods in Mexican immigration, see Broadbent, Elizabeth, "The Mexican Population in the Southwestern United States," *Texas Geographic Magazine*, vol. 5, Autumn, 1941, pp. 16–24.

27. Included among those sent out were many for whom the return to Mexico meant a real hardship. One, for example, was a young man who had been brought to the United States by his parents in his infancy. He had grown

up in Chicago, knew no Spanish, and had no ties with Mexico. He was nonetheless "repatriated."

28. A conspicuous exception is the Los Angeles Special Service for Groups Agency, which is reported to be doing an excellent job of providing group-work services to Mexican-American teen-age gangs.

29. There have been many reports on the problems, conditions, and prospects of migrant agricultural workers, including the large number who are Spanish-speaking. The best recent study of the whole problem is that made by the President's Commission on Migratory Labor, *Migratory Labor in American Agriculture*, Government Printing Office, Washington, 1951. Earlier reports dealing largely with Spanish-speaking migrants include the fine series by Paul S. Taylor, *Mexican Labor in the United States*, University of California Press, Berkeley, 1930–1934; also the following studies: Menefee, Seldon C., *Mexican Migratory Workers of South Texas*, Division of Research, Work Projects Administration, Washington, 1941; Brown, Malcolm, and Orin Cassmore, *Migratory Cotton Pickers in Arizona*, Works Progress Administration, Washington, 1939; Warburton, Amber A., Helen Wood, and Marian Crane, *The Work and Welfare of Children of Agricultural Laborers in Hidalgo County, Texas*, Children's Bureau, U.S. Dept. of Labor, Publication 298, Government Printing Office, Washington, 1943; and Thomas, Howard E., and Florence Taylor, *Migrant Farm Labor in Colorado*, National Child Labor Committee, New York, 1951, mimeographed.

30. Acculturation is the process by which individuals reared in one culture take on the characteristics of another. For a description of the process of acculturation and related phenomena, see Walter, Paul A., Jr., *Race and Culture Relations*, 1952, pp. 43–58; and Park, Robert E., "Human Migration and the Marginal Man," *American Journal of Sociology*, vol. 33, May, 1928, pp. 881–893.

Differential acculturation among various Spanish-speaking groups in the Southwest is discussed by Donovan Senter in "Acculturation Among New Mexican Villagers in Comparison to Adjustment Patterns of Other Spanish-Speaking Americans," *Rural Sociology*, vol. 10, March, 1945, pp. 31–47. See also Hawley, Florence, and Donovan Senter, "Group-Designed Behavior Patterns in Two Acculturating Groups," *Southwestern Journal of Anthropology*, vol. 2, Summer, 1946, pp. 133–151; Idem, "The Grammar School as the Basic Acculturating Influence for Native New Mexicans," *Social Forces*, vol. 24, May, 1946, pp. 398–407; Samora, Julian, *The Acculturation of the Spanish-Speaking People of Fort Collins, Colorado, in Selected Culture Areas*, Master's thesis, Colorado Agricultural and Mechanical College, 1947; Sánchez, George I., "New Mexicans and Acculturation," *New Mexico Quarterly Review*, vol. 11, no. 1, 1941, pp. 61–68.

31. An analysis of the pressures making for acculturation and of the extent of cultural change among Spanish-Americans and Mexican-Americans will be found in Saunders, Lyle, "The Social History of Spanish-Speaking People in Southwestern United States Since 1846," *Proceedings of the First Congress of Historians from Mexico and the United States*, 1950, pp. 152–165.

32. Background information on the group here defined as Mexicans will be found in the works on Mexico cited in note 24. For additional information on this group and their relationships with groups in the United States, see: Idar,

Ed, and Andrew C. McLellan, *What Price Wetbacks*, American G.I. Forum of Texas and Texas State Federation of Labor, Austin, 1953; a series of five articles by Gladwin Hill in the *New York Times*, March 25–29, 1951 (reprinted in *Congressional Record* as an elaboration on the remarks of the Hon. Paul H. Douglas of Illinois in the United States Senate, April 9, 1951); McWilliams, Carey, "California and the Wetback," *Common Ground*, vol. 9, Summer, 1949, pp. 15–20; Saunders, Lyle, and Olen E. Leonard, *The Wetback in the Lower Rio Grande Valley of Texas*, University of Texas Press, Austin, 1951; and Stilwell, Hart, "The Wetback Tide," *Common Ground*, vol. 9, Summer, 1949, pp. 3–14.

33. The statement that most of the group herein designated as "Mexicans" are in this country illegally is based on the fact that in recent years the numbers of illegal aliens apprehended by the Border Patrol has been many times greater than the number of Mexican citizens legally admitted to the United States for other than temporary residence. In the fiscal year ending June 30, 1951, for example, 6,153 immigrant aliens were admitted from Mexico, whereas 510,355 illegal Mexican aliens were picked up by the Border Patrol. For figures on other years see the *Annual Reports* of the Immigration and Naturalization Service.

34. A study by Manuel Gamio published in 1930, which we have already cited, indicated that most of the Mexican immigrants to the United States come from the central and northern plateaus, with more than half coming from the three states of Michoacán, Guanajuato, and Jalisco. (*Mexican Immigration to the United States*, pp. 13–29.) Dr. Gamio's findings were based on a study of post-office records of money orders sent to and from various areas in Mexico. A 1950 check by Saunders and Leonard, using the records on wetbacks voluntarily returned through the Hidalgo, Texas, office of the Immigration and Naturalization Service, confirmed Gamio's general findings. More than 70 per cent of the wetbacks for whom information was recorded in the Hidalgo office were from the states of Nuevo León, Guanajuato, San Luis Potosí, Jalisco, and Michoacán, only one of which has a common boundary with the United States. Saunders, Lyle, and Olen E. Leonard, *Op. cit.*, pp. 28–32.

35. It should be remembered that the term "Mexican," as used here, does not refer to the population of Mexico, but only to Mexican citizens who have recently come to the United States.

36. For information on the ages, sex ratio, marital status, occupations, places of origin, and length of residence in the United States for two samples of wetbacks, see Saunders, Lyle, and Olen E. Leonard, *Op. cit.*, pp. 26–41.

"The vast majority of wetbacks are plain agricultural workers, including women and children, mostly from the peasant class in Mexico. They are humble, amenable, easily dominated and controlled, and accept exploitation with the fatalism characteristic of their class. A common term applied to them is Guanajuato Joe, for the Mexican state of Guanajuato which supplies a large percentage of wetbacks apprehended in farm work. This type of wetback wants only to find work on a farm, mind his own business, and be left alone by the Border Patrol. He accepts good or bad treatment, starvation wages, diarrhea and other sickness for his children from contaminated drinking water and unsanitary living conditions—all this he accepts stolidly and philosophically. He does not think in terms of native labor displacement, lowering of economic standards and the socio-economic effects of his presence in the United States. Ideologies are beyond his comprehension. He understands only his way of life: to work, to suffer, and to pray to the *Virgen de Guadalupe* for a better life in the hereafter," Idar, Ed, and Andrew C. McLellan, *Op. cit.*, p. 6.

37. These terms are used more or less interchangeably to designate persons who are believed to have some special knowledge of illness and its treatment and whose services are for sale.

38. In areas where the concentration of wetbacks is heavy there is marked migration across the border on weekends as these agricultural workers cross over to the more congenial Mexican border towns for their Saturday night fun.

39. See Tables 3 and 12, pp. 290 and 300–307.

40. There are many revealing descriptions of living conditions of both urban and rural Spanish-speaking people. For detailed accounts see Brown, Malcolm, and Orin Cassmore, *Migratory Cotton Pickers in Arizona*, 1939; Kibbe, Pauline R., *Latin Americans in Texas*, 1946; Loomis, Charles P., and Olen E. Leonard, *Culture of a Contemporary Rural Community, El Cerrito, New Mexico*, 1941; McWilliams, Carey, *Brothers Under the Skin*, Little, Brown and Co., Boston, 1943; Menefee, Selden C., *Mexican Migratory Workers of South Texas*, 1941; President's Commission on Migratory Labor, *Migratory Labor in American Agriculture*, 1951; Sánchez, George I., *Forgotten People*, 1940; Taylor, Paul S., *An American-Mexican Frontier, Nueces County, Texas*, 1934; Thomas, Howard E., and Florence Taylor, *Migrant Farm Labor in Colorado*, 1951; Tuck, Ruth, *Not with the Fist*, 1946; and Warburton, Amber A., Helen Wood, and Marian Crane, *The Work and Welfare of Children of Agricultural Laborers in Hidalgo County, Texas*, 1943.

41. See Soil Conservation Service, U.S. Dept. of Agriculture, *Federal Relief Expenditures for Labor in Three Sub-Areas of the Rio Grande Watershed During 1935–36;* Geddes, Anne E., *Trends in Relief Expenditures, 1910–1935*, Division of Social Research, Works Progress Administration, Research Monograph 10, Government Printing Office, Washington, 1937; Harper, Allan G., Andrew R. Cordova, and Kalervo Oberg, *Man and Resources in the Middle Rio Grande Valley*, 1943.

42. Job referrals in a south Texas office of the Texas Employment Commission during the month of November, 1948, were as follows:

Job category	Anglo		Spanish-Name	
	Number	Per cent	Number	Per cent
Professional and managerial	0	0	0	0
Clerical and sales	17	65	9	35
Domestic service	10	20	40	80
Agriculture, fishery, etc.	0	0	0	0
Skilled labor	1	100	0	0
Semi-skilled labor	6	50	6	50
Unskilled labor	4	4	107	96

Source: Unpublished Study of Spanish-Speaking People, University of Texas. The county studied, in 1950, was about 70 per cent Spanish-speaking.

The following conclusions were obtained in a study of the occupational distribution of Spanish-name people in Austin, Texas, in 1948:

"(1) The Spanish-name citizens of Austin, Texas, are most likely to be found in certain occupational classes in greater proportion than are their Other-White neighbors.

"(2) The occupational classes in which the Spanish-name people are most often found are those which are regarded as semi-skilled and unskilled.

"(3) The Other-White workers have a better chance of being offered jobs which are the same as or similar to the job for which they seem best qualified.

"(4) The educational level of the Spanish-name and Other-White groups has a high coefficient of correlation with a rank order of job classifications from most skilled to least skilled.

"(5) The educational level of the Spanish-name group is of major importance in explaining differential job placement.

"(6) The lack of Spanish-name members in local trade unions is of major importance in explaining the difference in the proportionate numbers of Other-White and Spanish-name men classified in such skilled trades as carpentry, painting, masonry, and electrical work.

"(7) Discrimination is practiced by some employers in hiring Other-White women in preference to Spanish-name women where training and ability are equal. This is most apparent in the Clerical and Sales occupations." Crain, Forest B., *The Occupational Distribution of Spanish-Name People in Austin, Texas,* Master's thesis, University of Texas, 1948.

See also Nelson, Eastin, and Frederic Meyers, *Labor Requirements and Labor Resources in the Lower Rio Grande Valley of Texas,* University of Texas Press, Austin, December, 1950; Meyers, Frederic, *Spanish-Name Persons in the Labor Force in Manufacturing Industry in Texas,* University of Texas Press, Austin, 1951; Denver Area Welfare Council, *The Spanish-American Population of Denver,* 1950, mimeographed; Denver Unity Council, *The Spanish-Speaking Population of Denver,* 1946.

Information on the income and occupation of Spanish-speaking people in the five southwestern states will be found in Tables 8 and 9, pp. 296–297.

43. A survey of the water supply of 62 communities in 18 New Mexico counties in 1947 showed only one that was adequate from a public health standpoint. For a list of these communities and an evaluation of the water supply and sewage disposal facilities of each, see *New Mexico Health Council News-Letter,* May–June, 1947.

44. Comparative information on the housing of Spanish-speaking people in the Southwest is available in the U.S. Bureau of the Census 1950 reports on housing. Also of interest are: Bureau of Business and Social Research, University of Denver, *Housing Trends in Denver, 1939–1949,* University of Denver Reports, vol. 25, November, 1949; a survey of housing conditions in Corpus Christi, Texas, published in the *Corpus Christi Public Housing Market Review,* March, 1948; Hall, William C., *A Study of 281 Farm Labor Families of South Texas,* Master's thesis, Texas College of Arts and Industries, Kingsville, 1942; Broom, Perry M., *An Interpretive Analysis of the Economic and Educational Status of Latin-Americans in Texas,* Ph.D. dissertation, University of Texas, 1942.

45. For a comparison of the education attainments of Anglos and Spanish-speaking in the five southwestern states, see Table 10, p. 298. Wilson Little, in his study of the Spanish-speaking school children of Texas in 1942–1943, found only 53 per cent of those from six to seventeen years of age were enrolled in school; more than half of all enrolled were in the first three grades; over-ageness was characteristic of all grades; average daily attendance was low; and children tended to enroll late and leave early. See his *Spanish-Speaking Children in Texas*, University of Texas Press, Austin, 1944, pp. 63–66. For further information see: Manuel, H. T., *The Education of Mexican and Spanish-Speaking Children in Texas*, 1930 [the children whom Manuel was concerned with are now adults!]; Tireman, L. S., and Mary Watson, *La Comunidad:* Report of the Nambé Community School, University of New Mexico Press, Albuquerque, 1943; Sánchez, George I., *Concerning Segregation of Spanish-Speaking Children in the Public Schools*, University of Texas Press, 1951; and the excellent reports that have been made by the several state departments of education, particularly those of California.

46. Information about health conditions and problems of small groups within the total Spanish-speaking population will be found in the following: de la Rosa, L., "Ministry of Public Health and Welfare of Mexico on Sanitary Problems of Mexicans Living in the United States," *Boletín de la Oficina Sanitaria Panamericana*, vol. 27, August, 1948, pp. 752–755; Denver Area Welfare Council, *The Spanish-American Population of Denver*, 1950, pp. 21–33; Denver Unity Council, *The Spanish-Speaking Population of Denver*, 1946; Elliott, Robert S., *The Health and Relief Problems of a Group of Non-Family Mexican Men in Imperial County, California*, Master's thesis, University of Southern California, 1939; Gregg, R., "Medical Examination and Vaccination of Farm Laborers Recruited from Mexico," *Public Health R ports*, vol. 65, June 23, 1950, pp. 807–809; Heller, C. A., "Regional Patterns of Dietary Deficiency: Spanish-Americans in New Mexico and Arizona," *Annals* of American Academy of Political and Social Science, vol. 225, January, 1943, pp. 49–51; Kibbe, Pauline R., *Latin Americans in Texas*, 1946, pp. 123–156; Longmore, T. Wilson, and Theo L. Vaughan, *Taos County Cooperative Health Association, 1942–1943*, Bureau of Agricultural Economics, U.S. Dept. of Agriculture, Little Rock, September, 1944, mimeographed; Peters, LeRoy S., "New Mexico Medicine," *New Mexico Quarterly Review*, vol. 11, 1941, pp. 322–329; Pijoan, Michel, *Certain Factors Involved in the Struggle Against Malnutrition and Disease*, University of New Mexico Press, Albuquerque, 1943; Idem, "Food Availability and Social Function," *New Mexico Quarterly Review*, vol. 12, November, 1942, pp. 419–423; Pijoan, Michel, and R. W. Roskelley, *Nutrition and Certain Related Factors of Spanish-Americans in Northern Colorado*, Rocky Mountain Council on Inter-American Affairs and Western Policy Committee, Denver, 1943; President's Commission on Migratory Labor, *Migratory Labor in American Agriculture*, 1951, pp. 153–159; Saunders, Lyle, and Olen E. Leonard, *The Wetback in the Lower Rio Grande Valley of Texas*, 1951; Smith, R. M., "The Problem of Tuberculosis Among Mexicans in the United States," *Transactions* of the National Tuberculosis Association, vol. 34, 1938, pp. 247–253; Division of Maternal and Child Health, Texas State Dept. of Health, *The Latin American Health Problem in Texas*, Austin, 1940; Thomas, Howard E., and Florence Taylor, *Migrant Farm Labor in Colorado:* A Study of Migratory Families, 1951, pp. 35–69.

47. Thomas, Howard E., and Florence Taylor, *Op. cit.*

48. Among the few reports on political participation of Spanish-speaking people are: Chambers, R. L., "The New Mexico Pattern," *Common Ground*, vol. 9, Summer, 1949, pp. 20–27; Donnelly, Thomas C., editor, *Rocky Mountain Politics*, University of New Mexico Press, Albuquerque, 1940; McCully, John, "The Spanish-Speaking: North from Mexico," *The Reporter*, vol. 3, December 26, 1950, pp. 25–28; Ross, Fred M., *Community Organization in Mexican American Colonias:* A Progress Report, typescript prepared for the American Council on Race Relations, 1947; Russell, John C., "Racial Groups in the New Mexico Legislature," *Annals* of the American Academy of Political and Social Science, vol. 195, January, 1938, pp. 62–71; Idem, *State Regionalism in New Mexico*, Ph.D. dissertation, Stanford University, 1938; Idem, "State Regionalism in New Mexico," *Social Forces*, vol. 16, 1937, pp. 268–272; Tuck, Ruth, *Not with the Fist*, 1946.

49. The concept of class is one on which there is still much disagreement among social scientists. The term as used here refers to a population aggregation marked off from other parts of the population by common characteristics and differential status. One of the most important characteristics is the subjective identification of a person as belonging with certain other persons and sharing with them a set of social norms. Class is thus simply a convenient term to designate categories based on *subcultural* differences. The evaluative terms "upper," "middle," "lower" have been borrowed from everyday commonsense usage and are intended to be descriptive of differences in prestige and privilege rather than qualitative judgments about the comparative merits of one group or the other. The importance of class distinctions for anyone working in the field of health lies in the fact that there are correlations between class membership and the ways in which persons feel about or respond to illness and those who treat it.

Extended discussions of the concept of class and of differences among various class groups in the United States will be found in Centers, Richard, *The Psychology of Social Classes*, Princeton University Press, Princeton, N. J., 1949; Hollingshead, August B., *Elmtown's Youth*, John Wiley and Sons, New York, 1949; Jones, Alfred W., *Life, Liberty, and Property*, J. B. Lippincott Co., Philadelphia, 1941; Warner, W. Lloyd, Marchia Meeker, and Kenneth Eells, *Social Classes in America*, Science Research Associates, Chicago, 1949.

50. Much of the discussion of class differences among Spanish-Americans is based on Donovan Senter's "Acculturation Among New Mexican Villagers in Comparison to Adjustment Patterns of Other Spanish-Speaking Americans," *Rural Sociology*, vol. 10, March, 1945, pp. 31–47.

51. One of the few good analyses of class differences among Mexican-Americans and of the place of Mexican-Americans in the Anglo class system is that by Ozzie Simmons, *Anglo Americans and Mexican Americans in South Texas: A Study in Dominant-Subordinate Group Relations*, 1951, on which some of the discussion here is based.

52. Included in this class are many of that large body of migrant agricultural workers who in terms of almost any set of criteria would be assigned lower-class status.

53. This conclusion is based on extensive observation over a period of years of the marriage license notices published in newspapers in various parts of the Southwest. Sample tabulations made by Ozzie Simmons covering a thirty-seven-year period in one Texas county (*op. cit.*, p. 163) also show the proportion of intermarriages to be very low. The reason is probably not so much antagonism between the two groups—although this is a factor in some parts of the Southwest—as lack of opportunity for Anglos and Spanish-speaking people to come together in situations that lead to the development of intimate relationships.

54. For the twelve-month period ending June 30, 1951, the Immigration and Naturalization Service of the federal Department of Justice recorded a total of 51,058,946 persons coming into the United States across the Mexican border. This figure includes 25,939,023 aliens and 25,119,923 citizens. It does not include border crossings from the United States to Mexico or the extensive immigration of illegal and, hence, unrecorded wetbacks. Since multiple crossings by the same person are counted as separate entries, the total number of different persons crossing must have been considerably under 51 million. *Annual Report of the Immigration and Naturalization Service, for the Fiscal Year Ended June 30, 1951*, Table 25, mimeographed.

55. Other immigrant groups coming into the United States—with the possible exception of French Canadians—have been largely cut off from their places of origin and have received relatively little cultural reinforcement, except that which they made for themselves by living together in separate enclaved communities. The Spanish-speaking people of the Southwest, by contrast, have continued to have close and easy contact with the culture from which many of them have come.

56. The little town of Three Rivers, Texas, attained national and international prominence in 1949 as a result of the alleged refusal of a local undertaker to allow the use of his chapel for services for a Spanish-speaking soldier killed in action. After considerable controversy and an investigation by a committee from the Texas legislature, the soldier was buried at Arlington National Cemetery. In Three Rivers, at that time, the "Mexican" section of the local cemetery was separated from the Anglo section by a barbed wire fence.

57. There is some evidence that this situation is rapidly changing. In every state of the Southwest there is a growing group of young Spanish-speaking men and women with college and university training—received for the most part as a result of veterans' benefits—who are both capable and interested in improving the position of the Spanish-speaking population.

For a discussion of leadership in general among Spanish-Americans and the leadership pattern in a particular community, see Samora, Julian, *Minority Leadership in a Bi-Cultural Community*, 1953.

58. A possible exception might be the ditch organization whose function was to repair and maintain the irrigation ditches so necessary to the economy of the villages. But even though these more or less autonomous organizations had a semi-formal structure with elected officers and delegated responsibilities, membership and, to a considerable extent, leadership were highly institutionalized.

Fairly typical of the situation in Spanish-American villages were the findings described by Sigurd Johansen in his study of eight villages in Dona Ana County, New Mexico: "There are no organized special interest groups in any of the eight centers studied. The only organized group activity has been in connection with the church, and this has not developed sufficiently to make for special interest groups. There are no educational, recreational, economic, or political organizations in the centers, and the residents belong to none outside the centers. Sociability and recreational activities through social organizations are quite limited." See his "Family Organization in a Spanish-American Culture Area," *Sociology and Social Research*, vol. 28, November–December, 1943, p. 124.

Reasonably typical, too, is the experience of Denver, whose 25,000 or more Spanish-speaking residents have fewer than 20 nonchurch organizations, none of which includes more than a few dozen members.

59. By late 1953 the Forum had expanded to include chapters in other parts of Texas as well as in New Mexico, Arizona, and Colorado. In 1952 an attempt was made to bring together the various organizations of Spanish-speaking people into a national association under the leadership of Dr. George I. Sánchez, of the University of Texas, who has long been the most able and effective leader among the entire Spanish-speaking group. But the new organization, the American Council for Spanish-Speaking People, has been hampered by lack of funds and had not, by the end of 1953, been able to develop the kind of national cooperation it was working toward.

60. Something of the meaning of language shifts for familial and other relations can be seen in the experience of a Denver man who could not speak English when he came to Colorado at the age of eighteen. His mother still does not know English. His children do not know Spanish. So there can be no communication in the family between grandmother and grandchildren, except through the father or mother, or someone else who speaks both languages.

61. In addition to the extensive movement back and forth across the international border, there is much moving about of Spanish-speaking persons within the United States. Two hundred thousand or more Spanish-speaking people annually migrate in search of agricultural employment and during the course of a year live in a number of communities. The Selective Service draft and voluntary enlistments in the armed services have resulted in a great deal of movement both within the United States and outside by large numbers of Spanish-speaking young men. Large-scale migrations out of New Mexico villages took place in the 1920's and early 1930's and again in the late 1930's and early 1940's as jobs opened up in war industries and on the West Coast. See Loomis, Charles P., "Wartime Migration from the Rural Spanish-Speaking Villages of New Mexico," *Rural Sociology*, vol. 7, December, 1942, pp. 384–395. Movement of persons out of rural areas and into cities has been and still is heavy.

62. The great interest and increased activity in education in Mexico during the 1930's and 1940's supports rather than contradicts this generalization. Had there been any particular emphasis on formal education prior to that time new programs on such a scale would not have been necessary.

63. The state departments of education in each of the five southwestern states have separate departments or special personnel largely concerned with the problems of getting Spanish-speaking children into school and keeping them there. For a number of years there has been a loosely organized association of persons interested in education of Spanish-speaking children, the Southwestern Council for the Education of the Spanish-Speaking, which has held several meetings in which common problems could be discussed and progress reported.

64. For an excellent illustration of this point, see Zborowski, Mark, "Cultural Components in Response to Pain," *Journal of Social Issues*, vol. 8, no. 4, 1952, pp. 16–31.

Chapter III.   THE CULTURAL CHASM

1. Many of these notions were recorded years ago by Paul Taylor in his penetrating study of Nueces County, Texas. See his *An American-Mexican Frontier, Nueces County, Texas*, University of North Carolina Press, Chapel Hill, 1934.

Anyone who spends time in the Southwest is certain to have many of these ideas about the supposed characteristics of Spanish-speaking people brought to his attention. Among those most frequently heard are that the Spanish-speaking pretend not to know English when they really do; that they like to be crowded; that they are artistic and like gaudy colors; that they have a mechanical aptitude and good manual dexterity; that they are peculiarly adapted for stoop labor and are not bothered by its discomforts as an Anglo would be; that they do not mind working in the heat; that they can do hard work on little food; that they have a "gypsy spirit" and enjoy wandering; that they are sullen and suspicious; that they are all potential lawbreakers; that they cannot handle liquor; that they are gamblers; that they are sexually passionate; that they lack initiative and cannot work without constant direction; that they are docile and take orders well; that they are clannish; that they have no ambition and are satisfied with things as they are. While there are culturally derived attitudes and practices that give some semblance of truth to some of these beliefs it must be emphasized that there is as wide a range of differences within the Spanish-speaking group as would be found in any large population and that no generalization can be descriptive of the entire group.

2. U.S. Congress, House of Representatives, *Hearings Before the Committee on Education and Labor* . . . 81st Congress, 1st Session, on H.R. 2033. Government Printing Office, Washington, 1949, vol. 1, p. 629.

3. *Ibid.*, p. 632.

4. "In the stereotyped prejudices concerning others, there is usually contained the assumption that these other people are peculiarly adapted to the particular places which they have held up to the present time; it is a corollary

implication that they are not quite fit for new positions to which they may aspire." Hughes, Everett C., "Dilemmas and Contradictions of Status," *American Journal of Sociology*, vol. 50, March, 1945, p. 356.

A comprehensive discussion of the Anglo stereotype of Mexican-Americans in one area of the Southwest and its relationship to existing status patterns will be found in Simmons, Ozzie, *Anglo Americans and Mexican Americans in South Texas: A Study in Dominant-Subordinate Group Relations*, Ph.D. dissertation, Harvard University, 1951, chap. 8.

5. Since these unpublished theses are cited for illustrative purposes rather than for their factual content, they will not be further identified. The point of view they express is commonly held in the Southwest and the traits listed are among those frequently mentioned as characteristic of the "Mexican race."

6. It is interesting to note that in many areas where there is a widespread belief that "Mexicans are lazy," nearly all the jobs requiring hard physical effort are held by members of the Spanish-speaking group.

7. Discussions of the extent and some of the implications of language difference between English-speaking and Spanish-speaking in the Southwest will be found in Barker, George C., "Growing Up in a Bilingual Community," *The Kiva*, vol. 17, November–December, 1951, pp. 17–32; Idem, *Pachuco: An American-Spanish Argot and Its Social Function in Tucson, Arizona*, University of Arizona, Social Science Bulletin 18, Tucson, 1950; and Tireman, L. S., "Meaning and Reading," *Proceedings of the Fifth Annual Conference, Southwestern Conference on the Education of Spanish-Speaking People*, Los Angeles, January 18–20, 1951, pp. 14–20.

In parts of the Southwest it is not uncommon to hear two people conversing, one speaking English, the other Spanish. Quite common too is the tendency of some people to switch from one language to the other in the middle of a sentence. An amusing instance of this practice is reported by E. E. Mireles in *Lulac News* in the story of a young Mexican-American who wanted to go hunting but had no saddle. Asked why he did not borrow a saddle from Lolo, he replied: "Yo quiero borrow la saddle de Lolo, pero tengo fraid que Lolo se get mad porque la saddle se scratch up con el chaparro brush." Mr. Mireles, in the same article on what he calls "Tex-Mex Dialect," also tells the story of an Anglo storekeeper, a newcomer to the Southwest, who, while sitting in front of his store with a friend, was approached by a Mexican-American with the inquiry, "Mister Jones, you gare eggs today?" "No, Tomas," he replied, "no gare eggs today, but maybe tomorrow kechy." Then, turning to his friend, "You know, you can sure learn this Spanish lingo in no time."

8. Excellent illustrations of the ways in which language difference can lead to misunderstandings are included in Campa, Arthur L., "Language Barriers in Intercultural Relations," *Journal of Communication*, vol. 1, November, 1951, pp. 41–46.

9. "A culture is more than a collection of customs; it is a system of customs, each more or less meaningfully related to the others. Culture has structure as well as content. Recognition of this fact would enable us to understand the

tenacity of certain customs: they are hard to move because they are geared to other customs. . . ." Paul, Benjamin D., "Respect for Cultural Differences," *Community Development Bulletin*, vol. 4, June, 1953, p. 44.

10. The orientation to time of Spanish-Americans is specifically discussed in *Cultural Patterns and Technical Change*, edited by Margaret Mead, United Nations Educational, Scientific, and Cultural Organization, 1953, Paris, pp. 179–180. See also Florence Kluckhohn's discussion of what she has called the *mañana* configuration in *Los Atarqueños*, Ph.D. dissertation, Radcliffe College, 1941.

11. Campa, Arthur L., "Mañana Is Today," *New Mexico Quarterly*, vol. 9, 1939, pp. 3–11.

12. These and other Anglo characteristics have been discussed by many competent observers. Among the better accounts are: "Major Value-Orientations in America" in Williams, Robin M., Jr., *American Society: A Sociological Interpretation*, Alfred A. Knopf, New York, 1951; Kluckhohn, Clyde, and Florence R. Kluckhohn, "American Culture: Generalized Orientations and Class Patterns," *Conflicts of Power in Modern Culture*, edited by Lyman Bryson and others, Seventh Symposium of the Conference on Science, Philosophy, and Religion, New York, 1948; Gorer, Geoffrey, *The American People: A Study in National Character*, Cresset Press, London, 1948; Coleman, Lee, "What Is American: A Study of Alleged American Traits," *Social Forces*, vol. 19, May, 1941, pp. 492–499; Laski, Harold, *The American Democracy*, Viking Press, New York, 1948.

13. Cultural differences in attitudes toward work and success are illustrated in the story, frequently heard in the Southwest and related by Bennett Cerf in the "Trade Winds" column of the *Saturday Review*, about an eastern businessman. While strolling the railway station platform at Albuquerque, he observed a number of Pueblo Indian men sitting in the sun and was moved to indignation by what he considered an appalling waste of manpower. He approached one of the Indians and, with some asperity, asked, "Why aren't you working?"
"Why should I work?" replied the Indian.
"To earn money," said the businessman.
"Why should I want to earn money?" asked the Indian.
"If you work and earn money and save it, some day you will have enough so that you can retire and won't have to work any more."
"I'm not working now," said the Indian.

14. The low value on practicality and efficiency in the culture of the Spanish-speaking is clearly illustrated in *Human Problems and Technological Change: A Casebook*, edited by Edward H. Spicer, Russell Sage Foundation, New York, 1952, pp. 35–40. Case 2, "Corn and Custom" describes the failure of an attempt to introduce an unfamiliar strain of high-producing corn into the agriculture of a New Mexican village. Even though the yields were much greater than with old strains, the use of the new hybrid was soon abandoned because the appearance and flavor were thought to be inferior to those of the corn traditionally grown in the village.

15. Leadership among Spanish-Americans and the amount of membership and participation in various types of formal organizations are discussed at length by Julian Samora, in *Minority Leadership in a Bi-Cultural Community*, Ph.D. dissertation, Washington University, October, 1953.

16. The reciprocal of leadership is, of course, followership. It should be emphasized that, just as the village culture of the Spanish-speaking people offered few opportunities for the development of leadership, there were equally few chances for anyone to learn how to be a follower.

17. Possible exceptions to this rather sweeping generalization are the American Council for Spanish-Speaking People, under the very able leadership of Dr. George I. Sánchez; the American G.I. Forum, which has been rapidly expanding and is providing opportunities for the development and testing of talents of young leaders; and the Community Service Organization, which has been doing effective organizational work in and around Los Angeles.

Chapter IV.   HEALING WAYS

1. "Disease and its treatment are only in the abstract purely biological processes. Actually such facts as whether a person gets sick at all, what kind of disease he acquires, and what kind of treatment he receives, depend largely upon social factors. . . . I have been particularly impressed in the course of my anthropological and historical studies by the degree to which even the notion of disease itself depends rather on the decisions of society than on objective facts." Ackerknecht cites the case of a South American tribe in which *pinto* (dyschromic spirochetosis) is so common that those who have it are regarded as healthy, those who do not as ill. Ackerknecht, Erwin H., "The Role of Medical History in Medical Education," *Bulletin of the History of Medicine*, vol. 21, March–April, 1947, pp. 135–145.

For a discussion of illness as a social role see: Henderson, L. J., "The Physician and Patient as a Social System," *New England Journal of Medicine*, vol. 212, May 2, 1953, pp. 819–823; Parsons, Talcott, "Illness and the Role of the Physician," *American Journal of Orthopsychiatry*, vol. 21, July, 1951, pp. 452–460; Idem, "Social Structure and Dynamic Process: The Case of Modern Medical Practice" in *The Social System*, The Free Press, Glencoe, Ill., 1951, chap. 10; Parsons, Talcott, and Renée Fox, "Illness, Therapy and the Modern Urban American Family," *Journal of Social Issues*, vol. 8, no. 4, 1952, pp. 31–44.

2. The distinction between these various types of lay practitioners is not always clear and the terms are sometimes used interchangeably. In general *parteras* are concerned with childbirth and associated illness conditions: *curanderas* and *médicas* devote themselves to what in Anglo culture is called internal medicine; *albolarias* and *brujas* represent, respectively, the benevolent and malevolent aspects of witchcraft.

3. Folk medicine, as the term is used here, is not identical with primitive medicine. Folk medicine, in any culture, consists of the beliefs, practices, and collective attitudes which are the common possession of all the people of that culture. See Saunders, Lyle, and Gordon Hewes, "Folk Medicine and Medical Practice," *Journal of Medical Education*, vol. 28, September, 1953, pp. 43–46.

4. The differences between folk and "scientific" medicine are sharply illuminated in a discussion of "Medicine and Magic in Rural Rajasthan, India" by G. Morris Carstairs, in a book of case studies on the social and cultural aspects of public health being prepared by Dr. Benjamin Paul, Harvard School of Public Health, for Russell Sage Foundation.

5. The principal source of information on Mexican folk medicine has been the studies of George Foster and his associates in the Smithsonian Institute of Social Anthropology, particularly their mimeographed report, *A Cross-Cultural Analysis of a Technical Aid Program*, Smithsonian Institution, Washington, July 25, 1951. Other helpful studies dealing in whole or part with the folk medicine of Latin America are: Adams, Richard N., *Un analisis de las enfermedades y sus curaciones en una poblacion indigena de Guatemala*, Instituto de Nutricion de Centro America y Panama, Guatemala, October, 1951; Foster, George, "Relationship Between Spanish and Spanish-American Folk Medicine," *Journal of American Folklore*, vol. 66, July–September, 1953, pp. 201–217; Gillin, John, "Magical Fright," *Psychiatry*, vol. 2, no. 4, 1948, pp. 387–400; Idem, *The Culture of Security in San Carlos*, Middle American Research Institute, Publication 16, Tulane University, New Orleans, 1951; Redfield, Robert, *The Folk Culture of Yucatan*, University of Chicago Press, 1941; Simpson, Eyler N., *The Ejido:* Mexico's Way Out, University of North Carolina Press, Chapel Hill, 1937; Whetten, Nathan L., *Rural Mexico*, University of Chicago Press, 1948.

6. "Good health involves also the maintenance of that median condition which the native expresses in terms of heat and cold. Some persons are naturally hot, others cold. Two persons representing the extremes of such natural conditions should not marry; the outcome will not be fortunate. Nor should a man whose blood is 'hot' attempt to raise kinds of domestic animals known to be characteristically 'cold.' The food one eats and the beverages one drinks are known to have their characters in terms of these opposites. Something that is a little too 'hot,' as beef, may be made safer for consumption by adding a little lime juice, which is 'cold.' But it is dangerous to bring the greatest extremes together: honey is very 'hot' and it should not be followed by water, which is 'cold.' If a man has a fever, he is hot, and he may be treated with moderate amounts of herbs or foods which are cold. On the other hand, a person who is weak is 'cold' and should be given 'hot' things to eat and drink." Redfield, Robert, *The Folk Culture of Yucatan*, University of Chicago Press, 1941, pp. 128–129. The concepts of 'hot' and 'cold' are not nearly so prevalent in the Southwest as in Mexico and other Latin American countries.

7. The vast sums spent on laxatives and the ubiquity of advertising references to the desirability of achieving "regularity" are evidence that the concept of a "clean" interior is also an important component in Anglo folk medicine.

8. Notions about the importance of blood for health and the dangers of losing any considerable amounts of it may be important factors in the reluctance of Spanish-speaking people in parts of the Southwest to contribute to blood banks.

9. Injections of various kinds may be obtained from druggists or other sellers of medicines or from an *inyeccionista*, a person, usually female and with some minimal training in a health field such as nursing, who specializes in the giving of this type of service.

10. Simmons, Ozzie, *Anglo Americans and Mexican Americans in South Texas*, Ph.D. dissertation, Harvard University, 1951, p. 98.

11. "In many cultures where the individual is continuous with his unit, the isolation of the ill is completely unacceptable. Dr. Carl Binger reports that when he was dealing with a typhus epidemic among the Greeks of Macedonia at the end of World War I, the family would hide its sick under piles of clothing or in the cellar rather than show them to a physician who might take them to a hospital, though they knew that to keep the sick with them might mean death for the family. This attitude is reported to be present today also, obstructing the campaign against tuberculosis. People do know the danger to which they are exposed, but they feel that to isolate the sick individual, or to take precautions protecting the rest of the family, would be to reject a member of the family. In West Africa 'the whole family would rather contract disease and die from it than part with the infected member.' Spanish-speaking people of New Mexico protest that no harm can come to them from their loved ones. . . ." Mead, Margaret, editor, *Cultural Patterns and Technical Change*, United Nations Educational, Scientific, and Cultural Organization, Paris, 1953, p. 247.

12. Extensive accounts of folk medical beliefs and practices of Mexican-Americans will be found in Dodson, Ruth, "Folk Curing Among the Mexicans" in *Tone the Bell Easy*, Texas Folklore Society, Publication 10, Southern Methodist University Press, Dallas, 1932, pp. 82–98; and Hudson, William M., editor, *The Healer of Los Olmos and Other Mexican Lore*, Texas Folklore Society, Publication 24, Southern Methodist University Press, Dallas, 1951.

13. Curtin, L. S. M., *Healing Herbs of the Upper Rio Grande*, Laboratory of Anthropology, Santa Fe, 1947. This fascinating book has been drawn upon as the source of much of the information presented herein on Spanish-American herbal lore. Other sources are: Campa, Arthur L., "Some Herbs and Plants of Early California," *Western Folklore*, vol. 9, October, 1950, pp. 338–347; Hurt, Wesley, *Manzano: A Study of Community Disorganization*, Master's thesis, University of New Mexico, 1941; Bourke, John G., "Notes on the Language and Folk-Usage of the Rio Grande Valley," *Journal of American Folklore*, vol. 9, April–June, 1896, pp. 81–115; Moya, Benjamin S., *Superstitions and Beliefs Among the Spanish-Speaking People of New Mexico*, Master's thesis, University of New Mexico, 1940.

14. Curtin, L. S. M., *Op. cit.*, p. 11.

15. van der Eerden, Sister Mary Lucia, *Maternity Care in a Spanish-American Community of New Mexico*, Catholic University of America, Anthropological Series 13, Catholic University of America Press, Washington, 1948.

16. When told that an eclipse was about to occur, a young Spanish-American married woman who was confined in a Denver hospital during 1953 requested a "pass key" to wear during the danger period.

17. It is easy to understand why the services of a *partera* might be preferred to those of more highly trained physicians and nurses. *Parteras* are known to be *simpatico*, or sympathetic, since they are themselves Spanish-speaking and understand the point of view and ways of thinking and feeling of the mother and her family. They are relatively inexpensive as compared with the costs of Anglo medical and hospital care. And they do not require that the patient leave familiar surroundings and go among strangers in what might become a period of crisis.

At the time of her study, Sister Mary Lucia found more than 50 *parteras* practicing in Taos County. None lived at Ranchos, but five were available in a nearby village and one, who owned an automobile, was able to come from Taos. No special qualifications were required for becoming a *partera*, but the job was regarded as a highly responsible one requiring considerable knowledge and a willingness to work hard, long hours, and at inconvenient times. Most *parteras* began their profession at a fairly advanced age, after having had much experience in bearing children of their own.

The information available to *parteras* came mainly from three sources: other *parteras* who were the repository of village knowledge about childbirth; Anglo physicians, with some of whom a number of the *parteras* had a good working relationship; and the New Mexico State Department of Public Health, which has been seeking in a systematic and organized way to make the midwives more proficient. The process of acquiring information about their work is difficult, for most of the *parteras* can read only Spanish or cannot read at all, and have reached the age where it is not easy to acquire new knowledge. Techniques must be memorized and retained in memory for use when needed.

For a number of years the State Department of Public Health has conducted a program for the training and supervision of midwives. The result has been a reduction in the number of practicing midwives, an increase in the competence of those who remain in the field, and the development of relations between physicians and midwives to the point where the latter feel free to refer cases in which labor is especially difficult or complications arise.

18. This is a highly generalized account, following the description as given by Sister Mary Lucia. Certainly today, and undoubtedly during the time about which she was writing, many local variations of each of these details exist and are followed by many families. In childbirth, as in the treatment of many diseases, the folk medicine of the Spanish-Americans is rich in alternative procedures.

19. Anglo physicians advise first of all that women be delivered in hospitals rather than homes. However, in northern New Mexico there are frequently many reasons why hospital delivery is either not possible or not preferred by the expectant mother and her family.

20. The catalogue of the Trinidad "laboratory" gives a long list of "yerbas and medicinales," priced at from 25 cents to $3.00, including (using the cata-

logue spelling) Raiz de Immortal, Yerba De El Manzo Raiz, Chuchupaste, Gobernadora, Alusema, Flor de Mansanilla, Polello, Yerba Buena, Oregano, Valeriana, Alumbre, Romero, Gardenias, Yerba Mora, Culiantrillo, and Flor de Asufre Mexicano, as well as syrup of onions, green oil liniment, an eye wash made of "el manzo herb," and a preparation advertised as a cockroach chaser.

21. Samora, Julian, *The Acculturation of the Spanish-Speaking People of Fort Collins, Colorado, in Selected Culture Areas*, Master's thesis, Colorado Agricultural and Mechanical College, 1947, pp. 120–125. It should perhaps be pointed out that there is no problem of availability of Anglo medical care in Fort Collins.

22. Thomas, Howard E., and Florence Taylor, "Medical and Health Care" in *Migrant Farm Labor in Colorado:* A Study of Migratory Families, National Child Labor Committee, New York, 1951, chap. 4. Inasmuch as these were low-income families living in rural areas, both the availability and cost of Anglo medicine would be limiting factors.

23. *Ibid.*, p. 55.

24. *New Mexico Health Council News-Letter*, November, 1946.

25. Foster, George M., editor, *A Cross-Cultural Analysis of a Technical Aid Program*, July 25, 1951, p. 85.
"The concept of modesty, closely allied to that of morality, is inculcated at an early age. Although an entire family may live in a single room, each turns to the wall when dressing and undressing. After childhood, individuals never see others, even of the same sex, unclothed. Intimacies between the parents do not occur until after all others are asleep. The subject of sex is not mentioned between husband and wife nor explained to the children. The young people are expected to observe life of farm animals and they are known to discuss between themselves the immoral conduct of certain villagers, especially those caught in the problems of what they conceive to be rapid Anglicization. But on the surface, modesty and morality are equally to be observed at all times. Even the use of better clothes and grooming than those of one's neighbors is considered immodest because it is believed to advertise a girl's intention of attracting men for immoral purposes." Hawley, Florence, and Donovan Senter, "Group-Designed Behavior Patterns in Two Acculturating Groups," *Southwestern Journal of Anthropology*, vol. 2, Summer, 1946, p. 139.

Chapter V. BRIDGING THE GAP

1. Taos and Costilla counties are believed to be fairly typical of the situation of rural Spanish-Americans. They are not, however, equally typical with regard to the conditions under which rural Mexican-Americans and Mexicans live.

2. Longmore, T. Wilson, and Theo L. Vaughan, *Taos County Cooperative Health Association, 1942–43*, Bureau of Agricultural Economics, U.S. Dept. of

Agriculture, Little Rock, Ark., September, 1944, mimeographed. This study reports the results of a series of interviews with about 10 per cent of the first year's membership.

3. Membership fees were computed in accordance with a complicated formula which provided for: (a) a flat annual fee of $32 for nonfarm families; (b) 1 per cent of annual family income up to $100 per person per year, plus 3 per cent of additional family income; (c) special rates, based on a proportion of family rates, for unattached individuals. Only families and individuals whose annual income was less than $1,200 were eligible.

It is perhaps significant that at the end of a year of operation more than a third of a sample group of member families interviewed had no knowledge of how their fee was determined. Longmore and Vaughan, *Op. cit.*

4. For a description of the County and its people see Sánchez, George I., *Forgotten People*, University of New Mexico Press, Albuquerque, 1940; and Reid, J. T., *It Happened in Taos*, University of New Mexico Press, 1946.

5. Longmore and Vaughan, *Op. cit.*

6. A fairly detailed analysis of the Costilla County Health Association by Julian Samora and Lyle Saunders is included in a forthcoming Russell Sage Foundation book on the social and cultural aspects of public health, edited by Benjamin Paul of the Harvard School of Public Health. Mr. Samora was the Association's first president.

7. The paid-up membership in the Costilla County Health Association by years from 1946 to 1952 is given below.

Year	Spanish-American	Anglo	Total paid-up member families
1946–1947	369	36	405
1947–1948	239	48	287
1948–1949	73	17	90
1949–1950	44	16	60
1950–1951	13	12	25
1951–1952	1	0	1
August, 1952	0	0	0

Source: Membership records of the Association.

8. In the summer of 1953 new efforts were being made, with the cooperation of the State Department of Public Health, the Extension Division of the University of Colorado, and the University of Colorado Medical School, to work out a satisfactory program for meeting the health and medical needs of the Costilla County population.

9. There were undoubtedly many factors other than cultural difference which influenced the outcome of the Taos and Costilla County projects. Health programs for low-income rural people anywhere are difficult to organize and finance, and the geographic location and economic situation of these two counties were such as to make them unpromising at best. But the type of medical

care provided and the kinds of relationships necessary to obtain it were relatively unfamiliar to many of the people of Taos and Costilla counties, whereas their former techniques and relationships were both familiar and reasonably satisfactory.

10. Foster, George M., editor, *A Cross-Cultural Anthropological Analysis of a Technical Aid Program*, Smithsonian Institution, Washington, July 25, 1951, mimeographed.

11. Personal communication received in August, 1952. Dr. Samora, a sociologist, is on the teaching staff of Adams State College, Alamosa, Colorado.

12. Insurance salesmen in Costilla County report that quite a few life and hospitalization policies are sold in the County. However, a very high proportion of them are allowed to lapse after the first payment.

13. For a description of leadership patterns and expectations in one part of Costilla County, see Samora, Julian, *Minority Leadership in a Bi-Cultural Community*, Ph.D. dissertation, Washington University, October, 1953.

14. This description, of course, represents a great oversimplification of leadership patterns in both cultures. It does, however, point up some of the essential differences in the approach of the two cultures to health services and medical care. The leaders in the Taos and Costilla programs were, in part, self-selected and, in part, chosen on the basis of their possession of achieved qualities: technical training, experience, specialized knowledge and skills. They were concerned specifically with providing medical care and were not expected to be leaders in any other type of activity. Their leadership was exercised through a formal organization—the Association—and they were interchangeable and, in fact, did change during the life of the Association. Community leaders within the Spanish-speaking group in Costilla County are largely selected on the basis of ascribed characteristics (age, sex, family membership) and tend to be looked upon as general leaders in a variety of situations and activities. Although they operate in and through the few formal organizations of Spanish-speaking people in the County, they do not always or necessarily hold office in these organizations and they are influential in areas outside the concern of existing organizations. Their position is not readily transferable.

15. In his study of organizations in "Mountain Town" Samora (*op. cit.*) found practically none that was not directly or indirectly related to membership in the Catholic or Protestant church.

16. "Not only must he [the physician] know the wide range of facilities and resources which the community provides for the health and welfare of its citizens—from visiting nurse to job placement service—and know how and when to direct patients to them, but he must also be prepared to assume a pivotal position on a health team of many players. He must know how to work in intelligent cooperation with representatives of more than a score of specialties and subspecialties of medicine itself; and with a great variety of other people on this team, within the hospital and within the community—dentists, nurses, technicians, occupational therapists, dietitians, medical and psychiatric social workers and many others. He must be aware of the contribution that each can

make to an improvement of individual and collective health in the community, and try to make the sum total of their contributions result in an integrated, rather than piecemeal, health service to his patients." Clark, Katharine G., *Preventive Medicine in Medical Schools:* Report of Colorado Springs Conference, November, 1952, published for the Conference as Part 2 of the *Journal of Medical Education,* vol. 28, October, 1953, p. 7.

17. President's Commission on Migratory Labor, *Migratory Labor in American Agriculture,* Government Printing Office, Washington, 1951, pp. 153–159.

18. "The Anglo himself is constantly rediscovering that the extended Spanish family must be considered in any plans made for or by the individual Manito [Spanish-speaking person]. To a people whose opportunities for accumulating world goods are so largely limited by their environment, spiritual and psychological values may loom larger than to peoples more materialistically blessed. . . . Through the delights and securities provided by social and economic cooperation within the extended Spanish family and the village, the poverty-stricken present can be eased, forgotten, or even made to appear desirable." Hawley, Florence, and Donovan Senter, "Group-Designed Behavior Patterns in Two Acculturating Groups," *Southwestern Journal of Anthropology,* vol. 2, Summer, 1946, pp. 136–137.

The importance of the family as a basic social institution in Spanish-American villages and in Mexico has been emphasized many times. See Johansen, Sigurd, "Family Organization in a Spanish-American Culture Area," *Sociology and Social Research,* vol. 28, 1943, pp. 123–131; Hayner, Norman S., "Notes on the Changing Mexican Family," *American Sociological Review,* vol. 7, 1942, pp. 489–497; Humphrey, Norman D., "The Cultural Background of the Mexican Immigrant," *Rural Sociology,* vol. 13, September, 1948, pp. 239–255; Idem, "The Changing Structure of the Detroit Mexican Family: An Index of Acculturation," *American Sociological Review,* vol. 9, 1944, pp. 622–626; Mead, Margaret, editor, *Cultural Patterns and Technical Change,* United Nations Educational, Scientific, and Cultural Organization, Paris, 1953, pp. 170–174; Walter, Paul A., Jr., "The Spanish-Speaking Community in New Mexico," *Sociology and Social Research,* vol. 24, November–December, 1939, pp. 150–157; Idem, *A Study of Isolation and Social Change in Three Spanish-Speaking Villages of New Mexico,* Ph.D. dissertation, Stanford University, 1938.

The extended family pattern frequently breaks down in the urban setting before the controls necessary for the successful functioning of the Anglo type family are learned. In such cases, medical and related problems are intensified. In instances where family ties have been kept strong, either because of fortunate circumstances, short residence in the city, or extraordinary strength of the family relationship, the family can be a powerful factor in resisting some types of Anglo medical service. It could also, properly used, be an equally powerful aid to the persons seeking to give medical assistance.

19. "One of the most difficult problems facing Anglo physicians in dealing with the Manitos [Spanish-Americans] is the concept that any discussion of the functions of the body is strictly taboo on the basis of modesty and is considered doubly obscene if given before a third person. As the Manitos customarily take

another member of the family with them when seeing a doctor, their sensitivities often are insulted as much by the words of the doctor as by his necessary physical examination. Enraged patients sometimes return home, throw their medicine away, and swear they will never take anything prescribed by these evil persons. The bases of such reactions usually are as little understood by the outraged physician as the physician's actions are understood by the modest Manitos." Hawley, Florence, and Donovan Senter, *Op. cit.*, p. 139.

20. Foster, George M., "Relationships Between Theoretical and Applied Anthropology: A Public Health Program Analysis," *Human Organization*, vol. 11, Fall, 1952, pp. 5-16.

21. For an elaboration of this point, see Saunders, Lyle, and Gordon W. Hewes, "Folk Medicine and Medical Practice," *Journal of Medical Education*, vol. 28, September, 1953, pp. 43-46.

Chapter VI.   A WIDENING VIEW

1. One significant project is the Demonstration Area program now being carried on in El Salvador as a cooperative venture of the government of that country, the World Health Organization, UNESCO, the Food and Agriculture Organization, and other international agencies. Its purpose is to work out a pattern for providing medical services and facilities in rural areas of Latin America and at the same time to serve as a training center for personnel who will staff the facilities and provide services in El Salvador and other countries. Of great interest and significance are the attempts being made here to foster the team concept in the giving of health service and medical care and the experimentation with new relationships within the team and new categories of auxiliary personnel to serve on it.

2. It can be expected that in the future more and more attention will be paid to the total social and cultural setting as attempts are made to improve the health levels and practices of what may now be referred to as "medically underdeveloped" areas. One impressive evidence of a trend in this direction is the report, edited by Margaret Mead, which was prepared by a group from the World Federation for Mental Health at the request of the United Nations Educational, Scientific, and Cultural Organization. Addressed to "all those who are immediately concerned, at any level, with purposive technological change" the report, *Cultural Patterns and Technical Change*, includes brief reports on five whole cultures, analyses of the types of problems that may be encountered in attempts to introduce technological change in agriculture, nutrition, maternal and child care, public health, industry, or education, and a statement of the principles involved in developing and preserving mental health during the period in which change is introduced.

Significant, too, is the action of the Institute of Inter-American Affairs which in the past few years has been utilizing the knowledge and techniques of cultural anthropologists in an effort to improve the effectiveness of their technical aid programs in the field of health. Some of the findings of this group of anthropologists are available in Foster, George M., editor, *A Cross-Cultural Analysis of a Technical Aid Program*, Smithsonian Institution, Washington, July 25, 1951, mimeographed; Foster, George M., "Relationships Between Theoretical and Applied Anthropology: A Public Health Program Analysis," *Human Organization*, vol. 11, Fall, 1952, pp. 5–16; and in the article by Foster in which the following recommendations were made to the Institute:

"Knowledge of the people is just as important in many aspects of a public health program as is knowledge of medical service. It is therefore recommended that, in Institute of Inter-American Affairs' program planning, provision be made for systematic research into the form and content of the cultures of each country in which work is carried out. Such research should include anthropological, sociological, psychological, and economic studies. It is further recommended that the information so obtained be utilized in planning and operation of *Servicio* projects, both to determine the economic and social potential of a country which sets absolute limits on the changes which can be brought about, and for the purpose of reducing to the lowest possible level cultural barriers to general acceptance of public health programs." "Use of Anthropological Methods and Data in Planning and Operation," *Public Health Reports*, vol. 68, September, 1953, pp. 841–857.

3. An illuminating and helpful analysis of the kinds of adaptations practitioners of scientific medicine must make if their techniques and services are to be acceptable to people of other cultures is that by Richard N. Adams in a report on the medical beliefs and practices of a town in Guatemala. Adams says, in part: "In dealing with the problem of making acceptable the use of the new drugs and other types of cures, there are a number of steps which can be taken. First, a compromise must be made between the local practices and those of a doctor. From the Magdaleño's point of view, a new drug, technique, or cure is reasonably acceptable if he can understand how it is going to work to get at the causes of the ailment. He will be much more prone to give it a chance if he thinks it may be effective. Also, if there is some unfortunate reaction, such as a child vomiting up the pills administered, he will be likely to blame the vomiting on the recalcitrant nature of the illness rather than on the pills. From the doctor's point of view, it will be necessary to do a number of things. As was mentioned earlier, he must make every effort to be sure that the specific remedy he recommends will have some degree of success. He must make it clear in giving the remedy that this remedy has a definite name and that it is good for only certain types of ailments. He must point out that it may not be good for other ailments and that it might actually be harmful in certain situations. This will make sense, since the taking of hot herbs is bad for hotness but good for coldness. The doctor must make a real attempt to understand the system of rationalization which underlines the beliefs concerning the causes of ailments. . . . He must attempt to talk with every patient to find out what things they have done in the recent past which might be interpreted in these terms and might be at the back of the

patient's mind as the real cause of the illness. He must then strike a mean somewhere between the patient's explanation of the illness and his own diagnosis, and explain the effectiveness of the remedy in terms which will make sense to the patient. If there is too great a discrepancy between his scientific explanation and the patient's conditional explanation, he must, at least for the present, let the scientific explanation go, and interpret the cause and cure in terms which the patient can understand. He must get to know his patients, if possible, so that he can judge which persons can understand explanations of a more scientific nature and which may have to be given explanations in strictly traditional terms. It will be easier for the medical man to do this if he realizes that the cures used at the present in Magdaleña, as those of the ancient Maya, are reasonably arrived at. . . . If we realize that the contemporary Magdaleña system of explanation and curing is, for the most part, a highly rational and to some degree pragmatic system and that divergencies from this rationalism are no more frequent than among laymen in our own society, perhaps the doctor will be a little less reluctant to make an attempt to understand and utilize the local practices and beliefs instead of refuting them and fighting them. It ought to be added that while theories and studies of medicine may be scientific, a great deal of the practice of scientific medicine involves psychological sensitivity on the part of the doctor. In our society, it may be permissible to give a pink sugar pill to an aged spinster since the doctor probably understands the psychology of this person well enough to know that it will at least do her some good psychologically; the same does not follow in the treatment of Magdaleños, however, because at present there are very few doctors who understand the psychology of the Magdaleño well enough to recognize what the equivalent of the pink sugar pill may be. To the Magdaleño there is no "cure-all." An illness is a specific thing caused by a specific set of conditions and curable by remedies which have specific qualities to affect those conditions." Adams, Richard N., *An Analysis of Medical Beliefs and Practices in a Guatemalan Indian Town*, Pan American Sanitary Bureau, Guatemala, April, 1953, mimeographed. (Spanish edition published by the Instituto Indigenista Nacional de Guatemala, 1952.)

4. "The time has long since passed when the medical lore, the leechcraft, of isolated peoples could be classified with the quaint and queer in the album of medical curiosities. Nor is it sufficient to record the bare details of that lore, as is almost invariably done in present-day histories of medicine. Medicine is a social phenomenon, and the medicine of any people can only be effectively understood as such. For this reason, it is necessary to gain an understanding of the society as a whole if its medical knowledge and practice are to be understood in their full significance—if, indeed, that knowledge and practice are to be understood at all. This is particularly the case in isolated societies, in which medicine is much more closely integrated with the institutions and beliefs of the society as a whole than it is in the diversified structures of Western societies. . . ." Ashley-Montagu, Francis, *New England Journal of Medicine*, vol. 235, July 11, 1946, pp. 43–49.

5. See Clark, Katharine G., *Preventive Medicine in Medical Schools:* Report of Colorado Springs Conference, November, 1952, published for the Conference as Part 2 of the *Journal of Medical Education*, vol. 28, October, 1953. With respect

to professional education the Report states on page 27: "College students preparing for a future of work with people must have a knowledge of people, both as biological and social organisms. Thus, as is becoming increasingly recognized, along with courses in sciences and mathematics, education in the humanities and in the social and behavioral sciences is extremely valuable."

6. The plan for the Institutes is discussed by Dr. George Packer Berry, dean of the Harvard Medical School, in his presidential address to the November, 1952, meeting of the Association of American Medical Colleges. Dean Berry's address was published in the *Journal of Medical Education*, vol. 28, March, 1953, pp. 17–42. One brief quotation from pages 32–33 will perhaps serve to underscore the point that there is a trend in medical education and medical programs toward enlisting the collaborative efforts of social scientists: "No one can seriously challenge the value of the contributions that natural science has made to clinical medicine. It is also important to appreciate that significant new avenues to understanding man are being opened up rapidly by psychology, anthropology, and other of the social sciences. To say this does not imply that any of the old ways of characterizing man are losing their value—quite the opposite! It means, rather, that students should have a better chance to view the patient in broader perspective, taking into account the entire family and community setting. Man shall not live by bread alone—the orthodox basic medical sciences, though more and more important, are less and less the *whole* story." (Italics in original.)

7. For an appreciation of the extent of that literature and annotated reference to specific titles, see Rosenfeld, Leonard S., Beatrice Crowther, and Martha D. Ring, *Social and Preventive Medicine:* Content and Technical Methods, Division of Public Health Methods, U.S. Public Health Service, Washington, September, 1952, mimeographed.

Indicative, too, of the increasing interrelations of medicine and social science are the inclusion in the *Quarterly Index Medicus* of such headings as anthropology, social conditions, sociology, economics, primitive medicine, race, social aspects of medicine, and the family; the growing number of publications by such social scientists as Bernhard Stern, Oswald Hall, Leo Simmons, Richard Adams, Benjamin Paul, Talcott Parsons, Margaret Mead, Frances Macgregor, Mark Zborowski, and others on various aspects of medical care and practice; the numerous projects listed in the annual reports of Russell Sage Foundation, Commonwealth Fund, the Kellogg Foundation, and similar organizations; and the recent creation by the Social Science Research Council of committees on Psychiatry and Social Science, and Preventive Medicine and Social Science.

8. A new curriculum is being organized at Yale which will provide to doctoral candidates in social science an opportunity to work in some field of medicine during their training period.

9. "Although no attempt was made to specify the particular subjects that should be prerequisite to medical education, it is clear that college courses in the physical sciences should give the student not only factual information but should emphasize the methods of approach to problems in science; courses in mathematics should lead toward his understanding of quantitative methodology;

courses in psychology should lay the groundwork for his appreciation of human behavior in the individual, and its variability; courses in the humanities should sharpen his appreciation of man as a creative, reasoning and emotional being; courses in history, sociology, and economics should give him an understanding of man's relation to society and the institutions society has evolved." Clark, Katharine G., *Op. cit.*, pp. 27–28.

10. A detailed discussion of this question will be found in *Preventive Medicine in Medical Schools:* Report of Colorado Springs Conference, November, 1952.

11. See Blackwell, Gordon W., "Behavioral Science and Health," *Social Forces*, vol. 32, December, 1953, pp. 211–215.

12. For a somewhat similar listing and discussion of preconceptions of types of bias that interfere with an objective evaluation of the responses of culturally different people to public health programs, see Paul, Benjamin D., "Respect for Cultural Differences," *Community Development Bulletin*, vol. 4, June, 1953, pp. 42–47. Dr. Paul centers his discussion in the meanings and assumptions that underlie the use of such terms as backwardness, superstition, customs, education, and apathy.

13. For a more detailed discussion of this bias than can be given here, see Dunham, Barrows, *Man Against Myth*, Little, Brown and Co., Boston, 1948, pp. 31–56; Lippmann, Walter, *Public Opinion*, Macmillan Co., New York, 1936, particularly pp. 121–126; and Faris, Ellsworth, *The Nature of Human Nature*, McGraw-Hill Book Co., New York, 1937.

14. This point is developed at some length in Lippmann, Walter, *Op. cit.*, pp. 3–32; and Davis, Kingsley, *Human Society*, Macmillan Co., New York, 1949, pp. 128–133.

15. "It should be constantly borne in mind in cross-cultural situations that the cultures in which we grow up predispose us to certain views and values. We come to another culture with preconceptions about what is good and what is rational or sensible which do not hold good universally and these preconceptions may result in great misunderstanding. Setting aside those preconceptions, especially in the highly developed fields of technical specialism and administrative management in our culture, is one of the most difficult, as well as most necessary, disciplines in any work that goes on across cultural boundaries." Spicer, Edward H., editor, *Human Problems in Technological Change*, Russell Sage Foundation, New York, 1952, pp. 291–292. See also in this work "Introduction by the Editor," pp. 13–20 and "Conceptual Tools for Solving Human Problems," pp. 283–294.

16. "The permissible and expected behaviors of the physician in our society have little meaning in the Guatemalan Indian culture. Premises of thinking, beliefs concerning curing, action patterns involved in curing and in gaining rapport, the patient-doctor relationship, and the general content of the physician's behavior are ambiguous in the Indian context. In order to make adjustments for this situation we need not only study the culture of the Indian; we must also have more systematic knowledge about the medical subculture from which the doctors, nurses, and other personnel come. It is not merely that

Indians are different, but that doctors and Indians are different. Coordination and integration of medical practice requires more than impressionistic knowledge of both sides of the meeting ground." Adams, Richard N., "Notes on the Application of Anthropology," *Human Organization*, vol. 12, Summer, 1953, pp. 10–14.

17. An illustrative case in the field of public health is the account of an attempt to establish a stable water supply in the Viru Valley of Peru. See Spicer, Edward H., editor, *Op. cit.*, Case 7, pp. 113–123.

18. The operation of this bias is illustrated by the case of a woman who came to the outpatient clinic of a public hospital in a southwestern city for the examination and diagnosis of a small lump that had appeared on her breast. The young physician whom she consulted bluntly told her, after just a few minutes' external examination, that she had cancer and must be operated upon immediately. She demurred; he insisted. Finally, after some minutes of discussion, the woman was told, "If you won't have an operation there is nothing we can do for you." Including the time spent in waiting to see the physician, this woman had spent approximately forty minutes in the clinic. Yet in that brief time she had been examined, informed that she had a very serious disease, and practically commanded to submit immediately to a dangerous and disfiguring operation. Also, in the twenty minutes or so that he spent with her, the physician had exhausted all of his medical resources except one, and that one was offered in a coldly impersonal take-it-or-leave-it manner. Obviously, here was no concern with anything but the disease.

An excellent discussion of the possible effects of this bias, written from the point of view of a physician, is "Patient Relations," in Truman, Stanley R., *The Doctor*, Williams and Wilkins Co., Baltimore, 1951, pp. 120–135. See also Ginsburg, Ethel L. *Public Health Is People*, Commonwealth Fund, New York, 1950; and Robinson, G. Canby, *The Patient as a Person*, Commonwealth Fund, 1939.

19. Stieglitz, Edward J., "The Integration of Clinical and Social Medicine" in *Social Medicine:* Its Derivations and Objectives, edited by Iago Galdston, Commonwealth Fund, 1949, pp. 87–88.

DEMOGRAPHIC CHARACTERISTICS OF THE SPANISH-SPEAKING POPULATION OF THE SOUTHWEST

It is very difficult to say with certainty how many Spanish-speaking people there are in the Southwest or in what ways they are like or different from the general population. Census tabulations, until recently, have been somewhat unsatisfactory, and the few studies undertaken either have been concerned with only small portions of the total Spanish-speaking population, or have represented little more than fairly well-informed guesses as to the numbers and characteristics of this population group.

Much of the lack of adequate demographic information has been due to the difficulty of finding any accurate and usable criterion by which the Spanish-speaking people could easily be distinguished from the general population. Various criteria have been used at different times—place of birth, mother tongue, surname—but none has been found to be entirely satisfactory and the change from one to another has made comparison between reports difficult.

The first attempt by the Bureau of the Census to make available separate information about the whole Spanish-speaking population came in 1930 when a special category of "Mexicans" was set up. The instructions given to enumerators were that they should count as Mexicans "all persons born in Mexico, or having parents born in Mexico, who were not definitely white, Negro, Indian, Chinese, or Japanese." Aside from the confusion of racial and nationality concepts and the fact that a high proportion of all persons born in Mexico are likely to have some Indian ancestry, the principal difficulty with this definition lay in its exclusion of the Spanish-American group and other Spanish-speaking persons who, although not born in Mexico themselves or having parents born there, were nevertheless the natively Spanish-speaking descendants of persons who had come into the Southwest by way of Mexico and were definitely a part of the culturally distinct Spanish-speaking population. In New Mexico, for example, where Spanish-Americans have lived for many generations, only 61,960 "Mexicans" were enumerated under this definition at a time when it was a matter of common knowledge that about half the population of the state, approximately 200,000 persons, were natively Spanish-speaking. Similar underenumeration of the Spanish-speaking group was undoubtedly made in Colorado, and to a somewhat lesser extent in Arizona, Texas, and California. The resulting count showed a

TABLE 1. WHITE SPANISH-SPEAKING POPULATION OF FIVE SOUTH-WESTERN STATES: NUMBER AND PROPORTION OF TOTAL POPULATION, 1940 AND 1950

	1940		
State	Total population	White population of Spanish mother tongue	
		Number[a]	Per cent of total
Arizona	499,261	101,880	20.4
California	6,907,387	416,140	6.0
Colorado	1,123,296	92,540	8.2
New Mexico	531,818	221,740	41.7
Texas	6,414,824	738,440	11.5
Total	15,476,586	1,570,740	10.1
	1950		
State	Total population	White population of Spanish surname	
		Number[b]	Per cent of total
Arizona	749,587	128,318	17.1
California	10,586,223	760,453	7.2
Colorado	1,325,089	118,131	8.9
New Mexico	681,187	248,880	36.5
Texas	7,711,194	1,033,768	13.4
Total	21,053,280	2,289,550	10.9
Per cent increase, 1940 to 1950	36.0	45.8	–

[a] Estimates based on 5 per cent sample. *Census of Population:* 1940, Series P-15, No. 10.
[b] *Census of Population:* 1950, Vol. 4, *Special Reports*, Part 3, Chapter C.

"Mexican" population in the five southwestern states of only 1,330,820 persons, or 9.9 per cent of the total population of these states.

In its 1940 tabulations the Bureau of the Census dropped the category "Mexicans,"[1] except to designate foreign-born persons actually natives

[1] In the tabulations of the 1930 Census the category "Mexicans" was classified as nonwhite. The resulting criticisms and protests, from individuals and organizations both within the United States and in Latin America, were undoubtedly a factor in the decision to drop this category in the 1940 Census.

of Mexico, and attempted to determine the size of the Spanish-speaking group by asking a 5 per cent sample of those enumerated the question: What was the principal language, other than English, spoken in your home during your childhood? From the answers to this question an estimate was made of the number of Spanish-speaking people in the states and large cities, but the sample was too small to permit estimates for counties, small cities, or rural areas, or to justify separate tabulations of the characteristics of the Spanish-speaking population. The total white population of Spanish mother tongue was estimated at 1,861,400 persons, of whom 1,570,740 lived in the five southwestern states, making up 10.1 per cent of their population, as shown in Table 1 on the opposite page.

In 1950 the Bureau of the Census again changed its criterion and made a count of the Spanish-speaking people of the Southwest on the basis of their surnames. Family name, as a criterion for delimiting the Spanish-speaking group, had been used by a number of investigators prior to 1950[1] and had been found to be fairly satisfactory although, like all single criteria, it probably tends to underenumerate the group. Tabulations of the 1950 Census show a total of 2,289,550 Spanish-name persons (10.9 per cent of the total population) in the five southwestern states. Examination of the list of names used by the Bureau of the Census for this purpose, however, shows that a number of names common to the Spanish-speaking group were not included.[2] Estimates of the Spanish-speaking population of Texas made in 1948 by independent investigators[3] using different methods tended to give somewhat higher totals than those of the Census of 1950. It is also unlikely that any of the counts or estimates that have been made adequately account for the large wetback population of the Southwest, which may include at times

[1] Sánchez, George I., *Forgotten People*, University of New Mexico Press, Albuquerque, 1940; Manuel, H. T., "The Mexican Population in Texas," *Southwestern Social Science Quarterly*, June, 1934; Little, Wilson, *Spanish-Speaking Children in Texas*, University of Texas Press, Austin, 1944; Saunders, Lyle, *The Spanish-Speaking Population of Texas*, University of Texas Press, 1949; Belden, Joe D., and associates, *The Latin American Population in Texas*, Austin, January, 1951, mimeographed.

[2] A discussion of the use of Spanish surname as a criterion for distinguishing the Spanish-speaking population and of the extent to which it is more or less satisfactory than other criteria which have been used will be found in U.S. Bureau of the Census, *U.S. Census of Population: 1950*, Vol. 4, *Special Reports*, Part 3, Chapter C, *Persons of Spanish Surname*, Government Printing Office, Washington, 1953, pp. 4–6.

Many Spanish-speaking persons do not have Spanish surnames and were thus not counted in the special tabulations. An investigator in Brownsville, Texas, for example, found that Spanish was the prevailing language in the homes of persons with such names as Morse, Strong, Baker, Meyers, Jones, Johnson, and Shanahan. Another source of underenumeration is the fact that at the time the Census was taken (April), large numbers of Spanish-speaking people who annually migrate in search of agricultural work were on the road or working outside the Southwest.

[3] Saunders, Lyle, *Op. cit.;* Belden, Joe D., and associates, *Op. cit.*

half a million or more persons, so that here again is a reason for thinking that the Census counts are low.[1]

The Spanish-speaking population of the Southwest, then, probably includes in 1953 from 2,500,000 to 3,000,000 persons, with the exact number fluctuating from month to month, not only as a result of births and deaths but also because of the large movement of Spanish-speaking persons into and out of the area. In addition, large numbers of Spanish-speaking people move about in the Southwest or between the Southwest and other areas, working in agriculture, seeking and finding other types of employment, or changing from rural to urban residence. Thus, no single population figure can have meaning except as a rough index of the size of the group relative to other population groups in the area.

Just as it is difficult to say how many Spanish-speaking persons there are, so it is also hard to know just what is happening in terms of numbers. The information that would permit precise comparison of this with other population groups is not available, but a comparison of the proportion of Spanish-speaking people in the five southwestern states as estimated in the 1940 Census sample based on mother tongue with that in the 1950 count based on Spanish surname indicates that the Spanish-speaking population is growing somewhat faster than the total population in the Southwest. During the decade 1940 to 1950, the total population of the southwestern states increased 36.0 per cent, while that of the United States grew only 16.8 per cent. During the same period the Spanish-speaking population appears from the available Census figures to have increased 45.8 per cent, a rate very much greater than that of the United States and somewhat higher than that for the total population of the Southwest. A part of this apparent large increase of Spanish-speaking population is undoubtedly due to the greater accuracy of the Census count in 1950.

Population change in an area in a given period is a function of four variables: births, deaths, migration to the area, and migration from the area. Estimated birth and death rates for the southwestern counties having more than 50 per cent Spanish-speaking population, given in Table 2, indicate the probability that most of these counties have a higher rate of natural increase than the total population of the states in which they are located.

There is no very good source of information on the relative mobility of Spanish-speaking people into and out of the Southwest, but such studies and reports as are available indicate a considerable movement in both directions. Of the nearly 26 million aliens who legally entered the United States from Mexico during the year ended June 30, 1951,

---

[1] If the estimate of half a million or more wetbacks seems startlingly high, it may be remembered that some 750,000 were apprehended by the Border Patrol in 1953.

TABLE 2. CRUDE BIRTH AND DEATH RATES IN 1949 FOR FOUR
SOUTHWESTERN STATES AND THEIR COUNTIES HAVING
MORE THAN 50 PER CENT WHITE SPANISH-SURNAME
POPULATION[a]

State and county	Population, 1950		Live births, 1949		Deaths, 1949	
	Total	Per cent white Spanish-surname	Number[b]	Per 1,000 population[c]	Number[b]	Per 1,000 population[c]
ARIZONA	*749,587*	*17.1*	*20,275*	*27.0*	*6,397*	*8.5*
Santa Cruz	9,344	56.6	304	32.5	76	8.1
COLORADO	*1,325,089*	*8.9*	*32,894*	*24.8*	*12,415*	*9.4*
Conejos	10,171	62.8	260	25.6	77	7.6
Costilla	6,067	76.5	152	25.1	44	7.3
NEW MEXICO	*681,187*	*36.5*	*21,620*	*31.7*	*5,576*	*8.2*
Dona Ana	39,557	52.8	1,501	37.9	329	8.3
Guadalupe	6,772	74.8	220	32.5	72	10.6
Mora	8,720	85.2	321	36.8	90	10.3
Rio Arriba	24,997	80.2	916	36.6	225	9.0
Sandoval	12,438	52.6	549	44.1	148	11.9
San Miguel	26,512	77.4	1,017	38.4	319	12.0
Santa Fe	38,153	60.4	1,248	32.7	296	7.8
Socorro	9,670	58.5	338	35.0	116	12.0
Taos	17,146	81.0	629	36.7	134	7.8
Valencia	22,481	50.1	738	32.8	207	9.2
TEXAS	*7,711,194*	*13.4*	*202,297*	*26.2*	*63,337*	*8.2*
Brooks	9,195	64.1	373	40.6	70	7.6
Cameron	125,170	64.8	5,346	42.7	1,369	10.9
Dimmit	10,654	72.1	357	33.5	121	11.4
Duval	15,643	68.6	475	30.4	129	8.2
Frio	10,357	60.3	389	37.6	114	11.0
Hidalgo	160,446	70.1	7,442	46.4	1,870	11.7
Hudspeth	4,298	66.7	221	51.4	22	5.1
Jeff Davis	2,090	55.2	62	29.7	13	6.2
Jim Hogg	5,389	76.0	164	30.4	38	7.1
Jim Wells	27,991	53.2	942	33.7	188	6.7
Kenedy	632	87.5	21	33.2	3	4.7
Kinney	2,668	53.7	75	28.1	18	6.7
La Salle	7,485	67.4	231	30.9	78	10.4
Maverick	12,292	73.6	459	37.3	101	8.2
Presidio	7,354	69.7	260	35.4	49	6.7
San Patricio	35,842	51.5	1,353	37.7	379	10.6
Starr	13,948	89.3	593	42.5	119	8.5
Terrell	3,189	51.7	97	30.4	24	7.5
Val Verde	16,635	63.0	558	33.5	151	9.1
Webb	56,141	84.7	1,981	35.3	533	9.5
Willacy	20,920	64.3	1,014	48.5	212	10.1
Zapata	4,405	94.1	118	26.8	18	4.1
Zavala	11,201	69.0	387	34.6	118	10.5

[a] This table contains data for only four states, because no county in California has
more than 50 per cent white Spanish-surname population.

[b] From *Vital Statistics of the U.S.: 1949*, Part 2, *Natality and Mortality Data for the
U.S.* Government Printing Office, Washington, 1951, pp. 2–93.

[c] Calculated by the author, using 1950 population data.

a very high proportion must have been Spanish-speaking. Relatively few of this group, however, remained in the United States for any extended time. The great majority were persons who live in border cities and pass back and forth across the border daily. About 4,000 represented legal immigrants; some 28,000 were nonimmigrant officials,

TABLE 3. CONCENTRATION OF WHITE SPANISH-SURNAME POPULATION IN COUNTIES OF FIVE SOUTHWESTERN STATES, 1950

1. Counties Distributed by Number of White Spanish-Surname Population

Number of white Spanish-surname population in county	Number of counties having specified number of white Spanish-surname population					
	Arizona	California	Colorado	New Mexico	Texas	Total
Under 100	–	6	22	–	74	102
100 to 9,999	10	34	38	24	164	270
10,000 to 24,999	2	11	3	7	9	32
25,000 to 49,999	2	6	–	1	2	11
50,000 to 74,999	–	–	–	–	1	1
75,000 to 99,999	–	–	–	–	2	2
Over 100,000	–	1	–	–	2	3
Total counties	14	58	63	32	254	421

2. Counties Distributed by Proportion of White Spanish-Surname Population

Per cent of white Spanish-surname population in county	Number of counties having specified proportion of white Spanish-surname population					
	Arizona	California	Colorado	New Mexico	Texas	Total
Under 5	–	32	34	2	144	212
5 to 24	10	24	22	9	63	128
25 to 49	3	2	5	11	24	45
50 to 74	1	–	1	6	18	26
75 to 89	–	–	1	4	4	9
90 to 100	–	–	–	–	1	1
Total counties	14	58	63	32	254	421

visitors, or students; about 100,000 were legally admitted agricultural workers.[1] A much larger source of increase for the Spanish-speaking population of the Southwest is the undetermined number of illegal migrants who cross the border mainly to seek employment in the United States. More than a million of these illegal entrants were apprehended by the Border Patrol in the two-year period ended June

[1] U.S. Dept. of Justice, *Annual Report of the Immigration and Naturalization Service for the Fiscal Year Ended June 30, 1951*, pp. 24 and 27, and Tables 13 and 25, mimeographed.

30, 1951,[1] and were permitted to depart voluntarily. How many escape capture and remain, nobody knows. But the number must be large, for groups of wetbacks are regularly rounded up as far inland as Chicago, and studies have shown not only large numbers of illegal entrants in border counties, but also that the number of Mexican-born residents in the United States exceeds by far the number of Mexicans legally admitted for permanent residence.[2]

Some detailed information about numbers, distribution, and selected characteristics of the Spanish-speaking population of the five southwestern states is included in the accompanying tables. Most of the data presented have been taken directly from publications of the Bureau of the Census. A part represents calculations made especially for this book from published Census materials. In a few of the tables data are provided for a comparison between Spanish-speaking and Anglo populations. The latter is a residual category obtained by subtracting figures for the Spanish-speaking population from those for the total populations of the several states. No allowance has been made for the fact that for some of the states the resulting figure for Anglo population includes sizable numbers of Indians, Japanese-Americans, Chinese-Americans, and Filipinos.

Except where specified, the data of the tables were taken from, or are based on, data of the following Census publications: *U.S. Census of Population: 1950*, Vol. 4, *Special Reports*, Part 3, Chapter C, *Persons of Spanish Surname*. *U.S. Census of Population: 1950*, Vol. 2, *Characteristics of the Population*. *U.S. Census of Population: 1940*, Series P-15, No. 10, *Mother Tongue of the White Population for States and Large Cities*.

Because of rounding off to one decimal place, percentage columns in the tables do not always add to exactly 100 per cent.

---

[1] *Ibid.*, Table 24A. Since many of these represent repeated entries by and apprehensions of the same individual, the total number of different persons involved is probably considerably fewer than half a million a year.

[2] In the summer of 1950 it was estimated that there were at least 100,000 wetbacks in three counties in South Texas, Cameron, Hidalgo, and Willacy. Saunders, Lyle, and Olen E. Leonard, *The Wetback in the Lower Rio Grande Valley of Texas*, University of Texas Press, Austin, 1951.

TABLE 4. NATIVITY AND CITIZENSHIP, WHITE SPANISH-SURNAME POPULATION OF FIVE SOUTHWESTERN STATES, 1950

Nativity and citizenship	Arizona	California	Colorado	New Mexico	Texas	Total
		Number of persons				
Total white Spanish-surname population	128,318	760,453	118,131	248,880	1,033,768	2,289,550
Nativity						
Native	105,310	594,448	113,057	239,154	845,221	1,897,190
Foreign-born	23,008	166,005	5,074	9,726	188,547	392,360
Country of birth of foreign-born						
Mexico	22,143	145,265	4,396	9,011	185,063	365,878
Other country	865	20,740	678	715	3,484	26,482
Citizenship of foreign-born						
Naturalized	6,583	42,546	1,419	2,728	43,179	96,455
Alien	14,468	110,451	3,172	5,678	130,705	264,474
Not reported	1,957	13,008	483	1,320	14,663	31,431
		Percentage distribution				
Total white Spanish-surname population	100.0	100.0	100.0	100.0	100.0	100.0
Nativity						
Native	82.1	78.2	95.7	96.1	81.8	82.9
Foreign-born	18.0	21.8	4.3	3.9	18.2	17.2
Country of birth of foreign-born						
Mexico	17.3	19.1	3.7	3.6	17.9	16.0
Other country	0.7	2.7	0.6	0.3	0.3	1.2
Citizenship of foreign-born						
Naturalized	5.1	5.6	1.2	1.1	4.2	4.2
Alien	11.3	14.5	2.7	2.3	12.6	11.6
Not reported	1.5	1.7	0.4	0.5	1.4	1.4

TABLE 5. DISTRIBUTION BY RURAL OR URBAN RESIDENCE, WHITE SPANISH-SURNAME POPULATION AND ANGLO POPULATION OF FIVE SOUTHWESTERN STATES, 1950

Population group and residence category	Arizona	California	Colorado	New Mexico	Texas	Total
		Number of persons				
Spanish-surname						
Total	128,318	760,453	118,131	248,880	1,033,768	2,289,550
Urban	78,723	576,334	58,704	101,939	704,112	1,519,812
Rural nonfarm	40,595	126,534	40,760	89,240	194,741	491,870
Rural farm	9,000	57,585	18,667	57,701	134,915	277,868
Anglo[a]						
Total	621,269	9,825,770	1,206,958	432,307	6,677,426	18,763,730
Urban	337,277	7,963,086	772,614	239,950	4,133,948	13,446,875
Rural nonfarm	216,078	1,352,038	254,830	118,235	1,386,126	3,327,307
Rural farm	67,914	510,646	179,514	74,122	1,157,352	1,989,548
		Percentage distribution				
Spanish-surname						
Total	100.0	100.0	100.0	100.0	100.0	100.0
Urban	61.3	75.8	49.7	41.0	68.1	66.4
Rural nonfarm	31.6	16.6	34.5	35.8	18.8	21.5
Rural farm	7.0	7.6	15.8	23.2	13.1	12.1
Anglo[a]						
Total	100.0	100.0	100.0	100.0	100.0	100.0
Urban	54.3	81.0	64.0	55.5	61.9	71.7
Rural nonfarm	34.8	13.8	21.1	27.3	20.8	17.7
Rural farm	10.9	5.2	14.9	17.1	17.3	10.6

[a] Residual group, obtained by subtracting Spanish-surname population from the total population.

TABLE 6. PERCENTAGE DISTRIBUTION BY AGE, WHITE, SPANISH-SURNAME POPULATION AND ANGLO POPULATION OF FIVE SOUTHWESTERN STATES, 1950

Age in years	Arizona		California		Colorado		New Mexico		Texas		Total	
	Spanish-surname	Anglo[a]	Spanish-surname	Anglo[a]	Spanish-surname	Anglo[a]	Spanish-surname	Anglo[a]	Spanish-surname	Anglo[a]	Spanish-surname	Anglo[a]
Total	100.0	100.0	100.0	100.0	100.0	100.0	100.0	100.0	100.0	100.0	100.0	100.0
Under 5	15.7	11.7	14.3	10.1	17.1	10.6	16.6	12.6	16.9	10.0	15.9	10.5
5 to 9	13.4	9.9	11.3	7.7	14.0	8.3	13.5	10.0	13.4	8.9	12.7	8.3
10 to 14	11.5	8.5	9.6	5.9	12.4	7.0	12.0	8.2	10.7	7.5	10.6	6.7
15 to 19	9.8	7.2	9.1	5.7	10.1	7.0	10.0	7.5	9.7	7.5	9.6	6.5
20 to 24	9.1	7.3	10.4	7.1	8.4	7.7	8.4	8.5	9.3	8.0	9.5	7.5
25 to 29	7.8	7.9	9.4	8.7	7.4	8.3	7.3	9.1	8.3	8.4	8.5	8.5
30 to 34	6.4	7.7	7.1	8.5	5.8	7.7	5.7	8.3	5.9	7.7	6.3	8.1
35 to 39	5.9	7.8	6.3	8.3	5.3	7.3	5.6	7.7	6.0	7.7	6.0	8.0
40 to 44	4.8	7.0	5.4	7.3	4.5	6.6	4.6	6.5	4.9	7.0	5.0	7.2
45 to 49	4.1	5.8	5.0	6.5	3.8	5.8	4.1	5.3	4.3	6.1	4.5	6.2
50 to 54	3.1	5.0	3.6	5.8	2.9	5.3	3.3	4.4	3.0	5.2	3.3	5.5
55 to 59	2.5	4.2	2.8	5.1	2.7	4.8	2.9	3.6	2.3	4.3	2.6	4.7
60 to 64	1.9	3.4	2.1	4.4	2.2	4.2	2.3	2.9	1.9	3.5	2.0	4.0
65 to 69	1.7	2.7	1.6	3.6	1.6	3.5	1.8	2.2	1.6	2.9	1.6	3.3
70 to 74	0.9	1.8	0.8	2.5	0.8	2.6	1.0	1.4	0.8	2.0	0.8	2.3
75 and over	1.1	1.8	0.9	2.7	1.0	3.1	1.3	1.6	1.0	2.2	1.0	2.5
21 and over	47.6	61.3	53.6	69.2	44.6	65.6	46.6	60.0	47.4	63.6	49.2	66.5
65 and over	3.7	6.3	3.3	8.8	3.4	9.2	4.1	5.2	3.4	7.1	3.4	8.1

[a] Residual group, obtained by subtracting Spanish-surname population from the total population.

Census reports give median ages for Spanish-surname and total population, but not for the Anglo, or residual, group. Median ages in years for the Spanish-surname and total population for the five states in 1950 were:

	Arizona	California	Colorado	New Mexico	Texas
Spanish-surname	19.8	22.7	18.2	19.2	19.6
Total population	26.8	26.8	29.5	24.0	27.9

294

TABLE 7. PERCENTAGE DISTRIBUTION BY MARITAL STATUS AND SEX, WHITE SPANISH-SURNAME POPULATION AND ANGLO POPULATION OF FIVE SOUTHWESTERN STATES, 1950

Population group and marital status	Arizona	California	Colorado	New Mexico	Texas	Total
Male						
Spanish-surname						
Total	100.0	100.0	100.0	100.0	100.0	100.0
Single	35.4	35.1	33.6	33.9	34.5	34.7
Married	59.0	59.4	61.0	60.5	60.5	60.1
Widowed or divorced	5.5	5.5	5.4	5.6	4.9	5.3
Anglo[a]						
Total	100.0	100.0	100.0	100.0	100.0	100.0
Single	24.1	23.6	25.1	25.6	23.5	23.8
Married	68.9	68.9	68.1	68.8	70.5	69.4
Widowed or divorced	7.0	7.5	6.7	5.6	6.0	6.8
Female						
Spanish-surname						
Total	100.0	100.0	100.0	100.0	100.0	100.0
Single	27.5	24.7	26.7	27.6	27.5	26.5
Married	59.1	63.1	63.9	61.6	60.5	61.6
Widowed or divorced	13.4	12.2	9.4	10.8	12.0	11.9
Anglo[a]						
Total	100.0	100.0	100.0	100.0	100.0	100.0
Single	16.7	15.3	17.6	16.4	15.4	15.6
Married	69.6	67.2	67.2	72.0	69.6	68.2
Widowed or divorced	13.6	17.4	15.1	11.5	14.9	15.6

[a] Residual group, obtained by subtracting Spanish-surname population from the total population.

TABLE 8. PERCENTAGE DISTRIBUTION BY OCCUPATION AND SEX, EMPLOYED WHITE SPANISH-SURNAME POPULATION FOURTEEN YEARS OF AGE AND OVER OF FIVE SOUTHWESTERN STATES, 1950[a]

Occupation group	Arizona	California	Colorado	New Mexico	Texas	Total
Male						
Total	100.0	100.0	100.0	100.0	100.0	100.0
Professional, technical, and kindred workers	1.6	2.6	1.9	3.0	1.6	2.1
Farmers and farm managers	1.8	2.8	7.6	13.1	5.2	4.9
Managers, officials, and proprietors, except farm	3.7	4.6	3.0	4.4	4.4	4.4
Clerical, sales, and kindred workers	6.1	6.4	4.4	6.5	6.6	6.4
Craftsmen, foremen, and kindred workers	13.1	14.0	9.1	13.0	12.4	12.9
Operatives and kindred workers	25.5	21.6	22.1	14.8	16.4	18.8
Private household workers	0.1	0.1	0.1	0.1	0.2	0.2
Service workers, except private household	5.5	5.6	5.4	6.9	6.5	6.1
Farm laborers, unpaid family workers	0.3	0.3	1.9	2.5	1.3	1.0
Farm laborers, except unpaid, and farm foremen	23.9	23.4	20.8	14.3	25.4	23.3
Laborers, except farm and mine	17.2	17.8	22.2	19.0	18.8	18.5
Occupation not reported	1.0	0.9	1.4	2.3	1.1	1.1
Female						
Total	100.0	100.0	100.0	100.0	100.0	100.0
Professional, technical, and kindred workers	4.3	4.6	5.6	8.8	3.8	4.6
Farmers and farm managers	0.2	0.2	0.6	0.8	0.4	0.3
Managers, officials, and proprietors, except farm	4.6	3.5	2.9	3.6	4.3	3.9
Clerical, sales, and kindred workers	28.4	23.7	19.5	27.5	23.5	24.0
Craftsmen, foremen, and kindred workers	0.6	1.8	1.3	0.8	1.2	1.4
Operatives and kindred workers	14.6	41.2	20.0	9.0	21.5	28.1
Private household workers	15.6	5.4	17.0	18.1	18.7	13.1
Service workers, except private household	22.1	11.5	22.3	21.9	14.8	14.7
Farm laborers, unpaid family workers	0.3	0.5	1.3	0.9	1.4	0.9
Farm laborers, except unpaid, and farm foremen	6.1	4.6	4.4	0.8	6.6	5.2
Laborers, except farm and mine	0.5	1.6	2.1	0.6	1.4	1.4
Occupation not reported	2.5	1.3	3.0	7.0	2.4	2.4

[a] Percentages calculated by author from Census data for 20 per cent sample of Spanish-surname population. *Census of Population: 1950, Vol. 4, Special Reports*, Part 3, Chapter C, pp. 23–42.

TABLE 9. PERCENTAGE DISTRIBUTION BY ANNUAL INCOME, AND MEDIAN INCOME BY RURAL-URBAN RESIDENCE, WHITE SPANISH-SURNAME POPULATION FOURTEEN YEARS OF AGE AND OVER OF FIVE SOUTHWESTERN STATES, 1950[a]

Annual income and residence category	Arizona	California	Colorado	New Mexico	Texas	Total
			Percentage distribution			
Total	100.0	100.0	100.0	100.0	100.0	100.0
Less than $500	19.6	17.7	24.9	25.5	26.6	22.7
$500 to $999	18.7	16.4	23.6	19.8	24.3	20.5
$1,000 to $1,499	14.3	13.0	14.1	15.1	17.5	15.2
$1,500 to $1,999	11.7	11.4	10.9	11.0	12.1	11.7
$2,000 to $2,499	10.6	13.1	10.7	10.8	8.8	10.8
$2,500 to $2,999	7.4	9.3	7.2	6.6	4.1	6.6
$3,000 to $3,999	13.1	12.5	6.2	7.3	4.0	8.2
$4,000 to $4,999	2.5	3.7	1.3	2.0	1.2	2.3
$5,000 to $5,999	0.7	1.3	0.5	0.6	0.5	0.8
$6,000 and over	1.3	1.6	0.6	1.2	0.8	1.2
			Median income			
Total	$1,408	$1,628	$1,052	$1,156	$ 980	—
Urban	1,406	1,783	1,316	1,400	1,134	—
Rural nonfarm	1,497	1,244	897	1,066	1,280	—
Rural farm	1,174	1,174	869	897	739	—

[a] Data are for income in 1949 of 20 per cent sample of Spanish-surname population in 1950. *Census of Population: 1950*, Vol. 4, *Special Reports*, Part 3, Chapter C, pp. 23–42.

TABLE 10. PERCENTAGE DISTRIBUTION BY SCHOOL YEARS COMPLETED, WHITE SPANISH-SURNAME POPULATION AND ANGLO POPULATION TWENTY-FIVE YEARS OF AGE AND OVER OF FIVE SOUTHWESTERN STATES, 1950[a]

School years completed	Arizona		California		Colorado		New Mexico		Texas		Total	
	Spanish-surname	Anglo[b]	Spanish-surname	Anglo[b]	Spanish-surname	Anglo[b]	Spanish-surname	Anglo[b]	Spanish-surname	Anglo[b]	Spanish-surname	Anglo[b]
Total	100.0	100.0	100.0	100.0	100.0	100.0	100.0	100.0	100.0	100.0	100.0	100.0
None	13.4	4.2	10.7	1.3	10.1	1.1	12.5	3.1	27.0	1.8	18.0	1.6
Elementary												
1 to 4	26.1	6.0	18.6	4.3	24.8	4.2	27.1	5.4	34.8	8.9	27.2	5.9
5 to 6	17.0	6.4	14.2	5.3	18.3	5.3	15.6	6.2	14.6	10.9	14.9	7.2
7	7.4	5.2	6.3	4.4	8.3	4.8	8.1	5.3	4.6	9.0	5.9	6.0
8	13.1	16.2	13.7	16.2	14.4	20.8	12.3	14.0	4.3	12.1	9.4	15.1
High school												
1 to 3	9.5	17.2	15.4	18.0	10.7	16.6	9.4	18.1	5.6	22.4	10.0	19.4
4	6.6	22.7	12.8	27.6	7.0	24.7	7.5	22.7	4.0	17.0	7.8	23.6
College												
1 to 3	1.7	10.9	3.1	11.6	2.0	11.3	2.6	12.0	1.1	8.9	2.0	10.7
4 or more	1.1	8.3	1.8	8.5	1.0	8.6	1.4	9.2	0.8	6.6	1.3	7.9
Not reported	3.9	2.8	3.4	2.9	3.5	2.6	3.5	3.7	3.0	2.3	3.3	2.7

[a] Percentages calculated by the author from data for 20 per cent sample of Spanish-surname population given in Census of Population: 1950, Vol. 4, Special Reports, Part 3, Chapter C, pp. 16–17.
[b] Residual group, obtained by subtracting Spanish-surname population from the total population.

TABLE 11. CHARACTERISTICS OF DWELLING UNITS, WHITE SPANISH-SURNAME POPULATION OF FIVE SOUTHWESTERN STATES, 1950[a]

Dwelling units occupied by white persons of Spanish-surname	Arizona	California	Colorado	New Mexico	Texas	Total
Total	27,375	171,039	23,349	54,425	209,178	485,366
Per cent dilapidated	32.3	19.5	24.3	19.6	35.2	27.2
Median number of persons per dwelling unit	4.1	3.7	4.2	4.0	4.3	4.0
Percentage distribution by persons per room						
Total	100.0	100.0	100.0	100.0	100.0	100.0
1.00 or fewer	47.6	61.4	43.0	44.2	36.9	47.3
1.01 to 1.50	19.6	18.2	19.6	18.8	17.7	18.2
1.51 or more	31.4	19.1	35.8	34.2	43.4	32.8
Not reported	1.4	1.3	1.5	2.8	1.9	1.7
Median gross rent of renter-occupied units	$23.75	$31.40	$24.42	$24.86	$19.76	$25.90
Median value of owner-occupied units	$2,250	$6,620	$2,220	$2,412	$1,883	$3,160

[a] Adapted from data given in *Census of Population: 1950*, Vol. 4, *Special Reports*, Part 3, Chapter C, pp. 18-19.

TABLE 12. WHITE SPANISH-SURNAME POPULATION: NUMBER, PER CENT OF TOTAL POPULATION AND PER CENT BORN IN MEXICO, FOR COUNTIES OF FIVE SOUTHWESTERN STATES, 1950

County	White persons of Spanish-surname		
	Number	Per cent of total population[a]	Per cent born in Mexico[a]
ARIZONA			
Apache	1,623	5.8	0.8
Cochise	10,146	32.2	25.1
Coconino	3,728	15.6	12.6
Gila	5,397	22.3	14.1
Graham	2,591	20.0	9.6
Greenlee	5,368	41.9	9.4
Maricopa	42,560	12.8	15.5
Mohave	635	7.5	9.1
Navajo	2,739	9.3	7.2
Pima	27,224	19.3	16.5
Pinal	10,794	25.0	16.1
Santa Cruz	5,287	56.6	34.3
Yavapai	3,903	15.6	19.5
Yuma	6,323	22.6	30.3
Total	128,318	17.1	17.2
CALIFORNIA			
Alameda	35,578	4.8	9.6
Alpine	4	1.7	—
Amador	643	7.0	5.7
Butte	1,119	1.7	14.8
Calaveras	477	4.8	11.9
Colusa	1,154	9.9	32.6

County	White persons of Spanish-surname		
	Number	Per cent of total population[a]	Per cent born in Mexico[a]
CALIFORNIA, *continued*			
San Diego	28,926	5.2	21.9
San Francisco	31,433	4.1	13.8
San Joaquin	19,739	9.8	18.7
San Luis Obispo	3,102	6.0	13.2
San Mateo	7,030	3.0	8.8
Santa Barbara	16,439	16.7	21.4
Santa Clara	35,306	12.2	12.1
Santa Cruz	2,511	3.8	13.4
Shasta	430	1.2	14.6
Sierra	81	3.4	11.1
Siskiyou	819	2.7	34.4
Solano	3,848	3.7	16.5
Sonoma	2,638	2.6	9.0
Stanislaus	5,875	4.6	14.0
Sutter	940	3.6	26.3
Tehama	356	1.8	25.3
Trinity	78	1.5	14.1
Tulare	16,743	11.2	16.8
Tuolumne	881	7.0	11.2
Ventura	21,697	18.9	25.6
Yolo	5,761	14.2	31.0
Yuba	430	1.8	18.6
Total	760,453	7.2	19.1

California			
Contra Costa	14,963	5.0	14.9
Del Norte	145	1.8	6.9
El Dorado	175	1.1	12.0
Fresno	32,678	11.8	18.9
Glenn	604	3.9	16.2
Humboldt	631	—	10.8
Imperial	19,028	30.2	42.0
Inyo	350	3.0	20.6
Kern	18,579	8.1	17.3
Kings	8,183	17.5	15.9
Lake	81	—	14.8
Lassen	877	4.7	16.9
Los Angeles	287,614	6.9	20.1
Madera	4,664	12.6	21.2
Marin	1,826	2.1	10.8
Mariposa	50	—	4.0
Mendocino	700	1.7	21.3
Merced	7,393	10.6	17.4
Modoc	163	1.7	34.3
Mono	9	—	22.2
Monterey	15,655	12.0	20.3
Napa	1,708	3.7	9.3
Nevada	231	1.2	29.4
Orange	23,680	11.0	19.8
Placer	2,374	5.7	24.0
Plumas	231	1.7	25.1
Riverside	19,979	11.7	21.7
Sacramento	14,883	5.4	18.1
San Benito	3,626	25.2	19.2
San Bernardino	35,330	12.5	18.8

COLORADO

County			
Adams	2,479	6.2	3.9
Alamosa	2,662	25.3	0.2
Arapahoe	1,088	2.1	1.8
Archuleta	1,397	46.1	0.1
Baca	32	—	6.2
Bent	1,318	15.0	5.7
Boulder	1,545	3.2	6.1
Chaffee	631	8.8	0.8
Cheyenne	6	—	—
Clear Creek	27	—	—
Conejos	6,387	62.8	0.1
Costilla	4,760	78.5	0.1
Crowley	978	18.7	9.6
Custer	40	2.5	2.5
Delta	968	5.6	6.9
Denver	24,950	6.0	3.3
Dolores	6	—	—
Douglas	66	1.9	16.7
Eagle	783	17.4	1.8
Elbert	29	—	6.9
El Paso	2,337	3.1	3.2
Fremont	1,175	6.4	7.6
Garfield	325	2.8	1.5
Gilpin	20	2.4	—
Grand	79	2.0	3.8
Gunnison	236	4.1	0.8
Hinsdale	—	—	—
Huerfano	3,437	32.6	1.2
Jackson	11	—	—

(Continued on following page)

TABLE 12. WHITE SPANISH-SURNAME POPULATION: NUMBER, PER CENT OF TOTAL POPULATION AND PER CENT BORN IN MEXICO, FOR COUNTIES OF FIVE SOUTHWESTERN STATES, 1950—*Continued*

County	White persons of Spanish-surname			County	White persons of Spanish-surname		
	Number	Per cent of total population[a]	Per cent born in Mexico[a]		Number	Per cent of total population[a]	Per cent born in Mexico[a]
COLORADO, *continued*				NEW MEXICO, *continued*			
Jefferson	744	1.3	2.4	San Juan	1,742	9.5	0.3
Kiowa	68	2.3	13.2	San Miguel	20,524	77.4	1.9
Kit Carson	102	1.2	1.0	Santa Fe	23,034	60.4	0.5
Lake	891	14.5	0.7	Sierra	1,534	21.3	5.1
La Plata	2,240	15.1	0.3	Socorro	5,661	58.5	1.1
Larimer	1,780	4.1	7.0	Taos	13,884	81.0	0.1
Las Animas	11,031	42.6	1.6	Torrance	3,865	48.2	0.2
Lincoln	69	1.2	2.9	Union	1,635	22.2	0.5
Logan	719	4.2	11.8	Valencia	11,271	50.1	0.6
Mesa	1,543	4.0	3.0	Total	248,880	36.5	3.6
Mineral	64	9.2	—				
Moffat	156	2.6	—	TEXAS			
Montezuma	770	7.7	—	Anderson	61	—	11.5
Montrose	1,028	6.8	2.4	Andrews	26	—	7.7
Morgan	1,088	6.0	10.7	Angelina	172	—	5.8
Otero	6,036	23.9	6.2	Aransas	783	18.4	5.9
Ouray	36	1.7	—	Archer	17	—	5.9
Park	—	—	—	Armstrong	76	3.4	—
Phillips	—	—	—	Atascosa	9,441	47.1	5.5
Pitkin	4	—	—	Austin	153	1.0	9.8
Prowers	1,142	7.7	14.9	Bailey	147	1.9	10.2
Pueblo	14,802	16.4	6.2	Bandera	167	3.8	9.6
Rio Blanco	16	—	—	Bastrop	1,737	8.9	12.5
Rio Grande	4,605	35.9	0.1	Baylor	91	1.3	13.2
Routt	557	6.2	12.2				

County			
Saguache	1,410	24.9	0.1
San Juan	205	13.9	—
San Miguel	82	3.0	—
Sedgwick	371	7.3	15.6
Summit	—	—	—
Teller	20	—	—
Washington	112	1.5	3.6
Weld	8,647	12.8	7.5
Yuma	21	—	—
Total	118,131	8.9	3.7

NEW MEXICO

County			
Bernalillo	43,729	30.0	1.2
Catron	1,201	34.0	0.2
Chaves	6,318	15.6	4.7
Colfax	7,835	46.7	1.6
Curry	3,660	15.7	2.7
De Baca	1,029	29.7	0.2
Dona Ana	20,883	52.8	16.4
Eddy	8,896	21.9	10.5
Grant	10,112	46.7	10.0
Guadalupe	5,065	74.8	0.4
Harding	1,456	48.3	0.3
Hidalgo	2,036	40.0	17.6
Lea	718	2.3	13.5
Lincoln	2,840	38.3	2.3
Los Alamos	978	9.3	0.7
Luna	3,183	36.4	16.5
McKinley	4,067	14.8	8.3
Mora	7,433	85.2	0.1
Otero	3,469	23.3	7.5
Quay	3,599	25.8	2.0
Rio Arriba	20,056	80.2	0.1
Roosevelt	622	3.8	0.6
Sandoval	6,545	52.6	0.6

County			
Bee	7,961	43.8	4.2
Bell	2,524	3.4	11.0
Bexar	176,877	35.3	14.6
Blanco	190	5.0	4.7
Borden	110	9.9	0.9
Bosque	79	—	5.1
Bowie	200	—	38.5
Brazoria	2,187	4.7	16.0
Brazos	2,499	6.5	11.6
Brewster	3,056	41.8	13.6
Briscoe	12	—	—
Brooks	5,894	64.1	5.6
Brown	681	2.4	10.9
Burleson	1,032	7.9	17.1
Burnet	417	4.0	7.4
Caldwell	5,547	28.7	15.0
Calhoun	2,001	21.7	7.9
Callahan	153	1.7	11.1
Cameron	81,080	64.8	26.3
Camp	3	—	—
Carson	169	2.5	19.5
Cass	33	—	6.1
Castro	78	1.4	6.4
Chambers	22	—	—
Cherokee	74	—	20.3
Childress	83	—	7.2
Clay	12	—	8.3
Cochran	355	6.0	6.8
Coke	260	6.4	8.1
Coleman	513	3.3	8.4
Collin	403	1.0	8.4
Collingsworth	131	1.4	1.5
Colorado	930	5.3	10.9
Comal	4,440	27.1	13.1
Comanche	29	—	24.1
Concho	943	18.6	8.0

(Continued on following page)

303

TABLE 12. WHITE SPANISH-SURNAME POPULATION: NUMBER, PER CENT OF TOTAL POPULATION AND PER CENT BORN IN MEXICO, FOR COUNTIES OF FIVE SOUTHWESTERN STATES, 1950—*Continued*

County	White persons of Spanish-surname			County	White persons of Spanish-surname		
	Number	Per cent of total population[a]	Per cent born in Mexico[a]		Number	Per cent of total population[a]	Per cent born in Mexico[a]
TEXAS, *continued*				TEXAS, *continued*			
Cooke	24	—	—	Hockley	1,000	4.9	11.2
Coryell	333	2.0	7.5	Hood	41	—	29.3
Cottle	311	5.1	12.5	Hopkins	38	—	5.3
Crane	34	—	11.8	Houston	48	—	10.4
Crockett	1,404	35.3	19.9	Howard	3,137	11.7	11.3
Crosby	571	6.0	8.7	Hudspeth	2,866	66.7	46.0
Culbertson	719	39.4	14.7	Hunt	297	—	14.1
Dallam	508	66.6	5.1	Hutchinson	230	—	3.0
Dallas	14,430	2.3	15.7	Irion	292	18.4	3.1
Dawson	2,885	15.1	7.5	Jack	16	—	—
Deaf Smith	618	6.8	10.0	Jackson	1,865	14.4	6.6
Delta	43	—	—	Jasper	34	—	—
Denton	242	—	8.3	Jeff Davis	1,153	55.2	15.9
De Witt	4,071	17.7	6.0	Jefferson	4,274	2.2	14.2
Dickens	463	6.5	6.0	Jim Hogg	4,098	76.0	11.3
Dimmit	7,683	72.1	21.7	Jim Wells	14,878	53.2	6.3
Donley	17	—	5.9	Johnson	278	—	9.0
Duval	10,724	68.6	5.1	Jones	1,222	5.5	7.1
Eastland	400	1.7	15.0	Karnes	6,786	39.6	5.4
Ector	1,599	3.8	8.1	Kaufman	136	—	16.2
Edwards	1,044	35.9	23.8	Kendall	711	13.1	7.4
Ellis	1,276	2.8	13.4	Kenedy	553	87.5	15.9
El Paso	89,555	45.9	27.8	Kent	125	5.6	20.0
Erath	51	—	7.8	Kerr	1,400	10.0	8.8
Falls	2,021	7.6	13.7	Kimble	599	13.0	9.5

County			
Fannin	92	–	7.6
Fayette	617	2.6	8.9
Fisher	809	7.3	11.4
Floyd	175	1.7	2.8
Foard	146	3.5	4.1
Fort Bend	6,597	21.2	13.4
Franklin	–	–	–
Freestone	54	–	20.4
Frio	6,250	60.3	11.1
Gaines	232	2.6	7.3
Galveston	6,914	6.1	16.5
Garza	612	9.7	7.8
Gillespie	470	4.5	10.0
Glasscock	102	9.4	11.8
Goliad	2,173	34.9	3.7
Gonzales	4,357	20.6	7.1
Gray	81	–	12.3
Grayson	466	–	9.0
Gregg	144	–	11.8
Grimes	442	2.9	14.9
Guadalupe	6,047	23.8	11.9
Hale	1,251	4.4	6.9
Hall	136	1.2	11.8
Hamilton	39	–	5.1
Hansford	5	–	–
Hardeman	22	–	9.1
Hardin	166	–	12.6
Harris	39,171	4.8	15.4
Harrison	34	–	–
Hartley	27	1.4	3.7
Haskell	870	6.3	10.2
Hays	6,130	34.4	15.2
Hemphill	69	1.7	20.3
Henderson	50	–	18.0
Hidalgo	112,422	70.1	31.1
Hill	393	1.3	14.0
King	21	2.4	14.3
Kinney	1,432	53.7	15.9
Kleberg	10,306	46.9	9.4
Knox	858	8.5	8.3
Lamar	88	–	3.4
Lampasas	1,097	5.5	7.6
La Salle	575	5.8	6.9
Lavaca	5,044	67.4	12.1
Lee	592	2.7	5.7
Leon	118	1.2	26.3
Liberty	31	–	3.2
Limestone	279	1.0	8.6
Lipscomb	480	1.9	9.2
Live Oak	20	–	30.0
Llano	3,382	37.4	4.9
Loving	137	2.5	14.6
Lubbock	45	19.8	17.8
Lynn	6,477	6.4	8.1
McCulloch	1,117	10.1	7.0
McLennan	1,660	14.2	11.2
McMullen	4,445	3.4	13.8
Madison	431	36.3	3.2
Marion	35	–	8.6
Martin	1	–	–
Mason	1,011	18.2	12.4
Matagorda	357	7.2	9.2
Maverick	2,242	10.4	9.4
Medina	9,047	73.6	34.2
Menard	5,757	33.8	12.7
Midland	741	17.7	10.0
Milam	1,584	6.1	9.8
Mills	1,676	7.1	16.4
Mitchell	65	1.1	10.8
Montague	1,503	1.0	9.3
Montgomery	20	–	–
	524	2.1	13.5

(Continued on following page)

TABLE 12. WHITE SPANISH-SURNAME POPULATION: NUMBER, PER CENT OF TOTAL POPULATION AND PER CENT BORN IN MEXICO, FOR COUNTIES OF FIVE SOUTHWESTERN STATES, 1950—*Continued*

County	White persons of Spanish-surname			County	White persons of Spanish-surname		
	Number	Per cent of total population[a]	Per cent born in Mexico[a]		Number	Per cent of total population[a]	Per cent born in Mexico[a]
TEXAS, *continued*				TEXAS, *continued*			
Moore	199	1.5	9.5	Starr	12,452	89.3	8.3
Morris	56	—	—	Stephens	153	1.4	18.9
Motley	135	3.4	5.9	Sterling	249	19.4	5.6
Nacogdoches	492	1.6	1.6	Stonewall	155	4.2	10.3
Navarro	410	1.0	1.2	Sutton	1,577	42.1	16.9
Newton	—	—	—	Swisher	73	—	6.8
Nolan	1,215	6.1	14.0	Tarrant	8,552	2.4	17.2
Nueces	58,939	35.6	10.0	Taylor	2,026	3.2	11.5
Ochiltree	8	—	—	Terrell	1,648	51.7	21.0
Oldham	16	1.0	—	Terry	1,084	8.3	7.1
Orange	419	1.0	12.4	Throckmorton	34	—	—
Palo Pinto	185	1.1	6.5	Titus	62	—	19.3
Panola	18	—	5.5	Tom Green	6,896	11.7	10.2
Parker	289	1.3	10.7	Travis	15,365	9.5	11.0
Parmer	140	2.4	3.6	Trinity	34	—	20.6
Pecos	3,576	36.0	12.4	Tyler	42	—	4.8
Polk	83	—	14.4	Upshur	24	—	4.2
Potter	1,847	2.5	10.9	Upton	471	8.9	7.4
Presidio	5,133	69.8	15.7	Uvalde	6,807	42.5	14.2
Rains	2	—	100.0	Val Verde	10,488	63.0	25.2
Randall	101	—	5.9	Van Zandt	100	—	16.0
Reagan	148	4.7	11.5	Victoria	7,334	23.5	5.8
Real	356	14.4	9.3	Walker	328	1.6	26.8
Red River	21	—	19.0	Waller	227	1.9	10.6
Reeves	4,605	39.2	18.8	Ward	2,524	18.9	14.4

County			
Refugio	2,630	26.0	6.7
Roberts	18	1.7	11.1
Robertson	1,267	6.4	14.0
Rockwall	78	1.3	20.5
Runnels	1,372	8.2	9.1
Rusk	75	—	4.0
Sabine	10	—	40.0
San Augustine	—	—	—
San Jacinto	7	—	—
San Patricio	18,462	51.5	7.9
San Saba	571	6.6	9.1
Schleicher	530	18.6	16.8
Scurry	565	2.5	7.4
Shackelford	16	—	—
Shelby	25	—	—
Sherman	26	1.1	19.2
Smith	216	—	13.0
Somervell	4	—	25.0
Washington	120	—	6.7
Webb	47,525	84.7	24.3
Wharton	4,670	12.9	10.9
Wheeler	18	—	5.5
Wichita	1,808	1.8	14.9
Wilbarger	274	1.3	16.4
Willacy	13,472	64.4	29.3
Williamson	3,706	9.5	13.5
Wilson	5,070	34.6	4.6
Winkler	392	3.9	9.7
Wise	64	—	18.7
Wood	8	—	50.0
Yoakum	78	1.8	14.1
Young	44	—	—
Zapata	4,144	94.1	20.5
Zavala	7,690	68.6	24.7
Total	1,033,768	13.4	17.9

a Percentages calculated by the author.

A NOTE ON WITCHES AND
WITCHCRAFT

THE BELIEF IN SOME FORM OF WITCHCRAFT has been widespread in the culture of the Spanish-Americans and many writers have mentioned it. However, it is difficult to make an accurate assessment of the extent to which the belief persists, for individual Spanish-Americans are understandably reluctant to discuss the matter with persons whom they do not know well. Furthermore, there is a reluctance to admit belief in witchcraft which seems to develop during the acculturative process, so that, on the whole, younger Spanish-Americans and those most nearly acculturated deny any acceptance of the concept. Many know about it, however, and can name other persons who they think continue to believe. A school teacher in a southern Colorado town, who has discussed the matter with his students, feels that about 5 per cent of them and about a quarter of the adults in his community hold some form of belief in the powers of *brujas* (witches). His grandmother, now nearly a hundred years old, is a strong believer.

The vitality of a belief in witches is seen in stories that crop up from time to time in newspapers of the Southwest. One such story, sent out by United Press under a Phoenix dateline September 18, 1952, reports the arrest of an Arizona rancher who shot a woman because she was a witch and had put a curse on his wife that blinded her. The rancher was quoted as saying, "She sprinkled powder on my wife back in 1942 and she started going blind. Doctors, healers, and all the others couldn't help her. I spent a lot of money and traveled many miles trying to get her cured, but she just got worse. There was no cure but this."

Many people in the San Luis Valley of southern Colorado know of a recent case in which one man was accused of bewitching another. Legal action was threatened, the *brujo* apparently capitulated, and the case was settled out of court. *Time* magazine in 1946 reported the instance of a lawsuit brought against a Spanish-speaking *bruja* of Denver by three clients who had paid her $24 for a bewitchment, $40 for a stomach remedy, and $40 for a love potion, none of which produced the promised results. Some years earlier a case came to trial in Mora, New Mexico, in which a woman charged that her husband had changed himself into a frog so that he could get into a closed house, and then had resumed his normal form and had beaten her.

In Spanish-American villages the belief in witches and witchcraft has persisted in relatively unchanged form for more than three hundred years. Witches are credited with the powers of transporting themselves through the air, changing their form, influencing the emotions of people, and causing sickness and death. They work by casting spells, by preparing and administering potions, by polluting air, by poisoning food, and by the use of imitative magic in which control over a person is attained through the preparation and manipulation of an image. They are thought to be effective and are therefore feared, and the belief in their powers forms the basis for a pervasive anxiety throughout much of the area where Spanish-Americans are concentrated and provides professional opportunities for *albolarias* and *curanderas*, who are consulted for both physical and psychological ailments thought to result from witchcraft.

A Spanish-speaking interviewer, working in the San Luis Valley of Colorado in the summer of 1952, was able easily to find a number of stories of witchcraft and its treatment in that area. The death of an old man from cancer and an unhealed sore on the nose of his wife were widely believed to have resulted from a bewitchment. A candidate for county office lost a daughter several years before as a result of the activities of a witch. The daughter became ill after eating a piece of bread given her by a woman she was visiting. Physicians were consulted, so the story is told, but could do nothing to help. The girl was hospitalized but without result. She was then taken to an *albolaria* in northern Colorado, but by that time she was too far gone for him to help her and she eventually died. Another girl who was *embrujado*, or bewitched, became paralyzed. She, also, was taken to various doctors and to a hospital, but without any noticeable improvement in her condition. Finally she was taken to a *médica*, who was able to overcome the magic of the witch, and the girl recovered. The wife of a southern Colorado man was *embrujado* by another woman who had wanted to marry the man herself. The wife came under the influence of the *bruja* through accepting and eating some candy the *bruja* gave her. Shortly thereafter she began to experience severe headaches and a constant fever. Doctors were unable to diagnose her trouble or to relieve her, and she died about seven months after her marriage. A New Mexican man fell ill and went to see a *médica* in Santa Fe. She told him he was *embrujado* and that he should go home and look for a *monito* (a doll in his image) behind the toilet. He followed her instructions and found one buried a few feet behind the privy. He destroyed the *monito* and was cured.

Stories such as these, which are told and accepted throughout the Southwest, are evidence of the vitality of the witchcraft tradition. Frequently included in these stories is an account of the sick person's consulting one or more physicians without success. An *albolaria*, a *médica*, a *curandera* is expected to recognize the symptoms of witchcraft and to be skilled in treating illnesses that result from being *embrujado*. Such cures as are effected are frequently attributed to their help or advice. A physician, particularly an Anglo, is not expected to know anything about treating witchcraft illnesses, and even though cases may be taken to him because of uncertain etiology or a desperate willingness to try anything, there is no great expectation that his treatment will be effective. If the condition, thought to be caused by witches, is actually physiological in origin, his treatment may result in relief or cure. Credit for the improvement, however, is likely to be given, not to the methods of the doctor, but to supplementary treatment procedures which the patient was undergoing at the same time. If there are psychological factors underlying the appearance of the illness symptoms, treatment directed solely toward the physical symptoms has little chance of giving either relief or cure.

Important elements in the treatment of persons who believe themselves to be *embrujado* are acceptance of their statement of the cause of their illness and the instituting of a course of therapy which is not incongruous with their frame of reference. The successful *albolaria* who achieves a reputation for curing bewitched persons does so, to a considerable extent, because she uses procedures which fit into the framework of assumptions that the patient brings to the treatment relationship. The patient believes that his condition has been caused by a witch; he also believes that the techniques of the *albolaria* can give him protection against the source of his trouble. That the techniques often give such protection in the form of relief from the troubling symptoms is not surprising in the light of what is known in scientific medicine about psychosomatic conditions and their treatment.

As Donovan Senter has pointed out,[1] folk practitioners treating patients who have been *embrujado* utilize an approach and procedures very similar to those familiar to psychiatrists. In both the folk and scientific frames of reference, the illness is seen as a function of the maladjustment of the individual to some aspect of his environment. The principal difference is that the folk practitioner recognizes one aspect of the environment—the witch—which the scientific practitioner ignores. Where the psychiatrist is forced, by his conceptual scheme, to bring about an awareness in the patient of the source of the latter's troubles in terms of such abstractions as frustration, inhibition, anxiety, and repression, the *albolaria* can more easily accomplish her purpose by making the concrete, tangible person of the witch the focal source of the trouble and

[1] Senter, Donovan, "Witches and Psychiatrists," *Psychiatry*, Journal of the Biology and Pathology of Interpersonal Relations, vol. 10, February, 1947, pp. 49–56.

the equally tangible *monito* or other magic device the mechanism through which the damage is done. Thus, by destroying the *monito* or by beginning some protective procedures, she can break the link between the patient and the source of his illness or provide a type of psychic immunization which acts as a barrier to the harmful influence of the witch.

In treating a person who has been *embrujado*, the good *albolaria* does not ignore the possibility of other types of causation. The physical condition, the emotional state, and the social relationships of the patient are all taken into account in planning the course of treatment, and frequently types of therapeutic procedures applicable to all three may be utilized in a single case. Senter[1] cites the case of a wife who developed eczema when she began to suspect that her husband was paying attention to another woman. An *albolario* carefully assessed the situation from the standpoint of the social relationships involved, the physical condition of the wife, and the possible mental state of the husband. He made a diagnosis of witchcraft, deriving from the other woman, which had caused skin disease in the wife and was soon to bring about an illness in the husband. The treatment consisted in providing the husband with a charm to protect him against the witch and the wife with a number of remedies which included: a packet of herbs that would ensure her husband's affections; advice about the techniques of coquetry and love-making to make her more attractive to her husband; a standard ointment preparation for her skin; and a tonic of vitamin B and iron to make her feel better. The treatment resulted in a revival of the husband's interest in his wife, the breaking of his relationship with the other woman, and a clearing up of the wife's skin condition, which, taken together, represent probably as good an outcome as might be expected under any circumstances.

[1] *Ibid.*, pp. 53–54.

INDEX

313